GW00647600

In the same series

THE NATURALIST IN WALES
by R. M. Lockley

THE REGIONAL NATURALIST

THE NATURALIST IN
Devon and Cornwall

ROGER BURROWS

DAVID & CHARLES : NEWTON ABBOT

In memory of my mother

ISBN 0 7153 7360 8

Set in 12 on 13 point Bembo
and printed in Great Britain
by Latimer Trend & Company Limited
for David & Charles (Publishers) Limited
South Devon House Newton Abbot Devon

Contents

List of Illustrations

Plates

In text

Introduction

THE PENINSULA OF the South West is battered from the north by the Atlantic and Bristol Channel, and fretted from the south by the English Channel. It finds its south-eastern limit in the county boundary between Devon and Dorset, and its natural north-eastern frontier in the eastern foothills of the Exmoor uplands.

This is a part of Britain famed, on the one hand, for its lush, sunny coastline and dominated, on the other hand, by high open moorland. Bodmin Moor stretches over north Cornwall; Exmoor sweeps across the county border from Devon into Somerset; and the true wilderness of Dartmoor, the most majestic of them all, rises to over 2,000 feet. This high, exposed ground which covers so much of the peninsula endures a much harsher climate than that which gave the area its reputation as a tourist attraction. Altitude has, of course, a marked effect on temperature; in the far west the fall is 1°C for every 500ft rise, giving conditions which are similar in many ways to those of Southern Iceland. At 2,000ft, the climate in inland areas such as Dartmoor is sub-arctic and conditions are reflected in an impoverished flora on uplands much less favourable to plantlife than their continental equivalents at the same altitude.

Going down, however, into the lush, sheltered coastal districts of Devon and Cornwall, the contrast for the naturalist is complete. Here the warm air coming off the sea assists the growth of an almost sub-tropical flora along the south coast. The plantlife is often enriched by native species with Mediterranean affinities, as well as imported sub-tropical plants which flourish in ornamental gardens such as the Morrab Gardens in Penzance, and the Abbey Gardens, Tresco, on the Isles of Scilly. The warm water currents from the south Atlantic, in the form of the Gulf Stream bring not only floating forms of life from warmer waters but allow the development of a rather warmer water flora and fauna in the waters surrounding the peninsula. These climatic variations provide a wealth of habitats for the naturalist to study, as they affect both plant and animal life.

The hard, erosion-resistant, geologically ancient rocks which form much of the peninsula act as first landfall for winds sweeping across thousands of miles of open Atlantic, with Scilly and west Cornwall taking the full brunt of their force. Whilst the wind is often unwelcome to the visitor, it should be realised that it is a vital factor in the natural history of the area, affecting not only the native species, but allowing us to see North American birds who have a wind-assisted passage across the open ocean, aided in part, no doubt, by boats which act as temporary resting places. For the naturalist the winds bring in close to shore many otherwise oceanic birds such as petrels, shearwaters and skuas.

This wide variety of habitats and their attendant plant and animal communities is obviously an embarrassment in a book as small as this, and in a volume of this size the task is rather to select commonly occurring species, than to attempt to cover all-comers. No directions have been given for the finding of rarities, and indeed little mention has been made of them. In each chapter generalisations have had to be made and not all the species mentioned will necessarily be found although they are typical of the habitats described. Each chapter deals with one well-defined habitat and in some cases a typical example is considered in detail.

It is hoped that after reading this book the naturalist coming to the South West will at least know what to expect and will be able to choose, with the help of the maps and list of nature reserves in the appendix, where to go to see what most interests him. (The best times and places for seeing migrant birds for instance are marked on the maps for clarity.)

If a great deal of emphasis has been placed on the flora it should be remembered that the object of the book is to inform the visiting naturalist of what he or she is most likely to see. Plants being for the most part static have an obvious visual impact but the animals other than birds and butterflies have to be sought; all that this book can do is describe the main habitats and indicate where possible what the animal communities are and where they will be found.

The book is not intended to aid identification of species as it is hoped that the reader will be acquainted already with available books and have at least some natural history knowledge. Few photographs of species have been included as these are available, usually in colour, in previously published books; the illustrations included here are selected so that a general impression of the habitats under discussion can be obtained much more quickly and accurately than by written description. Some of the photographs illustrate the problems that the resident naturalists in the area have to face, namely china clay waste, reservoir construction, and of course pressure of people with their cars and houses and feet.

As much as possible, the information given throughout these chapters has been based on my own observations, but much information has had to be obtained from other sources, most of which are listed in the bibliography. But indeed, so little information has recently been published about the natural history of the area that the visitor could make very useful contributions in almost all fields by sending information either direct to the author or to the Cornwall or Devon Naturalists' Trusts, whose addresses will be found in the appendix.

Information about rainfall, sunshine and temperatures will be found in figure 23, page 187.

Roger Burrows
Breanoc Field Study Centre, St Agnes

CHAPTER ONE

Geology and Scenery

Rocks and their history–Soils

SCENICALLY THE SOUTH WEST is dominated by uplands and cliffs, and it is the geological structures of the area which determine their form and distribution. The area is for the most part composed of old rocks in the geological sense of the word; most were formed 300–150 million years BP and since their formation have been compressed, folded, faulted, and altered by heat from cooling granite masses pushed up into them. The resultant weathered, resistant, metamorphic and igneous rocks, together with hard sediments, form all the prominent topographic features from towering north Cornwall and Devon cliffs to peat-covered high moorland such as Dartmoor and Bodmin.

The following geological periods are represented by rocks of various types:

Pleistocene, eg St Erth, Crousa Downs, St Agnes
Tertiary, Bovey Beds in Devon
Cretaceous 'Greensands'
Trias
Permian—red soils of Devon farmland, South Devon cliffs
Carboniferous—culm of North Cornwall and Devon
Up, Mid, Lr } Devonian—covers much of Devon and Cornwall
Ordovician and Silurian, north of Lizard, thin, very contorted
Pre-Cambrian, Lizard and Start Point (perhaps Devonian)

The oldest rocks in the area are probably the Pre-Cambrian serpentines, granites and schists of the Lizard peninsula. The ultra basic serpentine gives rise to a relatively monotonous inland plateau devoid of trees but nevertheless carrying a fascinating and unique flora. But, if inland the Lizard is unimpressive scenically, the cliffs more than make up for this, producing dramatic and idyllic coves such as Kynance and Coverack. The green and red serpentine cliffs form the most southerly peninsula in England but the most southerly tip is occupied by schists of Lizard Point (see map, fig 18, p 157). Some of the serpentine is used by local traders to produce ornaments as the rock can be turned, albeit with difficulty due to the ease with which it fractures along small joints.

The South Devon headlands of Bolt Tail, Bolt Head, Start Point and Prawle Point are formed from schistose rocks which are of unknown age but most probably, like the Lizard rocks, are Pre-Cambrian. The rocks are divided into an east and west portion by the beautiful Salcombe estuary.

North of the Lizard serpentines and associated rocks come younger Ordovician and Silurian rocks, whilst Lower Devonian sediments abut on to the Start and Bolt Head schists. The Ordovician and Silurian deposits of the South Cornwall area are of specialist interest to geologists only and need not further occupy us. The same cannot be said for the succeeding sandstones, grits, slates and conglomerates of the Lower Devonian.

Devon gives its name to a series of deposits which are found in many other parts of the world; these rocks were first described in Devon where they are well if not exceptionally developed. (Devonian rocks do not, however, form the typical Devon red soils; this distinction is given to rocks of the Permian Age to be described later.) Large tracts of country in Devon, Cornwall and Somerset are formed by Devonian rocks which produce much of the spectacular south-west scenery such as the North Cornwall and North Devon cliffs, Exmoor and the Quantocks. Inland they give rise to many linear uplands due to the east–west folding of hard rock bands forming, for example, St Breocks and Denzell Downs near Bodmin Moor. The Devonian deposits are mainly marine except for the grits of North Devon which are continental and similar to those of the

English Midlands and Welsh Border region, where they are known as Old Red Sandstone. The south-west marine Devonian consist mainly of sedimentary rocks laid down on the floor of an old sea and containing fossils such as brachiopods and primitive fish. Few well-preserved fossils are found in North Devon and Cornwall but extensive limestone deposits near Torquay, Plymouth, Brixham and Totnes have yielded abundant well-preserved corals and brachiopods, particularly the former which can be well seen in some of the polished ornamental marbles produced in these parts. Beach pebbles containing fossil corals are extremely common in parts of South Devon.

Limestones are scarce throughout the peninsula of the South West but an interesting development of thin limestone lenses occurs near Ilfracombe where the intense folding to which the rocks were subjected by pressures from the south caused the 'rolling-up' of sections of the limestone to give the appearance of tree trunks protruding from the cliff. As already indicated the Devonian rocks, all heavily folded and faulted after deposition, produced shales, slates, phyllites and quartzites contorted like a wrinkled tablecloth by intense earth pressures from the south. These pressures were responsible not only for the folding and faulting but also for the elevation of a mountainous ridge of country running east to west across what is now South Cornwall. The ridge formerly extended both west into what is now the Atlantic and east for a considerable distance into what is now Brittany; it is after Armorica, the old name for Brittany, that these 250 million years old mountains are named. Into this mountain mass was injected fairly high up in the earth's crust, an igneous rock that has produced great scenic and economic effects—the Cornish and Dartmoor granite.

What we now see in the South West are the exposed roots of the Armorican mountains. Many hundreds of feet of rock originally covering the granite have been removed by erosion both above and below sea level and this has exposed the rigid granite backbone of the mountains which now form the upstanding moorlands of Dartmoor, Bodmin, St Austell, Carnmenellis and Land's End, not forgetting the low islands of granite lying some twenty-five miles off Land's End, forming the Scillies. The granite which was intruded at no great temperature, rather gently 'cooked' or metamorphosed the surrounding sedimentary rocks producing hard rock such as hornfelses, calc flintas and, more commonly, spotted slates for a short distance away from the contact.

Of more economic importance were the hot gases and liquids which were given off from the granite towards the end of its cooling, for these formed the valuable mineral deposits of tin, copper, wolfram, lead, silver and zinc, both within the granite and in zones around it in the country rock, the 'killas.' The late twentieth century will probably see a great resurgence of mining and many are rightly worried about the effect on the scenery of renewed activity; anyone knowing the central industrial strip of Cornwall will know of the existence of many hundreds of acres of derelict industrial sites. Fortunately, it seems to be mainly in these areas that the new development will take place. Many of the old mining areas on the coast will, it is hoped, not be reworked (although Botallack will be) as many of the old mine dumps have been recolonised by heather and furze and even the old derelict buildings have, for many people, added to rather than detracted from the natural beauty. This derelict land as we shall see, has a fairly varied and often interesting flora but has little else to commend it except to the growing numbers of 'rock hound' mineral hunters who are able to make an occasional good find among the old mine debris.

Other minerals, produced in the surrounding 'killas' or 'country rocks' as the granite cooled, include commercially worthless tourmaline, but very valuable china clay. Tourmaline-containing rocks are resistant to erosion and one very rich in tourmaline forms the well known feature of Roche Rock, near St Austell, capped by the hermitage, a light from which used to guide the traveller across Goss Moor.

The china clay belt centred on St Austell can be seen for many miles due to the often gleaming 'pyramids' of waste quartz sand from china clay production (see plate p 85). China clay deposits are also found in the North Cornwall coast, on the Land's End peninsula, and on Bodmin Moor, too, together with a number of sites on Dartmoor. Sand is not the only waste product, for the mica from the decomposed granite is dumped in vast quantities into the sea and local rivers. Pollution of the sea is a great problem and the small rivers flowing to St Austell Bay are heavily laden with white clay in suspension. The sea is turned turquoise by the clay, but less attractive are the piles of gluey clay washed in by the tide and mixed with the beach and to form sometimes quicksand-like deposits. A recent scheme to pipe the waste out to sea along the sea bed seemed to be a solution to the effluent problem although this idea has now been abandoned. The pollution has of course greatly affected the marine and river life of the area and will be considered in Chapter Six.

In North Cornwall the Devonian rocks forming towering cliffs, eg Bedruthan, locally contain large lava flows formed from sub sea volcanic activity in Devonian times. Such lavas now form the Pentires and a long ridge of country stretching eastward both north and south of Bodmin Moor, the southerly outcrop extending as far as Babbacombe. At Pentire, beautiful sections in the lavas show the pillow-like structure produced by rapid surface cooling as they flowed along the sea bed millions of years ago. Igneous rocks are responsible for many headlands on both north and south coasts, eg Rumps Point, Cataclews Point, Porthmissen Point, Trevose Head and, on the south, Nare Head, Caragloose Point and Black Head.

Anyone with an eye for building stone will be familiar with Delabole slate so often used for fireplaces and ornamental stone work but also for hedging purposes in North Cornwall From. the slates rather deformed fossils of brachiopods are obtained, known locally as Delabole butterflies but to the geologist as *Spirifer vernulii*. The deformation is due to earth movements affecting the rocks in which the fossils are preserved, rather than to original biological causes.

The Devonian rocks of North Devon are well exposed in the spectacular cliff scenery between Ilfracombe and Minehead in Somerset (see plate p 85). They form the wild uplands of Exmoor and to the east the Brendons and Quantocks. These old rocks run in bands striking west-north-west to east-south-east and are composed of grits and slates with very few volcanic rocks, unlike their equivalent in North Cornwall. Headlands such as Foreland Point, Hangman Point, Morte and Baggy Point are all formed from resistant bands of Devonian sediments. Not all these rocks are of marine origin, some as already mentioned being equivalent to the Old Red Sandstone facies further north in the British Isles.

Folding of the Devonian rocks also affected the younger Carboniferous deposits that lie on top of them in North Cornwall and Devon. The so-called 'Culm' deposits derive their name from the Devon term Culm for a poor quality sooty coal. Culm deposits occur over a wide area covering 1,200 square miles (see sketch map, figure 1). The folded Culm lies in a large downfold of the earth's crust known as the mid-Devon syncline, having its axis running east-west through Crediton. It therefore forms much of central Devon and ends in the rather spectacular cliffs between Boscastle and Appledore. The Culm deposits, shales, slate, sandstones, limestones and cherts often show alternating bands of sandstone and shale which are frequently zig-zag folded, a feature well developed at Millook Haven south of Bude. Scenically the Culm deposits form hilly ground including a series of whale-backed ridges arranged en echelon and composed of resistant chert, a material forming the Fire Beacon north of Boscastle. The Culm cliffs are unstable so are little colonised by plants or birds, but have an interesting woodland developed on land slips near Millook.

The typical red soils of Devon and Somerset are formed by the breakdown of Permian sandstones, breccias and marls deposited originally under desert conditions in a basin surrounded by mountains.

The mountains supplying the debris to fill up the basin which

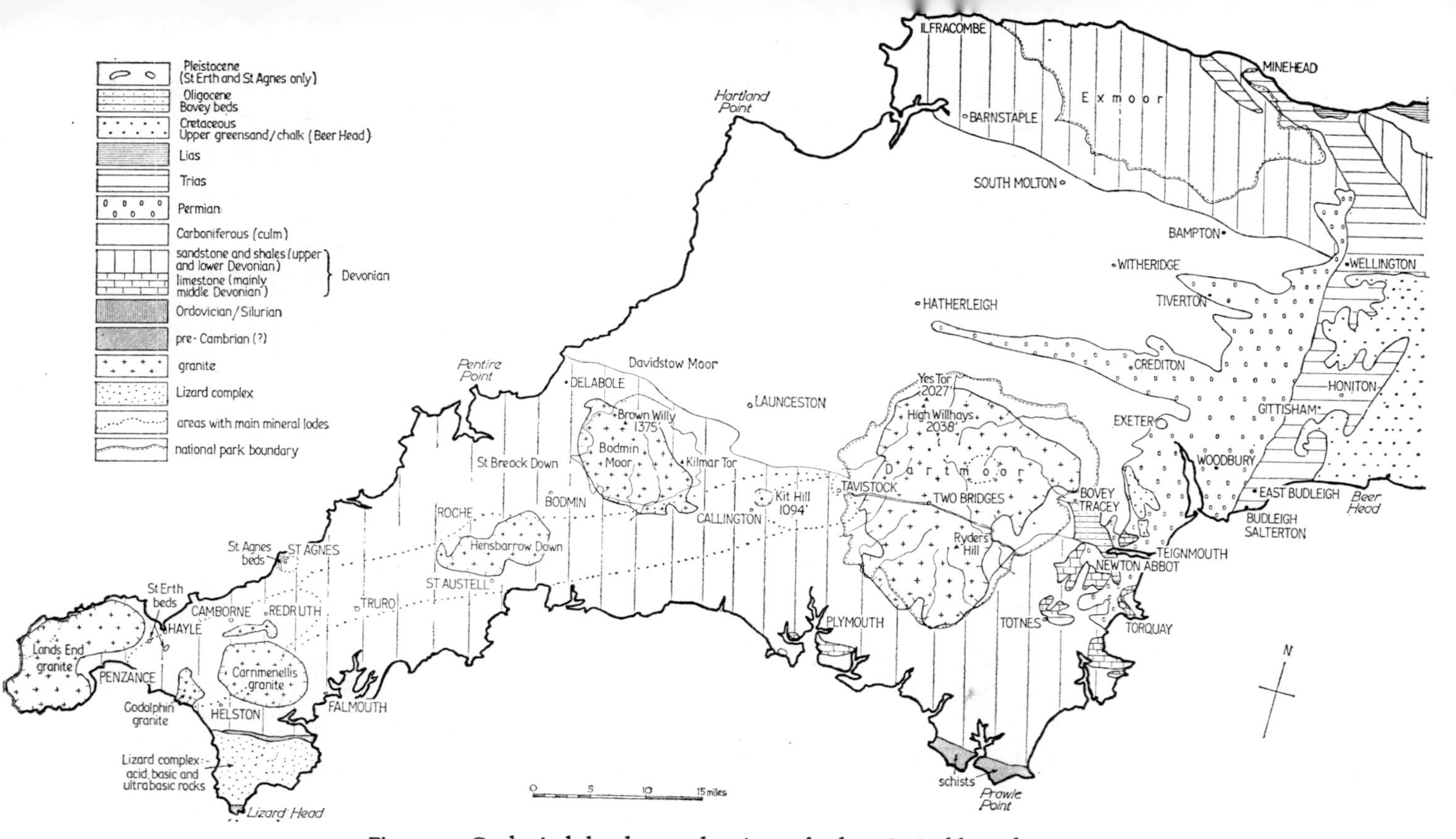

Figure 1 Geological sketch map showing only the principal boundaries

existed about 165 million years ago in what is now central and South Devon and Somerset, were the Quantock-Exmoor range on the north, and Dartmoor on the west. Contemporary volcanic activity in the Exeter area produced a variation in rock types but only over small areas. Permian rocks outcrop in a band from just south of the Quantocks through Taunton, with an elongated finger through Crediton to a point just north of Okehampton while the main band widens to about twelve miles just south of Exeter and then meets the coast as red cliffs between Budleigh Salterton and north of Torquay. The red cliffs will be known to rail travellers into the South West as the main line winds through tunnels cut in the red sandstone near Teignmouth. Permian deposits are succeeded by continental desert sandstones and conglomerates of the Triassic.

Geologically the most famous Triassic rock in the area is the so-called Budleigh Salterton pebble bed. This forms part of the cliffs between Budleigh Salterton and Sidmouth but inland gives an escarpment of rather waste land covered with heather, contrasting with the rich grasslands developed on the beds beneath. Triassic deposits are also found forming the cliffs in West Somerset where red, easily-weathered Keuper Marl is exposed.

A large gap in the geological column occurred in our area and the next beds to be formed, this time under the sea again, were those of the Cretaceous. These deposits are now only found in the extreme south east of the area in Devon; they probably formerly covered large areas to the west, possibly even Dartmoor, but if so they have long since been removed by weathering. It is suggested that the many flint pebbles forming barriers on the south coast are derived from a Cretaceous outcrop on the floor of the English Channel. Cretaceous rocks produce fairly high ground which forms part of a dissected sheet. They occur beneath the gravel-capped hills of Great and Little Haldon and here give rise to the most south-westerly outcrop of Cretaceous rocks in the British Isles. Rocks of this period are known locally as Devon 'Greensand' but seem to be equivalent to the Upper Gault and Upper Greensands of areas further east. They are covered in part by younger Cretaceous rocks forming the Chalk.

Chert beds in the Upper Greensand form abrupt scarps flanking high land such as Honiton Hill and Buckton Hill whilst the same beds form the Kempstone Rocks cliff near Dunscombe. Although the only modern use for the deposits is as road metal, Palaeolithic man used the cherts for tool making, the results of his labours now being found in the Axe Valley gravels. Beneath the Greensands the Gault forms the Blackdown Hills from which chert nodules were quarried as scythe stones, and the waste dumps yield beautifully preserved mollusc shells in chalcedony (for example the Downes' collection in Exeter museum).

The youngest Cretaceous deposits, the Chalk, form cliffs around Beer (see plate p 103) and on the north side of the harbour 130ft of middle chalk is exposed. The lower part has about thirteen feet of building stone known as Beer stone which is quarried and is excellent for carving, particularly for indoor work. The Upper Chalk is best exposed between Seaton and Beer Head, the latter being the most westerly extension of Upper Chalk in England.

The importance of the Chalk is that together with the Torquay Devonian Limestone it gives small areas of calcium rich soils, a none too frequent occurrence in the South West; the only other calcareous-rich deposits are those formed from blown shell sand particularly on the exposed north Cornish and Devon coasts as for example at Hayle, Perranporth and Braunton Burrows.

Deposits more recent than Cretaceous are uncommon, consisting of gravel capping to some hills, eg the Haldons, and some possible lake deposits at Bovey Tracey and Petrockstow (North Devon). All these beds are probably of early Tertiary age. In Cornwall an interesting deposit of blue clay containing fossils was found in 1881 in sand pits at St Erth near Camborne. Many fossil mollusc shells and foramanifera were obtained together with seeds of land plants and pollen grains. This deposit is thought to date from an interglacial stage about half way through the Pleistocene period (see S. M. Turk, *Cornwall Nats*

Trust Newsletter No. 11, September 1967, p. 3–4). Sands and clays probably of similar age occur around St Agnes Beacon where they were formerly used as candle clay for fixing candles to convenient places in the local mines, and for coarse pottery. Today these fossil sand deposits are dug for glass manufacture by man and for earths and setts by foxes and badgers. Superficial deposits of raised beaches occur commonly around the coasts of the South West at 65ft and 158ft above present day sea level. Head deposits formed under periglacial conditions and consisting of angular rock debris fill many of the valleys and are often exposed by coastal erosion. Due to the lack of glaciation of the area no boulder clay deposits are found.

Variation in sea level during Tertiary and Pleistocene times has produced overdeepened river valleys now filled in with silt, sand and peat, and submerged forests with remains of trees that formerly flourished on the coastal lowlands at times of lower sea level. The old tree trunks and peat deposits are sometimes visible at low levels in the cliffs, or are exposed at low tide by storms removing overlying sand and silt (see position on map, figure 10, p 123). The drowned river valleys formed when the over-deepened river valleys were submerged at the close of the last Ice Age, give rise to the typical 'rias' of the South West, eg the Tamar, Fal and Camel.

Apart from blown sand, which often has a high calcium carbonate content, the only other deposits in the area are those from caves and rivers. Kent's Cavern near Torquay is a classic area due to the association of extinct animal remains with Palaeolithic implements. Remains of hyaena, horse, woolly rhinoceros, cave lion, cave bear, grizzly bear, reindeer, stag and bison are common. Mammoth, wolf, brown bear and beaver, glutton, cave pika and sabre-toothed tiger are also found; this is a late-Pleistocene fauna.

The geology of the area has, as we shall see, an important role in determining the types of plant and animal communities in the South West.

Soils

Due to the lack of glaciation in the area many of the soils relate closely to the nature of the underlying rock but in a few cases soils have developed on material such as wind-blown loess, as on the Lizard and Scilly. Some soils are derived from head deposits whilst locally a number of different soils may be derived from a common rock as has happened on the Lizard for example. In general it seems that most of the soils have developed from brown earths originally formed beneath an oak woodland cover.

The following soil types are found in the South West.

Brown earth. This is the most widespread soil in the area and developed on a wide variety of bedrocks from shales and slates to granites, dolerites and serpentinites.

The brown earth is a loamy well-drained acid soil, pH about 4·5 and is known in Devon as the Mortonhampstead soil series. There is no surface peat and the vegetation is mainly bracken, gorse and bent fescue grassland, which produces good farmland in the lower flatter areas around Dartmoor.

The brown earths in Cornwall are orange-brown and despite their high clay content are not waterlogged even on fairly flat ground. Where there are fairly steep slopes in Culm shales and sandstones, a shallow well-drained brown earth occurs. It is good for cultivation throughout the year and is most important on the lower and western granite outcrops, but it is a very rare soil type on Bodmin granite.

Gleyed brown earths or surface water gley soils. Despite the high rainfall in the area these soils are of very limited distribution occurring occasionally on pre-Devonian and Devonian slates. In mid-Devon and East Cornwall gleyed brown earths are found on level ground on Culm shales and sandstones giving wet pasture land and extensive *Molinia* moorland with rushes. A good example is the Forestry Commission plantation around Halwill.

The soil is acid, pH about 5, and is wet in winter with surface waterlogging, but bakes and cracks in summer. It therefore gives difficult agricultural land.

Peaty gleyed podsol. These soils have a thin layer of amorphous peat over a thin iron pan. The latter not only causes surface waterlogging but prevents root penetration.

Such soils are extensively developed on Bodmin Moor and other upland areas such as St Breock's Down and Davidstowe Moor. They are known in Devon as the Hexworthy series and flank the high plateau of Dartmoor. The ground cover in this unenclosed area is a semi-natural *Molinia* grassland or wet heath.

The soil very acid and this is reflected in the heath vegetation of *Erica tetralix*, *Calluna* and *Vaccinium myrtillus*. Most of the Forestry Commission plantations on Dartmoor are on peaty gleyed podsol. The soil type also occurs on high ground in the Bude area and St Austell moors but is not common on the more westerly granites.

It is thought that these soils formed from brown earths of deciduous woodland after the trees had been cleared by early man and climatic changes.

Valley bogs and ground water gley soils. These occupy narrow bands along the sides of streams and on the margins of valley bogs, particularly in the granite areas. Valley and basin bogs are common on Bodmin and St Austell moors and were formerly so in South and West Cornwall river valleys. Valley bogs have been much modified by mining operations and few are left.

Blanket bog and peaty gley soils. The distinction between the two is arbitrary and based on the thickness of peat. If this is over 16in the term 'blanket bog' is used, if under 16in, peaty gley soil.

Blanket bog is rare in Cornwall occurring locally on Bodmin Moor but it is well developed in Devon particularly on the high plateaux of Dartmoor. Here, mainly above 1,500ft, the rainfall is over 80in per annum. On Bodmin Moor blanket bog occurs on gently sloping hill tops around the 1,000ft mark, eg Brockabarrow Common, where it has been extensively cut for peat. Peaty gley soils are common on Dartmoor, 1,000–1,100ft, and on the summit of Buttern Hill on Bodmin Moor. These soils form the typical rough unfenced moorland on Dartmoor. Much peat has been cut and erosion by natural causes gives rise to highly dissected or 'hagged' peat areas which are characteristic on the northern plateau of Dartmoor but do not occur in the south (see plate p 51).

Beneath the peat cover is a grey waterlogged mineral soil and the vegetation is mainly cotton grass, deer grass and rushes grazed by sheep and cattle.

Soils on serpentines. Soil types range from freely draining reddish-brown loams with a high base content due to magnesium ions, to poorly drained gley soils which are acid. In many cases the soil is acid on the surface but neutral down on the serpentine bedrock. The unusual soils of the area carry very distinctive and unusual flora which is discussed in Chapter Two.

Calcareous soils. These are of local occurrence only, mainly in South-east Devon on Cretaceous rocks and carry an interesting calcareous flora. Small outcrops of limestones or calcium-rich rocks do occur locally elsewhere, but in Cornwall the main calcareous habitats are provided by the north coast sand dunes.

CHAPTER TWO

Woodland

Early trees—Original oakwoods—Coppice and scrub—Woodland animal life—Other native trees—Introduced and imported trees—Coniferous forests

TO SAY THAT the South Western counties are well-wooded would be an exaggeration despite the first impression a visitor gets on entering Devon. Although roadside trees and hedgerow stands are common the winding, leafy lanes of the countryside obscure the fact that true woodland is rather sparse and found mainly in the sheltered valleys in South Devon and East Cornwall where it occurs often almost down to sea level. The Somerset part of Exmoor is well supplied with woods but they are rare features indeed in West Cornwall and natural woodland in the Isles of Scilly is non-existent, even though a few plantations do exist and many hedges have been planted as windbreaks.

These generalisations apply of course to deciduous trees, for there are very few native evergreens in the area apart from holly and juniper. The latter is still found rarely on the wind-ravaged heaths of the Lizard in Cornwall. However, Forestry Commission and private plantations have added many acres of coniferous woodland in Cornwall, Devon and neighbouring Somerset over the last fifty years.

Early trees

In the geologically recent past, woodlands existed that were subtropical and in these lived animal species long extinct, but similar to those now found in East Africa. The evidence for this is found at Bovey, north of Newton Abbot in Devon, where some ancient sediments occur which have for many years been exploited for the balt clay and lignite that they contain. Many species of plants contributed to the formation of the lignite or low rank brown coal which resulted from compression of plant remains. Twigs, whole trees and fragments such as leaves and seeds, were washed into the region by rivers which in Oligocene times, roughly 30 million years ago, formed an extensive lake near what is now Bovey Tracey.

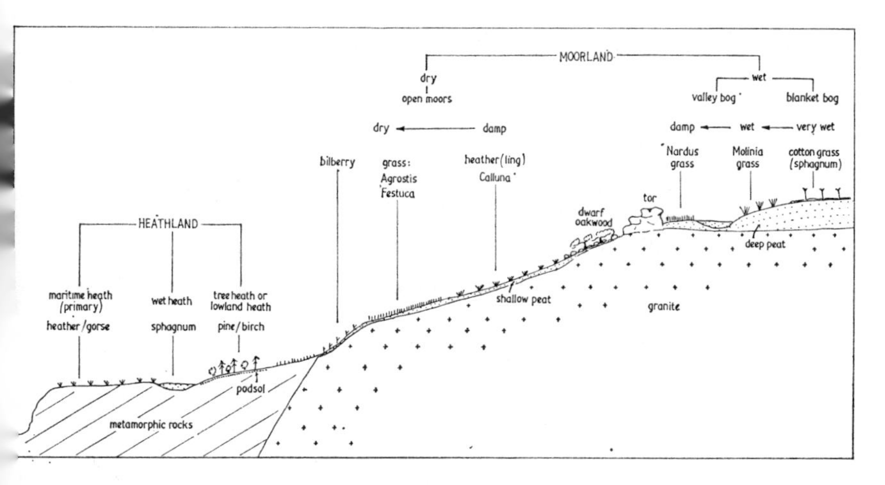

Figure 2 Classification of moorland and heathland habitats in the South West based on dominant plant species, depth of peat and altitude

When the fossils were identified it was found that many species of plant which were native to Oligocene Devon, have a strange similarity with the exotic trees and shrubs now found in the ornamental gardens in Devon and Cornwall. In both fossil lignite and modern gardens flourish magnolia, eucalyptus, *Ficus* (fig), gardenia, *Laurus* (sweet bay-tree), and members of the red wood or *Sequoia* family which are now found native only in North America. The native Oligocene species of *Sequoia* in Devon was a small tree *S. coultsiae*, but imported Californian

S. giagantea which grows now, has the distinction of providing for Devon the tallest tree (162ft) in the British Isles, at Endsleigh near Tavistock.

The climate of ancient Devon, when magnolia and eucalyptus grew wild, was warm and damp but as the climate changed, the warm flora disappeared, and it was only possible for man to re-introduce it after great environmental changes had taken place, hinging on the great cold of the last Ice Age.

During this time, over a million years ago, although great thicknesses of moving ice covered much of the British Isles, Devon and Cornwall were ice free but dominated by conditions described as periglacial which were too severe for all but the hardiest of the arctic-type shrubs and herbs. One of the few remnants of this tundra flora is the rare crowberry *Empetrum nigrum* of Dartmoor.

As the ice retreated farther northwards, so the warmer climatic conditions which crept up behind the ice fronts allowed the development of a succession of vegetation types. Even so, trees only became really well established in the area about 10,000 BC when a light forest cover of hairy birch and juniper was available for the first men in the area to use. The birch *Betula pubescens* is rarely found now in any quantity but stumps in peat indicate that it may in the past have occurred as it does in the north and west of the British Isles, above the limits of the oakwoods.

After another cold snap with tundra-type vegetation from about 9,000–8,000 BC, fossil pollen from the peat deposits tells us that rising temperatures and a more continental climate between 8,000–5,500 BC enabled aspen and willow to become established together with the birch and juniper. However, this age belongs to the pine trees *Pinus sylvestris* (Scots pine) which flourished at this time as great forests. Even so the presence of elm and oak foreshadowed the eclipse of the pine; it gradually lost ground to the deciduous trees which were more successful in dealing with the next major change, this time to a climate more coastal and wet, brought about by the establishment of the North Sea and the separation of the British Isles from the continent. This took place about 5,000 BC; the rising waters from the melting glaciers raised the level of the shallow seas around our coasts, and so brought about the extinction of the once large forests that existed on a low-lying coastal plain now well below the modern sea level. Such ancient vegetation forms submerged forests and peat deposits, which are common along many parts of the south-west coast and are indicated on figure 10, p 123. By studying the fossil pollen grains in such deposits we can reconstruct the geologically recent history of our area.

The cooler coastal climate with high rainfall and mild winters initiated the so-called Atlantic period which lasted from 5,500–2,500 BC and saw the establishment of oak and elm as the most important trees of the forest. A further period of more continental climate followed and during this time from 2,500–400 BC, oak finally became dominant over the elm. But man began to exert his influence on the oak forests and so reduced the length of the reign of 'king oak'; this we know again from studies of fossil pollen which show that heather was now much more common, indicating that man was clearing the oak forest cover by his cultivation techniques.

Man's onslaught, which has gone on ever since, was aided by further climatic changes from about 400 BC when a period of higher rainfall and cooler summers began, similar to the modern climate. The leaching effects of the rainwater on the felled woodlands and on the higher treeless hill tops allowed the progressive degeneration of the upland soils and the formation over 1,500ft of blanket bog, and lower down the spread of peat bogs and peaty gleyed soils, all of which meant the end of the soils as supporters of a deciduous forest cover.

Original oakwoods

The original oak forests dwindled rapidly until all that we have left are two or three isolated patches of stunted oak woods such as the famous enigmatic Wistman's Wood on high Dartmoor. Other more extensive areas of much modified oak woodland exist on the site of the former virgin oak woods, but most of them have been severely modified by man and can hardly be classified as natural. We shall first consider the high level relict oak woodland of Dartmoor.

From the open moorland on the east side of the West Dart valley, Wistman's Wood on the opposite slope looks anything but an impressive woodland of great botanical interest. This high Dartmoor, stunted, twisted oak woodland which covers only a little more than 8 acres of boulder- or 'clitter'-covered steep hillside, clings rather precariously to the valley at 1,250–450ft. Here it is subject not only to high winds and low swirling cloud cover for many days of the year, but during that time up to 70in of rain falls and removes from the soil any calcium and other soluble base material which might have begun to accumulate. The resulting highly acidic soil would seem to indicate by comparison with similarly situated woodland in the Lake District, that the dominant oak should be the sessile form *Quercus petraea* with its stalkless (sessile) acorn cups. The Wistman trees are, however, pure pedunculate oak *Q. robur* with long stalks or peduncles to the acorn cups (of the kind used, according to legend, as piskie pipes).

The trees are probably up to 500 years old but seldom rise more than 20ft above the angular granite scree blocks in between which the trunks and some lower branches are firmly wedged. It may well be that the protection given by the clitter has aided the establishment of the oaks in the past at what must now be the upper limits of their range, for outside the wood small saplings grow, sheltered in the granite debris weathered from nearby tors.

Although the oaks have only a limited height, their lateral spread is often considerable, up to 25ft (7·6m) for one tree only 10ft (3m) high. Despite their age the girth of the trees is not great, averaging about 50in for trees of about 15ft high.

The great humidity of the atmosphere provides ideal conditions for the growth of many non-flowering so-called lower plants; these are the ferns and the large group known as the bryophytes which includes the liverworts and mosses. A third

Page 33 (*above*) Sessile oak woodland with abundant scrambling ivy, young sycamore, holly and ground vegetation of bluebell, fern, wood sorrel and wood anemone. Mithian Woods, Cornwall; (*below*) epiphytic growths of moss and common polypody fern are typical of damp oak woodlands in the South West. Mithian Woods

Page 34 (*above*) Wild Exmoor looking across the Holnicote estate to Dunkery Beacon. Heather-topped moorland with thickly wooded combes, the latter excellent for bird watching in summer; (*below*) reclaimed Exmoor, typical field system with beech-topped hedges and beech shelter belts around isolated farms. Pasture invaded by bracken on drier slopes, and rushes on damper, former heathland areas

group of rather curious plants, the lichens, also occurs in profusion and makes up a large element in many woodlands in the South West. Lichens are an excellent example of co-operation in the plant world between two not very closely related groups, the fungi and the algae. The fungi are probably well known to many people but the land living algae are not as familiar as their first cousins the marine algae or seaweeds that we shall meet in later chapters.

The combination of a fungi and an algae living together to form an apparently unified single plant body or thallus, is what the botanist calls a lichen. If one wishes to study this group of plants there can be few finer places in the British Isles than Dartmoor and the other high moorland areas in the South West. In Wistman's Wood lichens, mosses and liverworts are abundant on the trunks and branches, and raggedly festoon even the higher twigs. There is evidence, however, of a reduction in the luxuriance and extent of lichen and moss growths.

Ferns flourish in the forks of trees and right along the horizontal branches, each of which has an accumulation of plant-sustaining humus. Common polypody *Polypodium vulgare* and the broad buckler fern *Dryopteris dilatata* are characteristic of plants growing on the surface of others, a habit known as epiphytic. Ferns and bryophytes are not the only epiphytes for rowan *Sorbus aucuparia* up to 10ft (3m) high also actually grow on the oaks, together with the whortleberry *Vaccinium myrtilus*. A few other species of shrubby plants do occur within the wood; of these, ivy *Hedera helix* and yellow-flowering honeysuckle *Lonicera periclymenum* are most frequently met. Occasionally a sallow *Salix atrocinerea* and holly *Ilex aquifolium* add diversity, and slightly more common is the rowan in its more usual ground-rooted situation rather than its epiphytic posture.

The woodland has changed considerably in the last fifty years and is no longer an almost impenetrable jungle of moss-festooned procumbent branches. Deeply crevassed clitter is still hard on the feet, but the moss and liverwort blanket has declined. Trees now grow taller and straighter, making it possible for grazing animals to enter the wood. As a result of both climatic and man-induced changes, the wood is becoming progressively less interesting.

Beneath the trees is a field layer community often dominated by the coarse foliage of the woodrushes, great woodrush *Luzula sylvatica* and hair woodrush *L. pilosa*. Ferns are represented by the narrow buckler fern *Dryopteris spinulosa* and the common male fern *D. felix-mas* together with bracken *Pteridium aquilinum* which dominates the clitter outside the wood and forms an attractive chestnut frame in the autumn.

Higher flowering plants are represented by wavy hair grass *Deschampsia flexuosa* and the paler green creeping soft grass *Holcus mollis* while larger-flowered species are scarce, but the yellow-flowered tormentil *Potentilla erecta* and the attractive wood sorrel *Oxalis acetosella* are present. Other flowering plants are heath bedstraw *Galium saxatile*, wood sage *Teucrium scorodonia*, English stonecrop *Sedum anglicum* and the less commonly seen white climbing corydalis *Corydalis claviculata*.

Similar to Wistman's Wood but having less deformed trees, is Black Tor Copse (or Beare) another forest nature reserve covering 72 acres about four miles south-west of Okehampton. Here the small oaks are mainly *Quercus robur* but sessile oak *Q. petraea* is also to be found. The woodland like Wistman's Wood grows on a clitter-covered steep hillside which gives way to open moorland at about 1,450ft. A third natural wood, Higher Piles Copse, is found high up in the Erme valley on Dartmoor. Despite the similarities in aspect, elevation and soil, Wistman's Wood is much richer in epiphytes and undergrowth than the other two woodlands but the reasons for this are not known. Likewise little work has been done on the animals of these elevated woodlands although the avifauna has been briefly studied by H. G. Hurrell (see *Dartmoor* by Harvey and St Ledger Gordon); further observations would be most valuable.

The sessile oak *Q. petraea*, which in other northern and western regions of the British Isles forms high level woodland, is on Dartmoor more or less confined to rocks surrounding the granite mass, particularly those forming the metamorphic aureole where the soils are better drained. One of the best remaining series of native deciduous woodlands on the margins of Dartmoor occurs in the Bovey valley about four miles north-west of Bovey Tracey. This area is now a national nature reserve and consists of a number of woods on a variety of soils. Both pedunculate and sessile oaks grow together with ash, birch and alder.

Another national nature reserve of 73 acres is Dendles Wood, nine miles north-east of Plymouth on the southern edge of the Dartmoor National Park. The woodland, on shallow soil derived from granite and upper Devonian sediments, lies between 475 and 900ft. The western part of the wood is mainly pedunculate oak but beech is common in the east. It may be that beech died out as a native tree during the last Ice Age in the South West but it now does very well regenerating naturally, and at Dendles Wood as elsewhere in the area it invades the native oakwoods. Ground cover is mainly provided by Yorkshire fog grass, bluebells and bracken, together with the usual luxuriant growth of mosses.

Geologically, sessile oak seems to be a later arrival on Dartmoor than the pedunculate form which it is suggested formed a once more extensive forest cover. Sessile oak woodlands are found mainly to the north and north-west of the Dartmoor granite, good examples occurring at Holne Chase and Yarner Wood. At the latter, which is now a national nature reserve, the sessile oak is accompanied by birch, rowan and holly. A great deal of experimental work is carried out at Yarner and a woodland trail has been established (see Appendix for details of location).

Thriving in the clean damp air of Wistman's Wood and Black Tor Copse are the mosses *Isothecium myosuroides*, *Scapania gracilis* and *Dicranum scoparium*. Other common species are:

On boulders: *Rhacomitrium heterostrichum*
Rhytidiadelphus loreus
Plagiothecium undulatum

On thin upper branches:

Hypnum cupressiforme var *filiforme*
Ulota bruchii
Antitrichia curtipendula

On overhanging rocks or tree trunks liverworts:

Douinia ovata
Plagiochila punctata

Higher Piles Copse which is the third example on Dartmoor of a relict woodland, differs from the other two mentioned above, in having little *Antitrichia* or *Douinia* which are replaced by three species confined to this area of Devon, *Jamesoniella autumnalis*, *Harpanthus scutatus* and *Dicranum flagellare*. These differences may be due to the milder even more humid climate of Piles Copse.

In the river valleys at lower altitudes woodland is similarly if less richly clothed with bryophytes. Here the two dominant species are *Isothecium myosuroides* and *Frullania tamarisci*. Locally common and frequently-found species growing on ash, oak, hazel and beech, are the mosses *Ulota bruchii*, *U. crispa* and *Orthotrichum* spp together with the liverwort *Frullania dilatata*.

Ground bryophyte flora in Devon is varied and in part at least dependent on the type of habitat. Rock-strewn woodlands either in valleys or on exposed clitter-covered uplands provide two common species *Isothecium myosuroides* and *Rhytidiadelphus loreus*. In less rocky woods occur *Polytrichum formosum*, *Mnium hornum*, *Dicranum majus*, *Thuidium tamariscinum* and *Plagiothecium undulatum*. Valley bottoms, where conditions are less acid due to the downwash of soluble salts from higher ground, support *Eurhynchium striatum*, *Mnium undulatum* and *Plagiochila aspenoides*.

In boggy woods such as Yarner Wood and Lustleigh Cleave where golden saxifrage *Chrysosplenium oppositifolium* occurs, may be found the mosses *Sphagnum subsecundum* var *inundatum*, *Thudium tamariscinum* and *Hookeria lucens*. Flourishing on rotting wood in these locations are liverworts such as *Lophocolea cuspidata* and *L. heterophylla* with two other species which also occur on peat, *Tetraphis pellucida* and *Cephalozia media*.

In Cornwall there are at present no natural woodlands of forest nature reserve status, although a very interesting and little-known woodland having similarities with the stunted oak woods of Dartmoor is found in North Cornwall at the Dizzard. Some of the oaks here are very stunted and occur on a much land-slipped precipitous cliff of Culm shales above the Atlantic. It may be that the constantly slipping materials cover the base of the oaks and only allow the topmost branches to protrude. In clefts sheltered from the sea, however, the oaks grow fairly well and the influence of salt-laden wind would seem to be the main factor causing the dwarfing of the cliff-face trees. Possibly these stunted oak woodlands were once more common on the north coasts but the tin smelters took most that were available, as they did no doubt on Dartmoor, and those that were left were coppiced to provide charcoal for the blowing houses until the demise of the latter in the mid-nineteenth century.

Coppice and scrub

Apart from the high level relict woodlands there are in the South West many acres of typical woodland which are in part natural but severely modified by man, particularly by his ancient management technique known as coppicing. This involved the felling of the tree, usually oak, so that from the cut stump near ground level numerous thin pole-like growths would sprout. These were harvested every twenty years or so and used for a variety of purposes from charcoal manufacture and fencing to the use of the bark for leather tanning. Woodland resulting from such management is called coppice but not all trees were so treated; some were allowed to grow up as standards to produce timber for ship building, and roof or lintel construction in houses. The coppicing technique was dependent on the local rural industries and when these ancient crafts died out so the coppice woods changed.

Ecologically, coppice woodlands are very unstable unless regularly cropped. When neglected they grow up, or in forestry terms degenerate into an almost impenetrable thicket of what is called scrub woodland; this is economically rather useless but is for natural history purposes very productive, providing plenty of shelter and food for a wide variety of birds, insects and small mammals, and an interesting ground flora.

The Somerset part of Exmoor has many acres of scrub woodland and the county as a whole has more woodland of this type than any other English county. Much of the 17,000 acres of Exmoor woodland, including that spilling out into Devon, is of scrub oak type and of this 9,000 acres are controlled by the Forestry Commission, with National Trust and County Councils holding much of the remainder.

Devon also has a great quantity of scrub oak, and with its nearly 2½ thousand acres is second only to Somerset in the scrub oak league table. The woodland in the two counties typically follows the sides of steep river valleys, for example the Barle, Upper Exe and Haddeo in Somerset, and the Taw–Torridge, Upper Dart and the Tamar–Tavy in Devon. The Exmoor coast of Devon has a fringe of woodland, so forming one of the finest tree-covered coasts in the country. The beauty of the woodland is enhanced by the magnificent, often inaccessible sea cliffs, many of these tree-clad precipitous slopes. Further inland a good example of well-preserved, coppiced oaks form Burridge Woods near Dulverton.

In Cornwall oak coppice mainly of sessile oak *Quercus petraea* is common and typical along the river valleys running down to the wind-sheltered south coast. Many of the oaks are trimmed by the salt water and are joined by other species such as beech, ash, elm and the imported evergreen oak and sycamore. Much of this woodland of over 30,000 acres is privately owned, mainly by the Duchy of Cornwall, while Lord Falmouth has an extensive woodland along the Fal in South Cornwall.

The diverse fauna found in old coppice oak woods is encouraged by the deep layers of leaf mould, an abundance of rotting tree trunks, and fallen branches in all stages of decay. Coppiced oak woods are seldom pure oak stands for beside the dominant oaks *Quercus robur* and the more abundant sessile oak Q. *petraea*, ash, holly, birch and rowan are found while in the underscrub which is often rather sparse, grow hazel, blackthorn, honeysuckle, holly and the equally prickly, almost natural, barbed wire jungle of bramble. Brambles seem to flourish in woodlands where natural browsing species such as deer are absent.

Ground flora is commonly wood anemone *Anemone nemorosa*, bluebell *Endymion non scripta*, primrose *Primula vulgaris*, ling *Calluna vulgaris* and whortleberry *Vaccinium myrtilus*; less abundant although frequently adding splashes of colour to the woodland edge are golden rod *Solidago virgaurea* and cow wheat *Melampyrum pratense* which occurs on dry banks and is much sought after by the larvae of the heath fritillary *Mellicta athalia* an attractive speckled butterfly, found in a few woodland areas. Wood sanicle *Sanicula europaea* is common not only in woodland but along shady lanes. The huge pink and white flowers of bastard balm *Melittis melissophyllum* are a feature of Cornish woodlands where they are frequented by bees and hawk moths in search of the plants' abundant nectar.

Probably May and June are the best months for woodland flowers but many continue flowering right into September; after this it is fungi which dominate the oakwood floor, covering dead branches and fallen trees as well as the leaf debris with a variety of bracket and multicoloured parasol growths. Also present right through the winter in the South West are the graceful fronds of the abundant ferns which are so typical of local woodlands. Lady fern, male fern, golden scale and soft shield fern are all frequent. The lady fern fronds, however, do not usually survive winter frosts. Other regularly occurring species are the common buckler and the less frequently found narrow buckler, together with a south-west form often appearing in Cornish woodlands, the hay-scented buckler fern.

Sometimes many square yards of open woodland floor will be carpeted with the long strap-like leaves of the hartstongue and the lower branches of the trees covered with epiphytic growths of common polypody which with the impressive ground-rooted fern are characteristic of the damp lichen-rich woodlands. Diligent searching may reveal the rare Tunbridge filmy fern which is not confined to woodland but also occurs on exposed granite tors.

Most of these sessile oakwoods have abundant mosses, liverworts and lichens as we have already noted, but they are less rich in flowering plants than lowland oakwoods in eastern and central England where more species of continental distribution are found. To many visitors the prolific fern growths will, however, offer both visual and botanical attraction and compensate for the lack of variety of flowering plants found in these maritime areas.

Woodland animal life

In the often warm, damp woodlands the woodant *Formica rufa* is abundant. Its nests of great piles of leaves are often very obvious particularly in clearings and near pathways through the woodlands. Most invertebrate groups are well represented but due to the generally acid conditions snails are rare. Most of the predatory spiders are of the jumping and rapid running, hunting types rather than the web-builders, and belong to the *Lycosidae* and *Linyphiidae* families.

Butterflies such as the brown, purple and green hairstreaks, speckled woods and silver-washed, high brown and pearl-bordered fritillaries are familiar day fliers, while moths make use of the dusk and dark. Badgers and foxes often use the larvae of geometrid and noctuid moths as sources of protein in their diet; for similar purposes they take the long snorkle-tubed air-breathing rats tail maggots of the abundant hover flies whose larvae are often found in woodland pools.

One of the most striking features of the oak coppice and also of the standard trees, is the very high gall fly population parasitizing the leaves and leaf buds. Golden-brown spangled galls on the undersurface of leaves caused by the small wasps of the genus *Neuroterus* are particularly abundant in late summer and autumn, as are the larger, familiar, soft oak apples which are produced by the cynipid *Biorhiza pallida* and the probably more familiar hard marble gall or Devonshire gall which should not be called an oak apple, and is produced by another cynipid wasp *Andricus kollari*. The hornets that occur in such oak woodlands will, it is hoped, be seen and heard rather than felt; they are attracted, as are many other insects, to the ubiquitous ivy flowers. The speckled bush cricket *Leptophyrs punctatissima* and the oak bush cricket *Meconema thalassinum* which is the only member of the Orthoptera to live naturally in trees, are likely to be heard after dark on late summer evenings. The oak bush cricket produces a peculiar drumming sound which can be heard over the distance of a few yards; once 'singing' it will continue even in torch light when the unique sound production mechanism can be studied. The speckled bush cricket has a very soft song which has to be listened for with great concentration. While so engaged, other rustlings will no doubt be detected as the small mammals move around in the deep leaf litter. Wood-mice are more arboreal than the voles and shrews and can sometimes be seen in daylight collecting acorns from the tips of even the most slender branches.

A familiar sound over the more remote woodlands is the mewing of the buzzard which nests in the taller trees, as do carrion crows, jays, kestrels and, more rarely, sparrowhawks. Insect-eating nuthatches, tree creepers and woodpeckers are all common although the spotted woodpecker is not a usual inhabitant of Cornish woodlands. In winter time many parties of tits can be seen moving along woodlands that border streams, where they are often joined by diminutive, very common goldcrest wrens. The mixed flocks are mainly of long tailed, coal and blue tits all of which are common breeding birds. Indeed, woodland bird life in the South West is particularly noteworthy for the species that are absent or in smaller numbers than elsewhere in the British Isles. This we shall see also applies to woodland plants in the South West.

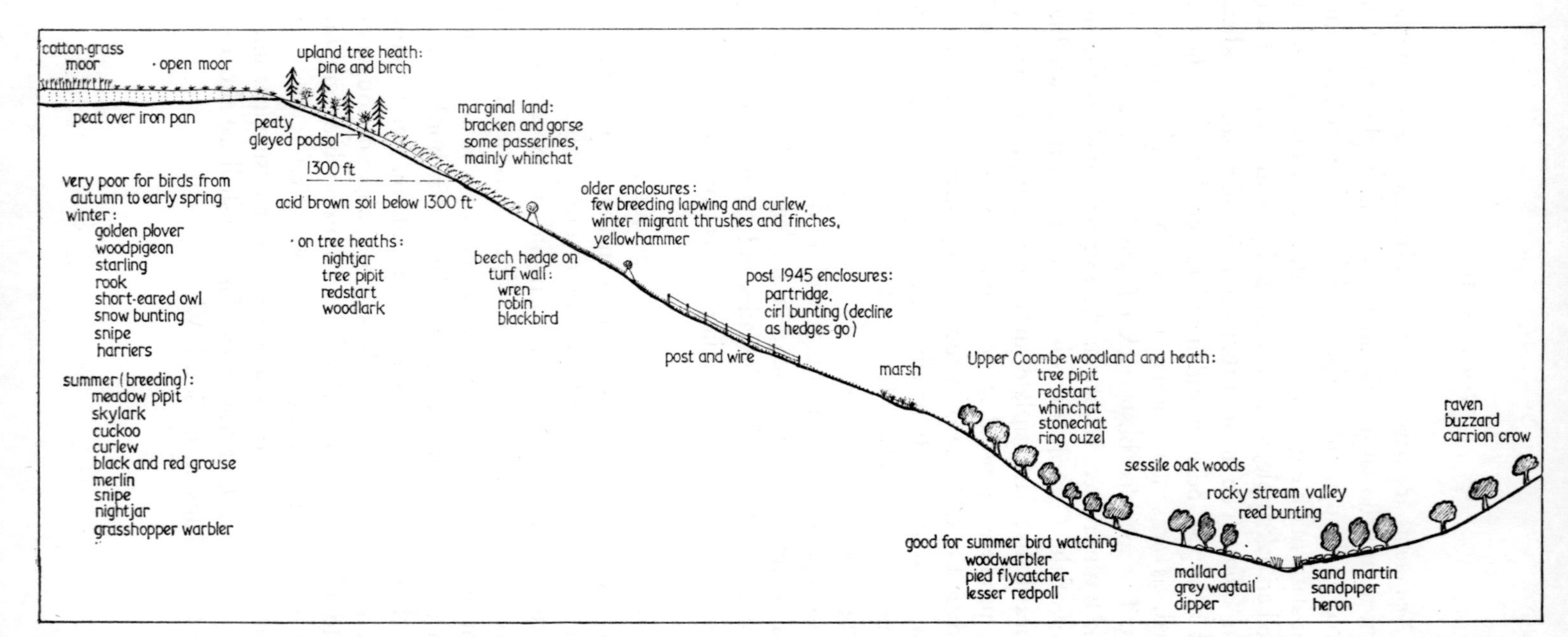

Figure 3 Diagrammatic section of a typical Exmoor area showing the main habitats and distribution of birds associated with them (not to scale)

In Cornwall the nightingale is absent as a breeding bird although passing through on migration, but the western limit as a breeding bird seems to be the Blackdown Hills in Devon. The garden warbler is another species that is absent as a regular bird in Cornwall. In the early part of the century starlings and woodpeckers seem to have been fairly rare in Cornwall as breeding species. Starlings now occur in vast numbers in the winter when on occasions small woods are destroyed by the accumulation of droppings. Green woodpeckers are now fairly common in Cornwall where they are creatures often of open ant-infested grasslands by the sea, rather than a woodland species. The spotted woodpeckers, not very abundant in Cornwall, can be seen commonly in Exmoor woodlands, but even so the lesser spotted is much more local than the greater spotted. Common summer woodland birds of Exmoor are shown on figure 3, opposite.

Some of the Dartmoor woodlands have recently been colonized by pied flycatchers which are encouraged to breed by the provision of nest boxes. Since 1955 pied flycatchers have also become well established in the national nature reserve at Yarner Wood.

In the drier coppiced woodland, adders, slow worms and common lizards make up what is for the British Isles a varied reptile population. Where thick undergrowth is found so is the grass snake which is unfortunately often killed in mistake for its venomous relative, the adder.

A good herd numbering 500–700 red deer, the largest native wild animal in the British Isles, still survives on Exmoor and also on the Brendon Hills and Quantocks. There have been red deer on Exmoor probably since the end of the Ice Age and the present animals represent descendants of the original indigenous animals. From their centre in the so-called Forest of Exmoor they stray into surrounding areas; there is a good herd in the plantation at Halwill near Okehampton, and they cross the border into Cornwall. A small herd exists in the Colquite and Glynn valley coverts near Bodmin and there is evidence too of red deer even in the conifer plantations on the Lizard. Roe deer are present in Somerset and Devon, and they have in recent years spread over the border into Cornwall. This tendency for deer to be found more widely distributed than in the past is due largely to the protection they are able to find in the new coniferous forests. Deer control may soon become a necessary task, particularly in Devon. They have no natural enemy except for man and so numbers tend to build up rapidly with consequently much damage, particularly to young conifers.

On Exmoor, of course, the Devon and Somerset stag hounds serve to limit the number of deer. Stag hunting has aroused great opposition and at present the League Against Cruel Sports is buying woodland in strategically placed areas on Exmoor in the hopes both of providing shelter for the deer and of frustrating the stag hounds and their followers by not allowing them to set foot on this land.

The red deer rut from roughly mid-October to mid-November which is the best time for observing and hearing their rutting roars; the peak time is around the third week in October depending on weather conditions, for a frosty spell is necessary to get the rut really under way. Fallow deer are also present in parklands and there are some feral herds. The other kinds present in the area are imported species now living and breeding in the wild state. The spotted sika deer *Cervus nippon*, an eastern relative of our native red, has spread from Dorset and Somerset and is well established in East Devon woodlands and also in parkland at Mount Edgcumbe near Plymouth. The little short-antlered large-toothed muntjac or barking deer is probably also present, and unconfirmed sightings of this species have been made right down in West Cornwall.

Other woodland animals such as the badger and squirrel are common. Both the red and grey squirrel occur but, as elsewhere in the British Isles, the red seems to be slowly yielding ground as the grey advances. Most stretches of woodland will be found to have a badger population, particularly in those areas with easily excavated soil. Pine martens are, unfortunately, now extinct in the South West, but there is a possibility that a few polecats still exist in the woodlands along the river valleys in Cornwall. Many suspected polecats eventually turn out to be either dark ferrets or 'fitchets', a polecat-ferret cross used in rabbit hunting.

Other native trees

Among the oaks other species are represented, many of these imported; they will be considered in the next section but mention must be made of a few other native species of tree. The Cornish elm is restricted as a native plant to the south-west peninsula. The tree, which is usually found in hedgerows where it is trimmed, is seldom able to show its natural pyramidal shape. The leaves of the Cornish elm are very much smaller than those of the English subspecies. Like the other elms found in the area, the wych and the common elm, the leaves are resistant to salt sea winds and sometimes the elm is able to form a wind-sculptured copse with a small amount of shelter from the winds. A good example of a natural elm wood has grown up in the last sixty years or so on the edge of a coastal heathland belt above Chapel Porth near St Agnes in Cornwall. Such woodland is not rich in herbs but growths of ferns, particularly the hartstongue, form a dense dark green carpet.

Ash, although a native species which is common in many places, does not form any natural woodlands in Cornwall probably due to the lack of basic soils but as we shall see, in Devon and further north-east in Somerset, it forms extensive woodland on more calcareous soils. Lime is another native species that is rare as a woodland tree in Cornwall where it mainly occurs planted in churchyards and parks, and on roadsides or in woods developed locally on limestone.

It may be surprising to learn that the yew is not apparently native in Cornwall although it has been much planted in churchyards.

Birch trees have lived in the South West for many thousands

of years and their fossilised remains in the upland peat are of hairy birch *Betula pubescens* of the same species as those which now form widespread growths in East Cornwall. In Devon over 4,000 acres of birch scrub is found which includes the second common species *B. verrucosa*—silver birch. In the same family, the *Betulaceae*, is grouped the alder *Alnus glutinosa* which is common in damper woodlands.

Beech behaves like a native species and produces ripe seeds and propagates very successfully. It probably arrived in the British Isles during the Atlantic period before the Bronze Age and for the last few thousand years it has seemed to be receding from the West. In places, however, the reverse process is taking place, and beech is invading old oak woods which fail to regenerate naturally. The beech woods that occur in Devon and Cornwall albeit covering a small area, are perhaps replacements of old native oak woodlands.

Once natural tree cover is destroyed it is sometimes difficult for it to become re-established if the climatic conditions are unsuitable; in the South West, wind is probably the greatest factor preventing tree growth.

The result is that Cornwall, if approached over Bodmin Moor along the A30 or along the north coast road, will present to the visitor an almost treeless scene. What tree cover there is in North Cornwall and adjacent parts of Devon is confined to valleys sheltered from the south-westerly winds, a few stunted wind-sculptured hedgerow trees, and small shelter belts of elm or beech planted around isolated farms. This picture is not true, however, as we have seen, of the English Channel coasts or inland in the east of Cornwall where fairly extensive deciduous woodlands, principally of oak, are associated mainly with the river courses. Only 4 per cent, however, of the land mass of Cornwall is still wooded, amounting to a little over 35,000 acres.

Devon is more wooded than Cornwall with tree cover a little more than 7 per cent of the county land area, which is only slightly higher than the national county average of 6·6 per cent. In terms of acreage this means that there are about 119,000 acres of woodland in Devon including up to 54,000 acres of hardwoods.

The policy of the National Trust is of course of great importance to the future of much of the woodland in the two counties, and the Trust's policy in seeking to protect the wooded valleys leading to higher moorland on Exmoor and Dartmoor, involves a great deal of management of these old woods.

Much of the Trust woodland is typical oak coppice which is common in the area, but such rich habitats are unfortunately, as we have seen, very unstable ecologically, tending to degenerate into scrub. Growth up to high forest is now encouraged by 'singling' coppice stems to about 100 per acre where it is felt vigorous growth can take place. Where the old woods have degenerated too far, particularly on exposed hilly areas with highly leached acid soil, birch and hazel have taken over from the oaks. In such situations the National Trust policy is to underplant with a beech/conifer mixture.

Although oak woodland is considered typical of the lower, more favourable regions of the South West, evidence suggests that an ecological change is taking place with open oak woods in some cases gradually being replaced by beech, ash and sycamore woodland as these species regenerate naturally, while the oak seldom does. We could now call this the Beech age, a tree normally associated with limestone woodland.

Base rich habitats are extremely local in the area, confined as they are to calcareous dunes and a few patches of limestone of Devonian and Carboniferous age (see map figure 1, p 21). In South-east Devon, however, on the younger Cretaceous rocks of Chalk and Greensand, ashwoods have developed; these appear on the exposed steep hillsides of small valleys leading down to the coast. Only when the Upper Greensand underlies the thin layer of Chalk is the Greensand highly calcareous and has, like the chalk rock, a shrubby calcicolous (lime-loving) ashwood community, for example Watercombe and Seller's Wood, Branscombe. In the aerial photograph of Beer Head (see plate p 103) the woodland can be seen beyond the level chalk downland in the foreground. Away from the Chalk, however, the Greensand is non-calcareous and is in fact highly acid, carrying a heathy type of oakwood with pedunculate oak *Quercus robur*.

Where the Greensand is calcareous, ash *Fraxinus* is the dominant tree with a rich flora particularly near the coast. In the field layer, early flowering dog's mercury *Mercurialis perennis* is dominant with abundant wild garlic or ramsons *Allium ursinum* in damper places, together with hartstongue fern *Phyllitis scolopendrium*. The dense thickets of wild clematis *Clematis vitalba* are an obvious feature of the area, particularly when the flowers have matured to white-plumed fruits. (For full species list see the Flora of Devon.)

Another region of natural woodland but of more recent origin than the ash woods, occurs in the Axmouth and Lyme Regis undercliff area. Here between Culvehole Point and Humble Point the undercliffs are of fallen Cretaceous deposits resting on Lias shore reefs. In 1838 cracks and fissures appeared in the cliff top and eventually a great landslip resulted in the formation of Downland's Chasm in 1839. About eight million tons of earth foundered forming a gash about half a mile long, 200ft wide in the west increasing to 400ft in the east. This classic example of a landslip is now a National Nature Reserve of great specialist ecological interest. An ash wood developed naturally in the chasm which, due to lack of human disturbance and its close proximity to the sea, created special conditions in which a wide variety of plants and animals flourish.

Introduced and imported trees

The other type of woodland in the South West is that planted for scenic and amenity purposes in the eighteenth and nineteenth centuries, much of which is mature parkland now owned by the National Trust or local authorities. It is not intended here to give a long account of the estates which add much to the beauty of the countryside; some of the most important are men-

Page 51 (*above*) A part of the high northern plateau of Dartmoor, much dissected blanket bog forming hags. Large conifer forests visible in distance on left; (*below*) southern area of Dartmoor near Shaugh Prior. Plateau in distance lacks peat hags but has wetter soil. Encroachment by agricultural reclamation and amenity use is obvious. Sheltered valleys support damp woodlands while more exposed areas are planted with conifers

Page 52 (*above*) Trevellas Valley, Cornwall, typical mine disturbed valle with spoil heaps recolonised by Euro pean gorse, heather and ling. Old mine buildings have man lichens and ferns of interest; (*left*) cock stonechat or 'furze-chip', a typical bird of coastal heathland

tioned in the Appendix and many are listed in the National Trust handbook. Reference must briefly be made to the introduced and planted native species which now add so much diversity to the woodland scene both inland and more particularly in coastal areas.

Trees and shrubs were planted not only in parkland and ornamental gardens but also for utilitarian purposes. Shelter belts of vegetation are vital if full benefit is going to be made of the mild coastal climate of the south-west peninsula. Gale-force winds laden with salt soon dessicate and kill the tender shoots in their path but some imported trees and a few native species are able to tolerate and even flourish under such conditions.

Native British species such as the wych elm *Ulmus glabra* is one such wind- and salt-hardy plant which even forms a small copse on the very exposed St Michael's Mount, a small rocky island just off Penzance. The Cornish elm can, as we have seen, grow up naturally in windy places; it has been planted for shelter purposes even along parts of the north coast and stands of this tree are common around coastal farms. The secret of the success of the elms and the equally tolerant ash, is that these trees produce their leaves late in the spring at the end of May and so the young buds are not blackened by early spring gales which are common in the area.

Beech, particularly in the form of hedges, has been planted in many areas away from direct contact with spray. Locations such as Exmoor are good places to see beech hedges which often retain their golden-brown dead leaves right through the winter so increasing their effectiveness in filtering wind.

Of the planted deciduous trees away from the sea many excellent mature beech stands occur in Cornwall; good examples of these can be seen at Boconnoc and Lanhydrock while in Somerset the Nettlecombe oaks are magnificent (see note in Appendix). Many other deciduous trees were also planted including ash, sweet chestnut, sycamore and, again, beech.

White poplar *Populus alba* with its heavy, pure white, downy cover on young twigs and the lower surface of leaves is another indigenous tree which does well, sometimes reaching 50ft even in salty winds; consequently this too has been planted as a windbreak. Its habit of producing many suckers helps form a dense low shelter.

The native but salt-intolerant Scots pine *Pinus sylvestris* was also frequently planted but many of these trees are now dead, particularly in Cornwall where some seem to have been killed by the droppings of countless winter starlings which have a habit of roosting in such places, destroying and then moving on.

Sycamore, unlike its smaller-leaved relative the field maple *Acer campestre*, is an imported species from central Europe, and probably arrived in this country during the fifteenth century. Despite early production of large leaves and consequent leaf loss during high winds, the sycamore grows well and regenerates often in very exposed areas open to salt-laden winds. Another hardy, large-leaved import is the attractive-leaved sweet chestnut which belongs to the oak family. Many fine trees of this species will be found in inland plantations and parkland but near the coast these trees also flourish. This species is native to the Mediterranean region and was probably introduced for its fruit by the Romans who must, however, have been disappointed with the nut crop that was obtained as the late flowering of the tree in July gives little time for fruit production before the winter winds and frosts. The trees were sometimes grown as coppice for the production of small poles.

Horse chestnut trees *Aesculus hippocastanum* produce the large ornamental candle-like inflorescences in late May, and are always an impressive sight and attractive to the young and not so young during the autumn when the large, brown, shiny smooth seeds are released from the prickly 'conker' cases. In parks the horse chestnut is not only decorative but the seeds provide a valuable autumn food supply for the deer. The tree was introduced in the sixteenth century from South-east Europe and has been widely planted in Devon and Cornwall although it does not seem to like exposure to strong winds and is seldom seen away from the sheltered areas.

Two imported species of oak add dignity and one gives winter colour to parkland. The Turkey oak *Quercus ceris* is a native of the Balkans and was introduced here in the eighteenth century; the acorns with their stalkless, green, scale-covered cups are unlike those of our native species and do not mature until the second year. The dark green foliage found on the second species *Quercus ilex* has caused the tree to be commonly called the evergreen oak. This epithet is apt as the leaves stay attached to the branches for two years and so the tree is always green due to the presence of successive crops of leaves. The latter are oval, have pointed tips and are often decidedly spiky which gives the alternative common name 'holly oak', reflected in the specific name *ilex*.

One tree which is now almost typical of the area is the fast-growing Monterey pine *Pinus radiata* which provides the main shelter on St Michael's Mount and Tresco in Scilly. Even this salt-tolerant species is subject to leaf scorch on the seaward side after very violent storms. The disadvantage of pines for a naturalist is the thick carpet of acid needles beneath the trees which will allow only limited natural vegetation, but during autumn a number of fungi are produced on the rotting vegetation. Also, bird life is locally enriched by the pine stands; in particular, the diminutive goldcrest wren's thin, high-pitched morse-like call note is frequently heard when the winds are not producing too much bass accompaniment. Coal tits, longtail tits and sparrow hawks sometimes nest, and the branches provide night roosting perches for wood pigeons and the recently introduced and extremely successful collared dove.

The Mediterranean maritime pine *Pinus pinaster* grows well in the South West with good examples clothing the north slopes of the beautiful Helford Passage at the head of the Lizard peninsula in Cornwall. The Monterey cypress *Cupressus macrocarpa* is also a common feature of the coastal strip, particularly along the more sheltered south coasts, for it is less salt- and wind-tolerant than the other species mentioned.

Not all the plantations are coastal and many fine examples of trees from other parts of the world were established out of reach of salt and high wind. In Somerset, Dunster Castle estate has some fine Douglas fir trees at Broadwood. These trees are among the best of their kind in the country; planted in 1874, some are now 155ft high and with a girth of 12ft.

It is not easy to find many examples of a beneficial effect to native species being brought about by introductions from other parts of the world. In the case of the giant wellingtonia or redwoods *Sequoia* spp, they are of great importance to a small, rather delicate native species of bird, the tree creeper. This often suffers badly in severe winter frosts but the birds have developed the technique of excavating a shallow crevice in the thick soft fibre-like bark of the redwood. The birds press themselves closely into this crack, and use the natural insulation of the bark to prevent undue heat loss from their bodies; so the species is able to survive in greater numbers. On the Isles of Scilly, as we shall see in Chapter Twelve, the local birds have found imported exotic trees provide a useful nectar source.

Much experimental work on the growth of trees and shrubs under adverse conditions is carried out near Camborne in Cornwall within two miles of the north coast. Here at the Rosewarne experimental station up to one hundredweight of salt has been found to fall per acre of ground each year; it is hardly surprising, therefore, that the greatest care has to be taken in selecting suitable species to plant along the coasts of the South West.

Coniferous forests

More recently, in this century, a third factor emerged to influence the woodland of the area in the shape of the Forestry Commission whose very first trees were planted at Eggesford in Devon during 1919. Much of the area used for planting was formerly open moorland and the Commission has thereby come in for criticism from other countryside users, particularly on Exmoor; however, for the record it should be stated that up to 1966 only 900 acres had been afforested in the area of Exmoor, while over 7,000 acres had been either partly or completely reclaimed for agricultural use. In many cases also the moorland soil is too poor to support deciduous trees, but it is hoped that these will be planted again when the conifers have improved the soil.

The South West Conservancy of the Forestry Commission which includes Devon, Cornwall and West Somerset, controls the bulk of the coniferous tree cover in the area, extending to over 200,000 acres. In some areas larch, spruce and Douglas fir have been planted after the clearance of the original coppice or scrub woodland.

In Devon the Commission has thirteen estates which it either owns or manages. Six of the plantations are situated on poor quality Culm measure soils including the largest forest in the South West covering 4,590 acres at Halwill about four miles east of Holsworthy. The smallest of the plantations is at Bampton, with others in order of acreage at Okehampton, Lydford, Eggesford, Hartland, and finally Halwill.

The Dartmoor and Fernworthy plantations are on exposed moorland, some of it over 1,500ft high where the tallest sikta spruce is over 70ft. Steep slopes have been planted with conifers in the Molton, Plym and Erme valleys. Of the remaining plantations those in the Honiton area consist of eleven separate acquisitions planted on gravel-capped Greensand hills giving a rather discontinuous pattern of dark trees dotted among rich agricultural land, unlike the more continuously wooded plantation at Haldon. These thirteen estates make up about one-sixth of the total woodland of Devon.

In Cornwall the first Forestry Commission plantation was established in 1922 in the Glynn valley, part of the beautiful Fowey valley. There are now five more plantations, at Bodmin in the Vale of Camel, at Herodsfoot associated with the Looe and West Looe rivers, at St Clement near Truro where a small estate runs along the River Allen, and two remaining exposed sites on open heathland. These two plantations are mainly experimental and the Wilsey Down plantation has a very poor growth rate, while the Croft Pascoe 100 acre site on the Lizard peninsula has been established to study the growth of trees under extremely exposed conditions.

In Somerset most of the older plantations are of larch and Scots pine but of recent years much spruce has been planted. The largest areas are on the north side of the Brendon Hills between Dunster and Luxborough. The tree cover on the hills between Dunster and Wootton Courtney and above Luccombe is also mainly coniferous. Scots pine was planted a great deal around Minehead, and there are smaller plantations to the east and north-east.

While there have been many objections to the coniferous plantations on purely aesthetic grounds and because of the dearth of animal and plant species, they have benefitted the avifauna, particularly on the higher moorland. Goldcrest, robin, coal tit and bullfinch populations have all increased. Other species to prosper and breed in these upland forests are sparrow hawk, merlin, Montagu's harrier, chiff-chaff, siskin and redpoll. The younger plantations attract grasshopper warblers and whinchat.

In the next chapter we shall consider the habitat which is now so abundant in the South West, namely heathland and moorland which as we have seen developed as a secondary vegetation cover after man, aided by climatic changes, brought an end to the great oak forests which covered most of the surface of south-western Britain until a few thousand years ago.

From those forests we have lost the once native bears, pigs, pine martens, polecats, lynx, wolverine, and wolf, but moorlands have their rewards although they tend to come in a botanical rather than a zoological form.

CHAPTER THREE

Heathland and Moorland

Heather moorland – Grass moors – Blanket and valley bog – Dry heathland – Wet heaths – Moor and heathland animals

IT IS APPROPRIATE I feel, that this chapter should be written by candlelight, living as we do on the edge of open heathland surrounding and crowning St Agnes Beacon and open to the gale force wind which sweeps from the south-west over the Atlantic and is even now bringing down the overhead power cables.

This North-west Cornish coast is dominated by salt-laden winds, open heath-covered high cliffs and, in many places to the despoilation of the view, poles which carry telephone and electricity to remote cottages and farms, each of which it seems must have its own separate line of dark stakes. However, in the almost complete absence of tall trees, the poles do provide perches for kestrels, carrion crows, rooks, and in the summer, cuckoos, often with attendant meadow pipits attempting to dissuade the parasites from their nesting areas.

If the wind influences the human way of life at times, it dominates the vegetation and to a lesser extent the animal life in many parts of the South West; it is with these regions of frequent wind, mist and rain that we are now concerned.

Physically brooding over much of the county of Devon are the two great upland regions of Exmoor in the north and Dartmoor in the south. Dartmoor is entirely in Devon but much of Exmoor spills out into neighbouring West Somerset and gives off outliers such as the Brendons and Quantocks. Apart from these two large moorland areas, smaller areas of heathland occur in

South-east Devon but the rest is good quality farmland. Like Devon, Cornwall is also dominated by moorland and heathland scenery but few of the 100,000 acres reach any great height.

The granite backbone of the south-west peninsula, eroded to exposure in Dartmoor, again appears on the surface in a string of outcrops running north-east to south-west to form the upland areas of Bodmin, Hensbarrow (St Austell), Carnmenellis, Land's End, and off-shore, the Isles of Scilly, the latter almost entirely composed of granite. Heathland occurs on some smaller granite outcrops in Cornwall, on the Killas and Culm of West and North Cornwall, and in fact around most of the coastal strip including the botanically fascinating flat-topped Lizard peninsula. But what is found in these areas and what is meant by the two terms 'moorland' and 'heathland' that so often are used as synonyms?

To the local farmers moorland or 'out country' consists of shallow, poor quality, cold, acid, often wet and stony soil areas on steeply sloping exposed uplands, useful only for rough grazing. Much of this land has been over the years converted to 'in country' by drainage, fencing and ploughing, and some old 'in country' has reverted to 'out', but the process is mainly one of reclamation. Much of the former wilderness area of the two counties has therefore been lost, notably on Exmoor (see plate p 34). This process is continuing with the encouragement of government subsidies, despite the attempts of conservation bodies, including the old Nature Conservancy, to protect these important open areas for long-term benefit of wildlife and man rather than short-term financial gain for the few.

Other competing factions for use of moorland are the army, who use a large area of Dartmoor for training, and local water boards who lay claim to it for reservoir construction. A further influence bringing change to the open areas are forestry interests, dealt with in Chapter Two.

To a naturalist, moorlands and heathlands contain a wide variety of plant and animal communities with transitions between those of wet and dry ground. However, for our purpose moorland (upland heath) will be considered as unenclosed high ground with peaty soil not used primarily as pasture, whilst the lower ground equivalent will be called heath—this is typically drier and with less peat deposit (see figure 2, p 29).

In many parts of lowland Britain heathlands developed after removal by man of the original tree cover. Leaching away of nutrient materials in the soil followed and the resulting acidic soils (podsols) were colonised by shrubby growths of heaths, ling, gorse, and later in some cases by birch and pine. These calcium-deficient soils are no longer capable of supporting the original deciduous-tree cover but pine heaths such as those in South-east Devon have been established locally, eg Bovey Heathfield, Woodbury Common and Gittisham Common, all of which have interesting bird populations.

Moorland and heathland develop on a variety of rock types but in most cases climate and exposure are probably more important in their production than local soil conditions.

The headings 'moorland' and 'heathland' are capable of further subdivision which here for discussion are based mainly on the amount of water in the soil which, in turn, often determines what sorts of plants and dependent animal communities will flourish.

Moorland—or upland heath

Dry (a) Heather moor—equivalent to grouse moor in North of England.
Bilberry locally dominant on steeper, damper slopes.
(b) *Festuca/Agrostis* grassland.

Damp (c) *Nardus* (mat grass)—acid grass moor on well-drained areas with little peat.
(d) *Molinia* grass moor.

Wet (e) Blanket and valley bog.

Heathland—or Lowland heath

Dry (a) Oceanic. Bilberry and heather heath.
(b) Inland. Grass pine and birch heath.

Wet (c) Mainly *Sphagnum* bogs in old river valleys.

An indication of the general distribution of these habitats is given in figure 2 (p 29); all will be considered and mention made of the dominant plant species in each community together with others that are characteristic and frequently seen.

The communities are often named after the dominant type of plant which sometimes has a common English name, but in other cases the Latin name for the plants dominating the community has to be used.

Heather moorland

All the moorlands are characteristically developed on dark peaty soils which are highly acidic and therefore very poor in calcium compounds and other so-called exchangeable base substances that are so vital to the growth of many plants. The only flowers found in peaty soils are those well able to cope not only with acidic soils but often temporary water logging due to the 60in of rain per annum.

Where the peaty soil is fairly well drained great expanses of purple heather (or ling) *Calluna vulgaris* dominate. In northern England these high moorland areas are known as grouse moors but this term can hardly be applied to those similar areas in the South West for red grouse are very few and far between. Characteristic birds here are pipits, larks and crows with a few breeding lapwings over the drier ground, whose numbers are supplemented during the colder months by visiting winter flocks. Other winter visitors foraging for what must be sparse pickings are northern thrushes, mainly redwings and fieldfares, and mixed flocks of finches and golden plovers.

Where the ling grows strongly and ungrazed it forms a dense tangle with little chance for other vegetation to reach the light except by actually growing upon the ling itself. Two characteristic epiphytic lichens are the grey, dainty, almost lace-like *Hypogymnia physodes* form *elegans*, and patches of *Lecanora varia* adding textural if not particularly colourful variations to otherwise rather drab, dark brown twisted stems of ling.

Where the ling growths are less dense a rather sparse yet colourful herb and dwarf shrub layer is formed. Among the tufts of grey-green bristle bent grass *Agrostis setacea* and the similar but dark green tufts of wavy hair grass *Deschampsia flexuosa*, are the straggling growths of the yellow-flowered tormentil *Potentilla erecta* and small white rather sickly scented flower clusters of *Galium saxatile*, the heath bedstraw. Other herbs are common, among them sorrel *Rumex acetosa* ('sour sobs' to the Cornish) and thyme speedwell *Veronica serpyllifolia*.

Shrubs, often low and matted, add colourful patches among the ling, particularly the contrasting yellow of the western gorse *Ulex gallii*. The long spikes of crimson purple bell heather *Erica cinerea* are often abundant but on wetter ground the cross-leaved heath *E. tetralix* takes over, with its rose pink flowers capping the greyish foliage. Locally abundant is the whortleberry *Vaccinium myrtillus* which in late summer produces small black fruits that are sought by many mammals and birds.

All the plants mentioned have adapted to life in a rather plant-hostile soil, but one plant, the dodder *Cuscuta epithymum*, forsakes free growth in the soil after a few days for a parasitic life attached to and sometimes covering a number of shrub hosts with cotton-like threads and delicate pink flowers. Dodder draws its food directly into its reddish twining stems from the living tissues of its host and so can dispense with both chlorophyll and leaves.

Of the plants much less highly evolved than dodder, the bryophytes make up in abundance for the rather sparsely represented species of flowering plants.

Grass moors

Sheep's fescue *Festuca ovina*, and fine bent *Agrostis tenuis* often form grassland when the ling is heavily grazed by rabbits or sheep. This vegetation which covers large areas of the higher moorland on the relatively dry shallow peat soil over granite, is usually known as festuca/agrostis grassland. Neither animal nor plant life is prolific in such sward but a few other grasses join the two dominant species. The bristle bent and wavy hair grass of heather moorlands are still present but they are now joined by mat grass *Nardus stricta*, purple moor grass *Molinia caerulea* and heath grass *Sieglingia decumbens*. The last two grasses are locally common, particularly in dampish spots. Flowering plants are similar to those of the ungrazed heather moorland apart from the scarcity of low shrubs.

A number of mosses are common between the grasses, particularly *Hylocomium splendens* with red-stemmed fronds of pale whitish green, *Hypnum cupressiforme* var *ericitorum*, and tufts of hair moss *Polytrichum juniperinum*. This latter upright, dark green, robust moss with its almost flower-like male reproductive structures, often follows another moss, *Funaria*, as a coloniser of recently burnt heathland.

On the Devonian slates and grits to the north of Bodmin a similar type of festuca/agrostis grassland is found on relatively dry soil. In the absence of grazing the grasses are accompanied by and often replaced by gorse and bracken.

The gorse most often associated with grassland in the South West is the western gorse *Ulex gallii* which forms a dense, low, extremely prickly scrub which is usually just over boot-high. On disturbed sites and along roadsides and tracks it is the common gorse *U. europaeus* which forms a prickly, often head-high barrier beneath which few plants can survive. There can be few weeks in the year when this gorse or, as it is locally called, furze, is not in bloom and its bright yellow insect-attracting flowers make up for the lack of floral diversity which it creates.

With a slight increase in soil moisture mat grass is the typical species of upland acid grassland forming, due to the bleached appearance of the leaves, what is known as white moor. This community is only really common on Bodmin Moor but it is well developed also on Dartmoor; it is only of local occurrence on Exmoor which is perhaps a good thing as the rank grass indicates an overgrazed and leached soil. The tough wiry leaves are unpalatable to sheep and grouse and often form an untouched white blaze of vegetation on the upper hillsides between the bent/

fescue grassland and the higher peat moors. A few insects can make a living from mat grass but bird life is almost absent and most animals seem to shun such areas. The only other plants to be found are a few whortleberries, *Sphagnum* moss and a few heath plants, particularly the wavy hair grass.

Nardus grassland is, like the following grassland type, closely related to the main areas of deep peat and is often found around the eroded edges of the blanket bogs.

Purple moor grass or flying bent, prefers a wetter soil with a fair thickness of fairly well aerated peat for it to produce its typically tussocky form of grassland. The grass forms purple moor due to the tinge of the leaf sheaths and flower spikelets. Progress across these moorlands is best accomplished by tussock leaping which will ensure dry feet for at least a few minutes before their owner discovers the cold, muddy, often *Sphagnum*-covered water courses between the grass roots.

Moor grass is useful pasture for cattle, sheep and ponies, at least during the summer, and forms the main vegetative cover on Bodmin Moor where it is extensively developed over the peat.

In contrast to the rather barren mat grass areas purple moor contains a large number of other plants in rather scattered communities amongst the tussocks; the latter also provide food and shelter for a variety of insects which form the basis of many foodchains.

Typical purple moor areas occur below 1,000ft on the flanks of Rough Tor, the highest point on Bodmin Moor. Here the moor grass often competes with the pale yellow, soft, highly water-absorbent carpets of bog moss *Sphagnum* which is locally the dominant plant. *Sphagnum* holds large quantities of the cold acidic water even during the relative warmth of summer in these exposed places, and among the moss growths will be discovered the red-tinted, spiky, curious leaves of the insect-consuming sundew *Drosera rotundifolia*; and more rarely, a plant with similar insect-eating ability, the pale butterwort *Pinguicula lusitanica* produces its pale lilac flower from the overwintering rosette of greasy, pale, insect-trapping leaves. This species is a western speciality replacing the common butterwort *P. vulgaris* which is the more northern form.

Plants with more normal feeding mechanisms include marsh bedstraw *Galium palustre*, marsh pennywort *Hydrocotyle vulgaris* with characteristic parasol-like centre-stalked leaves, marsh violet *Viola palustris*, tormentil *Potentilla erecta* and the attractive marsh St John's wort *Hypericum elodes* with its red-dotted yellow flowers. Lousewort *Pedicularis sylvatica*, a semi-parasitic plant, produces quite attractive leafy spikes of dark red flowers. Often found nearby are the hairy leaves of the devil's bit scabious *Succisa pratensis* whose well-scalloped leaf margins indicate its attractiveness to butterfly and moth caterpillars. The buttercup family is represented by yellow-flowered lesser spearwort *Ranunculus flammula*, and the more aquatic mud-loving ivy-leaved crowfoot *R. hederaceus* whose glorious masses of white flowers often float on the surface of any standing water. Another aquatic form is the creeping-stemmed bog bean *Menyanthes trifoliata* with its conspicuous white flowers projecting above the water in May and June.

In wetter areas of the moor with standing, rather stagnant water, the so-called cotton grasses which are in fact sedges, produce their conspicuous nodding white cotton-covered fruits. The common cotton grass *Eriophorum angustifolium*, in fact is less abundant than its relative the harestail *E. vaginatum* which is unlike the other species in having a tussocky habit and a single tuft of white down covering the mature fruits in summer.

Where drainage is better and mineral supply relatively good, sheeps fescue and fine bent grass take over from the *Molinia*, but in the event of mineral shortage only the tolerant mat grass and wavy hair grass can maintain themselves.

The flowering shrubs are well represented by cross-leaved heath and ling with much more rarely a patch of whortleberry. As one would suspect in such damp conditions, a variety of rushes and sedges flourish; most common are the compact rush *Juncus conglomeratus*, the toad rush *J. bufonius*, the heath rush *J. squarrosus* and bulbous rush *J. bulbosus*. The heath woodrush *Luzula multiflora* is abundant but sedges are less frequent, and moor sedge *Carex binervis*, common sedge *C. nigra* and the much rarer white beak-sedge *Rhynchospora alba* are the only members of their genus likely to be found.

Blanket and valley bog

Given an elevated stretch of poorly drained ground in a climate of low summer temperature, high rainfall, and great humidity due to frequent cloud cover and proximity to the sea, *Sphagnum* moss will flourish. The rather pale green spongy growths formerly spread out in an ever-growing, deepening layer over the surrounding ground; and this produced a flat, or sometimes hummocky, plant-suffocating mixture of living and dead moss, known descriptively as 'blanket bog'.

Sphagnum growth probably began during the wet Atlantic prehistoric period on the high plateaux of Exmoor, Dartmoor and Bodmin Moor (though blanket bog is not found further south-west). The moss contains within its spongy-textured leaves and stems considerable amounts of acid water which can easily be squeezed out in a clenched fist. Layer upon layer of moss and a few higher plants that can survive such conditions gradually compacted under the weight of the living blanket rising above, and formed deep peat deposits. Lack of oxygen and the aseptic acid conditions do not allow much decay as few bacteria can survive, so the remains of animals and plants are often well preserved. Few animal remains appear to have been found in peat of the South West, unlike the Irish blanket bog areas which have yielded the bones and antlers of giant deer. The peat bogs in Scandinavia also contain well-preserved human remains complete with soft tissues, tanned and therefore preserved by humic acids. But even though animals are not often preserved in the bogs of Devon and Cornwall, it is possible to find the remains of former forests, mainly of birch, which grew above the oak forests lower down the hillsides. During peat digging, well-preserved trees have been uncovered in the position where they were overwhelmed, killed and finally buried by the moss.

Despite high rainfall and high ground, *Sphagnum*, which is rightly considered typical, is not as widespread nor does it cover as great an area as one might expect.

Where the peat and living moss is thick, very few flowering plants are found except marsh violet, bog asphodel and sedges such as white beak, cotton grass and star sedge—plus the common soft rush *Juncus effusus*. On slightly drier ground such as drainage channel banks, cross-leaved heath, whortleberry and even ling will grow with an intertwining of yellow-flowered tormentil. Blanket bog is not uniformly composed of *Sphagnum* mosses for a small number of fairly well defined communities dominated by other plant species often add visual and botanical interest. Some of the plants already mentioned form communities, for instance, white beak sedge which commonly grows in the wetter patches where it produces small paper-white spikelets of flowers from June onwards. Amongst the sedge the insectivorous sundews are represented by two species the common *Drosera rotundifolia* and more rarely, the long-leaved form *D. intermedia*, both of which produce bright red splashes of colour against the background pale green of the moss. Bog myrtle, a low-growing shrub with reddish-brown twigs and buds containing a pleasantly aromatic resin, is locally common. The shrub produces attractive long orange male catkins, while on separate plants hang the smaller red female catkins. Bright yellow starlike flowers of bog asphodel *Narthecium ossifragum* add prominent spikes of colour in June and July. Lesser skullcap *Scutellaria minor*, with pale pinkish purple flowers borne in the leaf axils, is frequently found with a tiny prostrate plant, bog pimpernel *Anagallis tenella*, whose relatively large attractive pink bell-like flower unfortunately only seems to open when sunlight covers the moor. Less attractive visually are the deer grass and the grey-leaved carnation sedge *Carex panicea* but both are common.

A second common plant community is that of the bog rush *Schoenus nigricans*. The unusual feature of this tufted sedge which normally produces its blackish-brown flower spikelets in alkaline fens on chalk or limestone, is that here in South-west England (as in West Ireland) it grows in acid blanket bogs.

A conspicuous blanket bog plant which is familiar to the gaze of many summer visitors is the cotton grass which, when growing en masse, produces cotton grass moors commonly known as 'mosses'. In bogs, cotton grass occupies the wetter areas such as drainage channels and wet hollows; in these the dominant species is the common cotton grass *Eriophorum angustifolium* with the less abundant harestail *E. vaginatum* on slightly drier ground. Due to the increased drainage of the upland areas, cotton grass moor is becoming rarer but the wavy cotton ball-like heads are still commonly seen. On the peat islands or hags, whortleberry is common together with cloudberry *Rubus chamaemorus* which has a single bramble-like white flower and a large hard raspberry-like fruit. More rarely occurs the crowberry *Empetrum nigrum* which is a relic of an arctic-type flora which existed during the great Ice Age.

South-western blanket bogs also contain what is for southern England a unique subordinate plant community dominated by deer grass *Trichophorum cespitosum*. Even so, deer grass moor is not extensive but can be studied on both Exmoor and Bodmin Moor where it produces its typical densely tufted wiry stems.

There are at present little signs of further peat growth although it seems the reasons for this are not known. In a number of areas active erosion of the existing peat is obvious where upstanding islands of it are left rising above deep gash-like, dark, peat-lined drainage channels. The hags bear testimony to the erosive force of temporary streams born during heavy rain tearing at the soft peat and carrying it in fine suspension or fibrous chunks down to lower areas. Here, the eroded solids are deposited to contribute to valley bogs while the dark brown water flows on towards the estuaries.

Most of the major rivers of the South West have their origin in the blanket bogs from which they radiate away to lower ground, but the water current once generated by gravity is not continuous as there are a number of pauses induced perhaps rather unexpectedly by the sea. All the uplands in the area show evidence of old sea beaches marking pauses in the retreat of the sea which led, not many millions of years ago, to the uncovering of the present-day land mass. Where seas have paused, a gently sloping bench is now found in the present-day hill profile which appears like giant steps running from the highest ground to positions well below modern sea level. When upland streams meet such levels, the slackening of pace leads to the deposit of silt and lumps of peat during storms. Subsequently, vegetation growth helps to choke the water courses which are forced to divide and meander, and at times the water only makes progress by filtering away beneath the vegetation layers. Not only silt is deposited but the waters from the upland bogs do bring in a little soluble mineral matter eroded from even the most acid bed rock, granite. These salts produce a more favourable medium for plant growth which means that the flora of these valley bog areas is much more interesting than that of the blanket bog above.

Here again, however, bog moss is the dominant plant forming the usual lush green springy carpet which, when built upon rather spongy foundations of unconsolidated vegetation rafts over water, produces a quaking bog. Heavy footsteps here may produce ripples like undulations of the surface which can be quite disconcerting; however, even if the crust is broken the walker is unlikely to sink higher than knee-deep. Carver Doone, whose body was supposed to have been sucked down to a peaty grave on Exmoor, could be considered unlucky indeed to find one of the few areas of dangerous mire.

In valley bogs which are extensively developed along many of the stream courses, a rather uneven surface is sometimes produced by tussocky or hummocky growths of rushes or *Sphagnum* which provide locally drier conditions; the islands of vegetation so formed are much richer in higher plants than is the general bog surface. Similarly endowed are the bog margins where they abut on bedrock of granite or sandstone for here will be found more soluble mineral matter. One typical floral feature of valley bogs is the presence of many rushes and sedges, groups which are only locally represented on blanket bogs.

Unfortunately, many of the valley bogs, like their lower-ground equivalents, wet heaths, have been much disturbed by the old stream tinners who are known affectionately by the Cornish as 'the old men'; old they would now be, for most of the streaming took place before the last century. These early prospectors found alluvial tin in the form of rounded stones and sand-size grains of the oxide cassiterite. The alluvial deposits were often heavy in the valley bog areas where they were dropped by flood waters which collected the tin stones higher up the hillside from exposed mineral veins. The tin was removed after the *Sphagnum* moss had been cleared. Some of the moss was used as a natural filter for the finer tin sediments which it was able to retain and so concentrate, but much was dumped back on the living moss together with waste sand and silt. In this way many of the bogs were spoilt; fortunately, regeneration has taken place in many areas but the habitat is modified, as always, by man.

Another characteristic bog which is extremely common on Dartmoor is that resulting from local waterlogging of the ground by a small spring producing what is known as a flush. The boggy ground so produced gradually widens as the water spreads down the hillside and a number may merge together at lower levels to produce a long strip of boggy land.

The richer, more varied fauna of both valley bog and hillside flush is partly due to lower altitude which enables many visiting mobile animals to take advantage of the fairly rich flora. Here there are more permanent inhabitants such as insects with aquatic larvae, particularly the brightly coloured dragonflies which are usually common (although their cousins, the less vigorous, more delicately built, damselflies are more rare).

Frogs lay their eggs in the early months of the year but some of these, together with the adults, fall prey to visiting heron and even on occasion to the fox; the latter, as in other habitats, takes advantage of any easily procured food into which category also falls the common black slug *Arion ater*. Slugs are present almost to the exclusion of shelled molluscs as the snails' demand for shell-building calcium is unlikely to be satisfied in such acidic conditions as valley bogs. Summer visitors gorging on the abundant insect life are the skylark, meadow pipit and wheatear, with dippers and a few breeding sandpipers along the banks of local streams.

Dry heathland

Heathland is in most cases developed on relatively low ground on acid soils which originally were covered with deciduous forest. The soil often degenerates after removal of the trees and in many cases the soil from which most of the valuable mineral salts have been leached can no longer support the original vegetation.

It is now thought that the heathlands developed along the coastal strip of Devon and Cornwall may be the natural vegetation cover. Perhaps many of these present-day coastal heaths were never tree-covered but formed a narrow band, probably only a few hundred yards wide, separating the cliff vegetation from the original deciduous forests which developed out of direct reach of salt spray.

The effect of windblasting of the shrub vegetation can be clearly seen on Atlantic coasts: facing inland, brown dead clumps of gorse and heather will be commonly seen, but if the heathland is viewed from the opposite direction the leaves and flowers that flourish in the lee of the dead branches make a striking contrast.

Coastal heathland has a highly oceanic flora similar in many respects to that developed on the Atlantic coasts of southern Europe. Here, to the delight of visiting botanists, are species which are local or absent in other parts of the British Isles forming the so-called Lusitanian element in the British flora. One such plant, the dwarf western gorse, flowers from July to October and forms a brilliant carpet of yellow flowers mixed with the purple and pinks of the heathers and ling during the late summer.

Most of the coastal heathland is dominated by ling with cross-leaved heath in the wetter parts and locally with bilberry on better-drained soils.

Much of this habitat in Cornwall has been influenced, particularly in the far west, by mining activity but some of the old mine buildings add to rather than detract from the wild beauty of the areas, and provide interesting situations for plants, and nesting sites for a number of birds.

Animal life is abundant in summer when many visiting species can be found, among them cuckoos, wheatears and nightjars; of the residents the lizard and adder population is often high, and there are always the sea birds passing over, often accompanied by ravens and jackdaws. It is in such areas that the visitor might see a peregrine falcon since a few still nest and overwinter locally.

Away from the stunting effects of the winds, and particularly in South-east Devon, some very interesting lowland dry heaths have developed. These are mixed ling and grass heaths with some scrub, pine and a few deciduous trees such as oak and birch.

Woodbury Common developed on Triassic pebble beds is fairly typical, with its shallow-leached peaty soil overlying an iron hardpan. This is one of the largest common heathlands lying between the Exe estuary and the borders of Dorset. Similar areas occur at Colaton Raleigh, Bicton and Lympstone Commons, where none rise higher than 560ft. For the bird-watcher Woodbury is probably the best, having stonechats, nightjars, tree-pipits, redstarts, buzzards and at times crossbills and redpolls. Occasionally a red-backed shrike occurs which, together with the nightingale, was formerly more common. All these habitats suffer man's influence, from walkers and picnickers to military trainees. Chudleigh Knighton Heath is now a Devon Trust nature reserve but the nightingale population which used to be found there is now much depleted.

As an example of an elevated common in South-east Devon, a brief mention must be made of Gittisham Common developed on Cretaceous Greensand. This is situated on a high plateau extending from the Black Down Hills to the coast between Sidmouth and Beer. It appears in the aerial view of Beer Head (see plate p 103) where the Lower Greensand plateau, partly dissected and fairly well wooded, will be seen in the region above the flat arable farming area on the Chalk in the foreground. Gittisham Common is small, about one and a half miles from north to south and half a mile across east to west, and roughly bounded by the 700ft contour on the map, except locally in the south where the ground is rather peaty, allowing the development of a small bog in the south-east corner. The rest of the heath is dry with *Ulex gallii*, *U. europaeus*, *Erica cinerea*, *E. tetralix*, *Calluna vulgaris*, *Vaccinium myrtillus* and *Pteridium aquilinum*.

Wet heaths

These can be considered as lowland representatives of the valley bogs of upland moors and contain a similar flora but generally a much richer fauna. In places, of course, wet heaths show all stages in conversion to dry heaths and even eventually into woodland.

Wet heaths develop in regions of waterlogged acid soil along stream courses, and were probably of fairly common occurrence in Cornwall until the stream tin industry destroyed them. A conservation site of considerable interest and importance is the wet heath known as Ventongimps Moor, not far from Truro in Cornwall. Here is preserved one of the few remaining lowland valley bogs in Cornwall which still, despite drainage and present-day grazing, contains a fair amount of *Sphagnum* with the usual bog flora. In the South West, this includes Dorset heath, *Erica ciliaris*, a species only known from Dorset and Cornwall as a native species in the British Isles, and also pale butterwort *Pinguicula lusitanica*. The insect population is of great interest and is the object of active conservation efforts at present. The area is a nature reserve of the Cornwall Naturalists' Trust who are attempting to remove much of the gorse (*U. europaeus*) which invaded the area after wartime drainage. The gorse is choking out much of the smaller vegetation which is vital to the survival of the varied insect population, in particular, the marsh fritillary butterfly.

Of outstanding importance botanically and geologically is the world-famous Lizard heathland area in South Cornwall where in 1969 the Cornwall Naturalists' Trust took up a lease on Predannack Downs to be held as a nature reserve. This land on the west side of the peninsula has been leased from the National Trust after both the latter and the Cornwall Naturalists' Trust appealed nationally for money for its purchase.

Most of the Lizard heathland is unsuitable for agriculture and is now dominated physically by the Goonhilly Downs satellite-tracking station, but its flora should be safeguarded for at least the forseeable future. The flat-topped peninsula is in summer dominated botanically by the rare *Erica vagans* or Cornish heath which grows in lilac profusion together with yellow gorse. The bedrock of rotting serpentine rock provides magnesium compounds and the ground water and soil is therefore slightly alkaline but still deficient in lime. Some soils have developed here on granite loess giving a silty, badly drained clay soil on which Cornish heath is co-dominant with another moorland species, the bog rush.

The peculiar soil condition on the Lizard gives an almost unique juxtaposition of plant species characteristic of both acid and base-rich habitats. Not all the Lizard heathland is developed over serpentine, however, some lies over gabbro and granite bedrock (see geology map of Lizard, figure 18, p 157). In the past the peat developed in the area was cut but this practice no longer takes place.

Other damp heathlands in Cornwall are common, particularly in the north of the county over the Culm measures where they were formerly provided as poorly drained pastureland. Much of this land has been reinvaded by *Molinia* and *Juncus*, although the ridges and furrows of the eighteenth and nineteenth century cultivation can still be seen. *Molinia* and *Eriophorum* dominate much of this area now as they do further south on the flanks of the St Austell granite at Goss Moor.

Much of the St Austell or Hensbarrow Moor has been ruined by the china-clay workings, which not only physically remove the surface of the ground but disgorge the siliceous waste in gleaming white pyramids over hundreds of acres of land around the workings: no spoil is returned to the great pits from which it is taken. A large part of Hensbarrow Moor has also been reclaimed for agriculture but in the north there are still some extensive marshy pastures with a good deal of cotton grass.

On the granite boss of Carnmenellis little wild heathland still remains, mainly due to mining, farming and quarry operations.

Moor and heathland animals

A walk across moorland during the winter months would leave the naturalist with the impression of relative desolation, dead, often bleached, windswept vegetation stretching away probably into the mist with only an occasional rook or raven to break the sound of the wind.

In spring, however, some birds leave the estuaries and move to take up breeding grounds on the higher moorland. Curlew and a few common sandpipers will be found together with snipe in the wetter hollows, and a few pairs of golden plover and dunlin. Much more common and characteristic are the meadow pipits, skylarks and carrion crows and, commonly, a few buzzards and ravens.

Summer visitors breeding on the moorland include ring ousel, whinchat and wheatears. The lapwing, although common in winter on the lower ground around the moorland, is now less common as a breeding species. The traditional bird of the heather, the red grouse, is rare in the South West and even the few now occurring around Cranmere Pool on Dartmoor are descendants from introduced stock. The black grouse, although native, is by no means more plentiful than the red and is, unfortunately, now a rare bird indeed, mainly due to persecution.

Another declining species, rarely seen but more usually heard in the warm still summer evenings, is the nightjar which still manages to breed on moorlands although in very small numbers. Cuckoos are still fairly common even on the highest moorland, but the coastal heathlands provide the greatest number when up to ten can be seen perched on overhead wires.

Most of the breeding birds have gone from the moorland in autumn but are followed by a seasonal influx of starlings and northern thrushes, such as fieldfare and redwing, together with numbers of finches. Lapwings pass through with golden plover and the occasional hen harrier which may overwinter on the moor (see figure 3, p 44, showing main bird species on Exmoor in varied habitats).

The scarcity of food is probably one of the main reasons for the relatively poor bird population of moorland, and certainly insect life is not great, being limited to mainly strong-flying visiting species from surrounding habitats such as bumble bees, migrant Lepidoptera and the blundering dor beetles, with dragonflies locally more common in the richer areas of valley bog. The latter are much more favourable for animal life, due both to the lower altitude and the presence of a more diverse flora supporting the plant-eating (phytophagous) insect larvae that form, in many cases, the basis of the upland food chains.

Where the undergrowth is thick, a fairly rich beetle population can be uncovered, including both predatory and carrion feeders; very few are conspicuous except the common tiger beetle, while among the Hymenoptera there are usually a few ants. Of the bees found, only *Bombus lapponicus* is really a characteristic moorland species.

Lepidoptera are rather poorly represented, but fox, emperor and oak eggar moths can be considered characteristic, and butterflies are represented by the meadow brown, gatekeeper, small heath, common blue, and more locally, the grayling. Probably the best month for insects is August. Bodmin, Exmoor and Dartmoor are all good places for grasshoppers and crickets and the South West in general is well supplied with these little-studied but often very noisy insects.

The nature of the soil, either permanently waterlogged or very shallow and stony, excludes the common earthworms from the moorland and with them the worm-eating mole; its relative the common shrew *Sorex araneus* is frequently heard and even a few water shrews may be found far from open water. The short-tailed vole and woodmouse are plentiful in all but the wettest habitat and form the prey for the kestrel and the occasional short-eared owl and barn owl that cross the moor.

Voles are also useful as food for the foxes and badgers of the moorland which eke out what must be a rather meagre diet with the only common mollusc on the calcium-deficient soils, namely the black slug *Arion ater*. Both fox and badger frequently utilise the open moorland, particularly the former who often uses the clitter slopes below the tors to produce its cubs. The fox is much persecuted in these areas largely on the mistaken view that it is a major threat to moorland sheep. Carrion feeder it most certainly is but killer of sheep and lambs seldom.

Red deer *Cervus elaphus* also form part of the carrion prey for scavengers on moorland, and the native red deer herd on Exmoor is probably the most famous and ancient in the British Isles. Much controversy has centred around this particular herd over the past few years, respecting the pros and cons of the local Exmoor and Quantock stag hounds and many bitter episodes have been recorded. It is felt by many people, including specialists in deer study who have visited the area, that probably the best way to perpetuate deer on Exmoor is to allow hunting as it is hardly in the hunters' interest to exterminate its quarry. This does, of course, leave aside the ethics of the hunt but it is agreed that some control is necessary to avoid excessive damage to local agricultural and forestry interests; the question must really revolve around the way in which the deer are killed.

Various individuals have, from time to time, emigrated from Exmoor and red deer herds are now established around Dartmoor and Bodmin Moor.

The ponies of Exmoor and Dartmoor must be mentioned here as they form an obvious attraction for the visitor. The origins of the ponies are obscure but they probably represent the descendants of wild horses domesticated by man thousands of years ago. The Exmoor pony is only slightly larger than the New Forest form which is the smallest breed in the British Isles. Exmoors are a very uniform breed although there are two varieties: the Acland or Anchor type is smaller and lighter and has an s-shaped curve in the face; while the larger, darker Withypool has a straight Roman profile. Despite its lack of size the Exmoor is extremely tough, enduring not only the climate but carrying heavy loads with ease and so is ideal for trekking. There is an active Exmoor Pony Society and a short booklet describing the breed has recently been produced (1970) by the Exmoor Press, Dulverton.

Reptiles appear in the form of common lizards, grass snakes and adders, with a few frogs, common and palmate newts and toads representing the amphibian community which is most prolific in valley bog areas.

For the naturalist the summer is the best time to visit moorland but the winter visitor may be rewarded by the sight of a Montagu's harrier and, as is so often the case with natural history, it is the observer and his patience that are the most vital factors in making a habitat give up its secrets.

CHAPTER FOUR

Dartmoor, Exmoor and Bodmin Moor

Dartmoor–Dartmoor tors–Exmoor–Bodmin Moor

As the wildernesses of Britain shrink and disappear, the three great open moorlands of the South West remain: Dartmoor, indeed, is the largest true wilderness left in England, rolling for 400 square miles and legendarily offering alien, exposed country to the unwary traveller. To the north and south, Exmoor and Bodmin stretch, comparatively untouched by civilization: but it is only a relative state. Much of the great moorland has been reclaimed for agriculture, especially on Exmoor. Many acres, in all three areas, have been planted with conifers; and reservoirs cover some hundreds of acres, with others under construction and more proposed.

Although we think of the three great moors as unspoilt, all have been affected to a great extent by man, and indeed the present wilderness is largely a result of man's activities; but even so the communities are of great general interest, and of importance also to the specialist, especially those with interest in rushes, sedges, lichens and bryophytes. For the naturalist these areas are still unique in Great Britain as representatives of high, unglaciated moorland which, during the last great glaciation, probably acted as last strongholds for plant and animal species which were eliminated by ice action further north. The plant communities embrace many essentially southern species also found in Southern Ireland. And if southern species are a speciality, northern forms at the southern extremity of their range also occur: these include cowberry *Vaccinium vitis-idaea*, crowberry *Empetrum nigrum*, cranberry *Vaccinium oxycoccus*, and the cotton grasses.

Dartmoor is the most important bog land in the South West and has a very rich and fairly well documented bryophyte flora. These, together with fascinating relict woodlands, discussed in Chapter One, are probably the most important features of the area, although orthopterists will know Dartmoor as a good hunting ground for grasshoppers and bush crickets.

Both Dartmoor and Exmoor have interesting and varied bird populations, away, that is, from the relatively barren blanket bog areas, and the visitor can expect to see at least two of the following breeding birds of prey: merlin, buzzard, kestrel, hobby, sparrow hawk, Montagu's harrier and peregrine.

Exmoor is less important as a bog land than Dartmoor but has a wide variety of habitats including extensive heather moor and important woodlands. The red deer will be well known even to people unfamiliar with the area and form the oldest native herd in the British Isles.

Of the three sites, it is at present more threatened than the others by man's agricultural activities and tourist pressure. Exmoor, unlike the two granite moorlands further south, developed on sandstones and shales of Devonian age and provides a tolerably good soil when the ironpan has been broken. The granite under Dartmoor and Bodmin Moor produces a badly-drained, thin, highly acid soil of little use to the farmer other than for rough grazing. Bodmin Moor, which is the most important moorland in Cornwall, is lower and smaller than the two Devon moors.

Large areas of Dartmoor are used for military training but this does not despoil the land as does the construction of great reservoirs to meet the needs of the area. The very high rainfall, lack of farming potential, sparse human population and apparent emptiness makes this an engineer's paradise providing very suitable sites for dam construction. Geologically, many of the sites are not so suitable; on closer inspection, much of the granite is highly rotten with many joints that have to be sealed, and mineral veins which, in the case of the new reservoir under construction at Meldon on the south-west flanks of Dartmoor, gave objectors to the proposal some cause for concern. Many battles have been and will be fought both by naturalists, amenity societies and landowners over the construction of reservoirs. On Dartmoor, Meldon is under construction but not Swincombe, for here the preservationists won the day; but another is planned for the National Park area of Exmoor; in Cornwall at least one new dam will be built, in the upper Fowey valley, to flood one of the most beautiful and interesting areas of Bodmin Moor.

Multi-purpose use may be made of the new reservoirs in which fishing, boating, shooting, water sports and natural history interests have to share the amenity created, but this does little to compensate for the destruction of habitats, for as we shall see in the chapter on freshwater, the new reservoirs have as yet little to commend them to the naturalist.

The lack of glaciation in the South West meant that no glacial lakes were formed, and lack of boulder clay together with rapid run-off of surface water results in few freshwater areas apart from a small number of pools and the large, rather barren expanse of water forming Dozmary pool on Bodmin Moor.

Dartmoor

The National Park includes much farmland; about two-thirds of the 400 square miles is on granite. The A384 road divides Dartmoor roughly into a northern plateau section of rounded hills with the highest points, Yes Tor and High Willhays, rising over 2,000ft (see figure 23, p 187), and a more gently rolling lower southern area with Ryder's Hill 1,692ft as its peak. 'Dartmoor forest' applies to an inner part formerly used as a royal hunting area, which is the original meaning of the term forest and should not be taken to indicate that a tree cover was present in recent historical times. It is only the open moorland that will be considered here; the woodland and streams are discussed in Chapters One and Ten respectively.

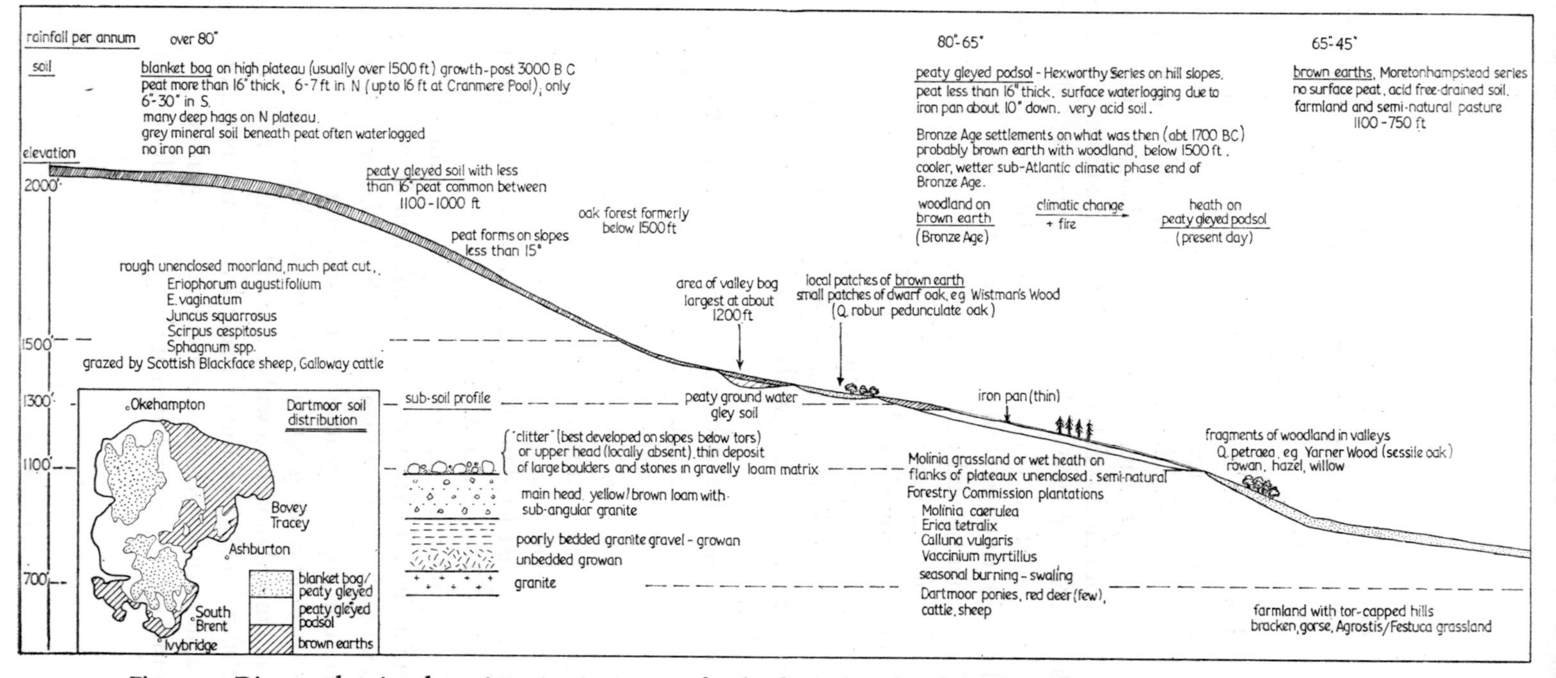

Figure 4 Diagram showing the main vegetation types and soils of Dartmoor based mainly on the work of Clayden & Manley 1964

Dartmoor is dominated by granite tors of resistant rock which may be only a few inches, or over 50ft high, often surrounded by boulder-strewn slopes and scree or 'clitter'. The highest ground, over 1,500ft, forming the wilderness of the inner high moor, is covered with either blanket bog or cotton-grass moor which occurs in two main areas, where it rests on rotten granite known locally as 'growan'. The thick moss blanket of *Sphagnum*, together with the growan, acts as a sponge, soaking up much of the 80in or so of rain that falls on the high north and south plateaux each year. Slow release of the rain water so captured allows the development of many small streams, and Dartmoor is the source of the major rivers in Devon (see figure 23, p 187).

Due to human and natural causes, there are strong signs of regression of the northern bog, and deep erosion gashes leave upstanding peat mounds, or hags, up to six feet above the channels where dark brown peat is exposed beneath the green growing moss. However, little evidence of peat growth can be found on Dartmoor except in a few places such as Taw Head and East Dart Head.

The southern blanket bog contains one of the few dangerous mires on Dartmoor, namely Fox Tor mire which would have been flooded if the proposed Swincombe reservoir had been built. The mire is an indication of the much wetter conditions found in this southern area where no hags appear; rushes are more common and less ling grows here. Blanket bogs up to 15ft thick carry a very restricted tundra-type flora which is characteristic of wet moors in the South West.

For the interested reader the bryophyte communities to be found in this important area are described in *Dartmoor Essays* by Proctor and only brief mention can be made here. Most of the Dartmoor bog is degenerate to the specialist botanist eye; but there is an interesting *Sphagnum* cover which gives way in drier areas to mixed moorland with sedge and heather. In the cushions of *Sphagnum* will be found many liverworts, but more conspicuous in these wetter areas are the cotton grasses.

Surrounding the wet moors are large areas of drier heather and

Page 85 (*above*) Coastal heathland on hogsback cliffs forming the northern boundary of Exmoor east of Combe Martin. Much of this coastal heathland has been reclaimed, but large areas are still dominated by western gorse and heathers. Great Hangman and Holdstone Down are prominent hill features. This cliffland is typical of the north and west coasts of the peninsula; (*below*) south Cornish coast with Hensbarrow (St Austell) Moor in the background. China clay production has replaced tin and copper mining as the main cause of derelict land. Quartz waste mounds and mica-filled artificial lakes cover many acres of moorland. The clay pollution of the sea is conspicuous

Page 86 (*above*) Panoramic view across the Land's End peninsula from Lamorna Cove in the foreground, to the Atlantic coast. Typical exposed, treeless upland with well-wooded steep-sided coves. Note castellated granite cliffs; (*below*) wheatear—a characteristic summer visitor to the cliffs and heathland. Grasshoppers which are abundant in such habitats provide plentiful food

grass moor. Here the plant communities depend largely on the amount of waterlogging of the soil. Figure 4 on p 83, shows a generalised section with vegetation types indicated: from this it will be noted that the wetter areas are dominated by purple moor grass, and locally by cotton grass and cross-leaved heath.

Over well-drained shallow peat a drier type of moorland flora occurs dominated by grasses. True grass moor is not very common on Dartmoor but heather moor on the other hand, is, extensive and dominated by ling. This is subject to seasonal burning (swayling) but if this is carried out either too enthusiastically or by the tourists' cigarette ends, the ling tends to be replaced by bracken. Despite the appearance of uniformity in plant cover, ling moors can yield up to 250 plant species, but unlike other similar upland areas further north the clubmosses are poorly represented, only *Lycopodium inundatum* and *L. clavatum* being present.

Where the slope of the ground makes rapid drainage possible, the resulting dry soil carries bilberry moor. Whortleberry patches also occur among the heather, and during the autumn provide food for a number of animals.

Streams draining the uplands fall fairly gently at first but then at about 1,200ft an area of less steep ground is marked by waterlogged patches forming valley bogs, eg Taw marsh. While valley bogs also occur lower down it is at about 1,200ft that they are best developed. Many valley bogs have been altered by tin streaming and later mining operations but they carry an interesting flora best developed, as far as species are concerned, at their margins, with rushes being the main vegetation in the more central floating bog area. Marginal *Sphagnum* tussocks are often crowned by ling, cross-leaved heath and gorse.

The soils of Dartmoor have been closely studied and a summary of the soil types and distribution will be found in the diagram figure 4, p 83.

Dartmoor tors

The granite core of Dartmoor is often exposed as tors which are upstanding masses sometimes many feet high and often sculptured by the weather into shapes reminiscent of animals—especially if seen in half-light or through swirling mist. The granite may show a pseudobedding and be highly jointed and cracked, whilst other tors have very little surface irregularity and thus provide few footholds for plant colonisation. Damper cracks do have liverworts and some ferns such as black spleenwort and with them are stunted heather and whortleberry bushes. Tors are used as shelter by sheep and ponies and the north-east side is often bare ground due to trampling and grazing.

Around the base of a tor the broken collection of large boulders forms the 'clitter'. The bryophyte flora of tors and clitters is varied if not extensive, but the thin open turf and rocks are commonly covered with a mat of *Rhacomitrium lanuginosum* which forms a conspicuous feature of the moor.

Due to the sparse plant cover few animals occur on the tors, but some springtails, pseudoscorpions, beetles, spiders, woodlice, earwigs, centipedes, millipedes, slugs and occasional snails can be found, together with a few ants, moths and flies. Larger animals such as rabbits and a few adders can live here and the clitters provide shelter for fox families and temporary homes for badgers. Tors provide rare perches for some moorland birds, mainly kestrels, carrion crows, ravens and buzzards.

Exmoor

Exmoor, which was designated as a National Park in 1954, covers 265 square miles, of which 188 lie in Somerset and the remaining 77 in Devon. The National Park includes a main upland plateau forming Exmoor proper, centred on The Chains which is a blanket bog area with the largest area of deer grass *Trichophorum cespitosum* in southern England. Here is the region of greatest rainfall and the bog acts like a sponge as it does on Dartmoor, controlling run-off, but not sufficiently effective to stop disasters such as the Lynmouth flooding in 1952.

Coastal heaths and often thickly wooded slopes form the

northern boundary, where impressive high cliffs are washed by the waters of the Bristol Channel. The upland area is mostly above 700ft, much of the land rising over 1,000ft with the highest point at Dunkery Beacon (see plate p 34) with open moorland rising to 1,706ft. These uplands are dissected by deep, well-wooded valleys through which flow rapid streams. The watershed, as in most of south-west England, lies near the north coast so the short northerly flowing streams run swiftly to the coast. These streams and their surrounding woodlands are dealt with in other chapters.

The relatively warm summers and influence of warm sea breezes means that the climate is less arctic than might have been expected despite over 60in of rain and more mist and snow than is usual for the South West. Even in deep winter, frost is not usually severe except in a few pockets on north-facing open slopes. Spring frosts are rare and a wide range of more exotic and rather tender trees and shrubs are therefore able to survive along the coastal strip.

Thick layers of peat developed over the impervious iron-panned soil on the higher moorland, but despite the high rainfall and presence of thick wet peat in places, *Sphagnum* moss can rarely be said to dominate the plant communities over a large area. Nevertheless, it does form in the wetter bogs a discontinuous blanket with typical bog plants.

In many places the upland is dotted with small plantations of beech, larch, pine and spruce although greatly stunted by wind action. A beechwood planted during the nineteenth century at Birch Cleave, Simonsbath, at an altitude of 1,100ft, is probably the highest such woodland in the country. Much of Exmoor has been enclosed with earth and stone banks built around the older fields. Characteristic are the beeches planted along the earth banks or forming shelter belts near farmhouses. (See plate p 34.)

Exmoor can be divided into three vegetative areas.

(a) In the north the coastal heaths occur on well-drained, shallow, acid soil supporting a mainly heath and gorse community. Both common and western gorse occur but much of this land has been ploughed up and enclosed (see plate p 34), east of Combe Martin. Excessive burning on these dry slopes has in places allowed soil erosion, eg Great Hangman: western gorse is prominent as an invader in such eroded areas as it is also in under-grazed grasslands.

(b) About 21,000 acres of heather moor bound the grassland heart of Exmoor (see figure 25, p 212). All this land is of high amenity value and is also potentially good agricultural land. On the heather moors ling is the most abundant species accompanied by bell heather and cross-leaved heath.

Swayling is not carried out systematically and instead of strip burning in rotation, large areas are burnt casually, often by tourists. Such fires are an increasing danger to the heather moorland, particularly in such popular regions as Dunkery Beacon.

(c) Grass moor forms the central area and its extent almost coincides with the boundaries of the old 'Royal forest' which, as with the Dartmoor Forest, was essentially a hunting area and not tree-covered in recent years. Purple moor grass is the dominant species in the old Royal forest area; the grass in fact covers 10,000 acres, about one-third of the total of Exmoor moorland.

Where a better type of mineral soil is found, fescue and bent grasses dominate. Such grass moor covers over 7,500 acres and as the sward is tolerant of human feet and car-tyre wear, this type of moor is increasing, particularly in parking areas and well-used heathland tracks.

Mat grass is poorly represented but may be increasing locally where it can invade degenerate acid soils. This grass offers little food value for grazing animals who tend to avoid such areas which occur mainly on west-facing commons; about 10,000 acres of steeply sloping land are covered by bracken which, although choking out much of the ground flora, provides a valuable visual amenity; and gorse moor with both European and western gorse, covers about 1,000 acres.

We have seen that the blanket bog area on Exmoor is limited but there are still relatively large areas of cotton grass with the common cotton grass *E. angustifolium* being less common here than harestail, *E. vaginatum*, the reverse of the Dartmoor position. There is seldom a pure stand of cotton grass as it is mixed with heaths and ling forming a mixed heath, eg Withypool and the surrounding commons.

On the northern and eastern edges of the moor, pine and birch trees join the heather to form a community more like the heathlands of lowland areas. The Brendon Hills form an outlier of Exmoor to the east and this was formerly heathland, but the area has now been either reclaimed or planted with conifers so that little open moorland remains.

Exmoor is still threatened with reclamation work, although less so than in the middle years of this century. Even after the establishment of the National Park, large areas were taken in as grassland and the average loss of moorland over the past decade has been about 1,000 acres per annum.

Much of this land is privately owned but fortunately more and more is coming under the supervision of the National Trust, who also control much of that coast with properties recently acquired by the Enterprise Neptune appeal. Devon and Somerset County Councils, too, are acquiring more property: in 1969 Somerset County Council took over the Emmett's Grange estate and much of the 1,990 acres north-west of Simonsbath will be managed and preserved as farmland and open country. In the past, little control could be exercised over the privately held land on Exmoor, and with the encouragement of grants for ploughing and drainage, many acres were taken in. Much of this land, it must be admitted, has made good economically, but not inconsiderable acres have reverted to rush infested pastures as the land was not suitable for agricultural activities.

Since the passing of the Countryside Act in 1968 some power, albeit limited, is available to protect open moorland in the National Park. Farmers must now give six months' notice to the local planning authority, during which time either formal agreements can be made concerning the management of the land or it may be purchased. Much depends on the attitude and efficiency of local planners to safeguard the land of which 43,500 acres, or 26 per cent of the total acreage of Exmoor park, has been designated as of critical amenity value.

The situation is now urgent in the area and there are still twelve species of plant that are in danger of extinction; already since 1930, thirty-one species of plants have become extinct in the area.

Nature reserves and waymarked routes are listed in the Appendix.

Bodmin Moor

Like Dartmoor, Bodmin Moor, which consists of 80 square miles of rough moorland, has its highest ground forming a northern mass, rising to 1,375ft on Brown Willy and 1,311ft at Rough Tor. Tors are fewer than on Dartmoor but those present are equally dominant. To the north and south-east there is much broadly undulating rugged country with a number of steep-sided hills such as Kilmarston and Caradon, both over 1,200ft high. An inner area of moorland is less steep and composed of gently rounded ridges aligned north-north-west/south-south-east.

Bodmin provides the source for a number of streams most of which produce gorges or waterfalls as they pass from the granite of the upland on to the lower metamorphic rocks. Blanket bog is rare but several feet of *Sphagnum* forming so-called 'Piskie Pits' occurs locally, while shallow peat is widespread. There are only a few water-filled hollows of which only the rather barren Dozmary Pool, over a mile in circumference, is worth close examination, although it is never very popular with water birds and the vegetation is very sparse. If open water is rare, some marsh-filled basins do occur most extensively in the north around the Rough Tor mass.

Bodmin Moor presents a mainly pastoral scene with many hardy cattle on the open moor. Patches of cultivated land appear in the lower areas and strips of woodland have developed along south-draining valleys. Some areas have been afforested, for example, 300 acres of Davidstow Moor. Such areas and particularly the Glynn valley to the east, contain at present a small number of red deer which have probably spread from Exmoor and now seem to be well established.

As would be expected Bodmin has a high rainfall, severe exposure to wind, and a wet, acid peaty soil, but despite its elevation and exposure the climate is generally mild. Much of the ground vegetation is dominated by *Molinia* and *Agrostis* grassland and there is little heather moor compared with Dartmoor or Exmoor. There are, however, large areas of rough grazing with bracken and gorse on the drier land, and much sedge and dwarf rush in the areas of slow or impeded drainage. On Bodmin Moor the deer grass grows in tufts with bare peat between and the area on which it grows is generally wetter than its Exmoor site.

A full list of species found in the two areas is given in Tansley, p 711.

The policy of the National Trust towards the moorland in the South West is of course of great significance for the future. At present the Trust owns relatively little of the open moorland but concentrates on preserving by acquisition or lease the wooded valleys leading to the moors.

On Dartmoor, most of which is owned by the Duchy of Cornwall, the conservation interests are well looked after by the vigorous Dartmoor Preservation Society. There, as for Exmoor, National Trust policy is to establish properties around the base of Dartmoor to protect the wooded valleys and the South Hams from destruction.

CHAPTER FIVE

The sea shores

Exposed mussel shores–Barnacle shores–Semi-exposed shores–Sheltered areas–Effects of the Torrey Canyon–Shingle beaches–Sandy beaches

IF THE HIGH moorland dominates much of the land mass of the South West, it is the sea which probably provides the greatest attraction for the naturalist.

The coast, roughly 600 miles long, is washed by the English Channel on the south and hammered by the Atlantic Ocean on the north which, with the muddy waters of the Bristol Channel, forms the northern limit of our area. The North Atlantic Drift divides on meeting the resistant mass of the Land's End granite which stands like the rest of the peninsula as a rigid block thrusting above the ocean. The streams of warm water from the South Atlantic move either eastwards along the English Channel or up the north coast towards Wales and the Bristol Channel.

Waves generated by storms off Cape Horn some 6,000 miles away are sometimes detected on the coasts of Devon and Cornwall and bring huge seas with attendant foaming surges of surf on even clear, almost windless days in summer. Autumn, however, is the time for the really rough seas when winds from the west bring in rolling spume-topped waves which break on the resistant granite and metamorphic rock cliffs. There is almost always surf on the north coast, but although the same is true in some parts of South Cornwall, the seas are seldom as spectacular except during a south-easterly gale. The relative shelter of the south coast can be judged by the trees which grow along the cliff tops almost down to high-tide level.

The water is relatively shallow and often waves break on rocky shore platforms which are treacherous for shipping. Wrecks such as that of the *Torrey Canyon* on the Seven Stones Reef still occur despite modern navigational aids and famous lighthouses such as Bishops Rock, Longships and Wolf Rock. Indeed, if the sea level were now only 200ft lower, as it was during part of the last Ice Age, there would be no Bristol Channel, and the granite island of Lundy would be part of the mainland, jutting above a wide area of gently sloping, low-lying country, backed by what are now the high sea cliffs.

The Isles of Scilly and Seven Stones rocks have, however, a deep-water channel separating them from the main land mass, but St Michael's Mount, off Penzance, has only recently, geologically speaking (about 1,700 BC), become separated from the mainland and then only at high tide. In the first century BC, the Mount was known as 'the hoar rock in the woods' and probably stood in swampy, tree-covered ground, much like the adjacent Marazion marsh (so important to the bird-watcher) which rests on the remains of former forest.

The presence of many low-level raised beaches suggests that the general outline of the coast has changed little over the past few thousand years. Many fossil beaches are just above present spring tide level and rest on a high-level wave-cut platform. This shows how slowly, with a few notable exceptions, the resistant rocks are being eroded in most parts of the area, but even so the general level of the peninsula is falling relative to sea level by an average of about 2·3mm per annum.

The general form of the coast in Devon and Cornwall is crenulate, and the majority of beaches have a smooth profile. In a number of cases, spits of shingle or sand have formed across the mouths of estuaries. At Loe Bar near Helston a terminal shingle barrier between two headlands impounds a large sheet of fresh water, forming the largest natural area of freshwater in Cornwall. There are now plans to increase the water volume in the lake to provide domestic water supply.

In Devon at Dawlish Warren, a sand spit across the mouth of

the river Exe is threatened now with complete destruction by wave action unless coastal defence schemes are put in hand at once.

Sandy beaches are the most common, but shingle beaches also occur, particularly in North Devon and the adjacent Somerset coast, and more locally in Cornwall, for example, south of Wadebridge and on the Lizard peninsula. In almost every case, except where there are sand dunes, the coast behind the shore is formed by high, often spectacular cliffs rising above a wave-cut rocky foreshore which provides the typical west-country shore with its multitude of rock pools. In some cases the rocks run out below low-tide level so allowing the full zonation of rocky shores to be studied, but in many cases it is only the upper zones above the sand line at about mid-tide level that are available.

Although the wave action is severe, the water pounding on the shore is relatively warm, coming as it does from the South Atlantic. During the summer it brings floating forms of life from these waters including jelly-fish such as the famous Portuguese Man-o'-War *Physalia*, the pretty By-the-wind-sailor *Velella*, often its delicate, transparent float found on the strand-line, and the stalked goose barnacle *Lepas* on driftwood. The warm waters also provide the correct conditions for the survival of many southern species of shore-dwelling organisms. Some of these are at the northern limit of their distribution, eg two species of seaweed, the yellowish-olive, regularly forked cylindrical branches of *Bifurcaria bifurcata* and the rare *Laminaria ochroleuca*, together with the low-shelled black-footed limpet *Patella depressa* and the large barnacle *Balanus perforatus*, the polychaete worms *Lepidonotus clava* and the honeycomb-like reef of *Sabellaria alveolata*. In deeper waters, southern species include the deep-bodied yet narrow, curiously shaped John Dory fish *Zeus faber* and the streaked gurnard *Trigla lineata*. Other species around the coast are at their southern limit of distribution including the cod *Gadus callarias* and the rock-clinging acorn barnacle *Balanus balanoides* which is absent from parts of South Cornwall. Northern forms include the large barnacle *Balanus crenatus*, the plumose anemone *Metridium* and the weed *Alaria esculenta* which is commonly found at low-tide mark on exposed rocks.

The comparatively narrow strip of coastline between the extreme high-water mark and the low-tide level is the hunting-ground of a rich and varied animal and plant life; and it is with the species found within these limits that this chapter is concerned.

The upper limit is indistinct due to the wide spray zone present, particularly on the north coast, which allows shore species to exist much higher above sea level than usual. On the lower shore, among the *Laminaria* or oar weed, many pools of exceptional interest may be found containing shallow-water or sublittoral forms which will be considered in the next chapter; so the lower limits will be taken as the top of the oarweed zone. Low spring tide in our area reaches its lowest point at a very suitable time for shore studies, occurring around midday. This allows the tide to be followed out during the morning and gives ample time for study of low-level populations at the warmest part of the day, a consideration of no mean importance when a strong wind is blowing or a persistent drizzle hampers the naturalist.

If we consider the shores from the viewpoint of the degree of exposure to wave action, we can distinguish three main communities associated with rocky shores in the South West.

(a) Exposed—Open to the full ocean. Such shores are mainly found on the North Devon and North Cornwall coasts but also occur locally on headlands on the south coasts. These shores are dominated by two animals—mussels and barnacles.

(b) Semi-exposed—These shores are subject to less violent wave action either due to aspect or local shelter provided by headlands or offshore rocks. This is probably the most common type of shore in the area and is dominated by brown seaweeds of the *Fucaceae* family—the wracks.

(c) Sheltered—Here wave action is far less important in determining which species survive. Such shores are found mainly along the south coast, particularly in lower reaches of the esutaries (see figure 7, p 106).

Exposed mussel shores

The dominant animal community in exposed, rocky situations is that of the common mussel *Mytilus edulis*. Mussel growth is favoured by the presence of ledges and platforms of rock which are abundantly provided around much of the north coast by the slaty killas, where the population is most dense on surf-swept slopes.

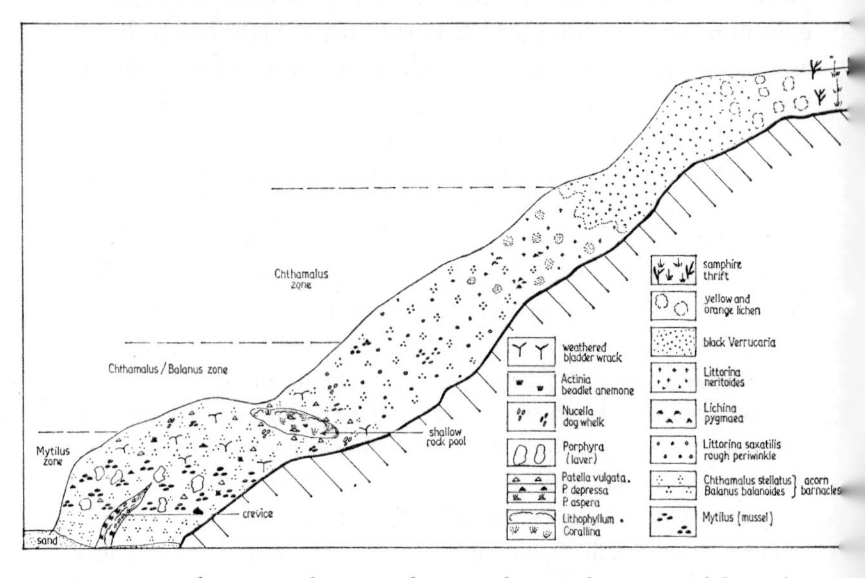

Figure 5 Belt transect diagram of a typical area of an exposed barnacle-dominated rocky headland commonly found on the northern and western coasts

The dark blue growths of mussels characteristically occur on low rocks at about mean low tide level where large colonies flourish with their attendant growths of red algae which form the co-dominant type of life in such exposed habitats. Oyster-catchers and sometimes turnstones probe for food at low tide among the mussels, while at higher states of the tide the area is fished by shags and grey seals.

Of the red algae, the thin purple laver *Porphyra umbilicalis*, which is still used to make laverbread in parts of the South West, is the most abundant. In summer it dries to a blackish polythene-like film stretched over the mussels at low tide, and retaining beneath it moisture which supports a varied small crustacean and mollusc population.

Other red algae also found associated with the mussels are:

Callithamnion	*Nemalion*
Ceramium	*Polysiphonia*
Corallina	*Rhodymenia*
Cystoclonium	*Laurencia*
Gigartina	

Above the red algae, particularly in regions subject to very violent wave action, is a small variety of *Fucus* that lacks air bladders and is known as *Fucus vesiculosus f. linearis*; this is often only represented by the tough, short black tufts of the resistant mid-ribs, from which all the blade (lamina) has been stripped by the pounding waves. If the mussels dominate the lower shore population, the barnacles often do well at higher levels forming a prominent white band contrasting with the darker mussel zone below. In the upper parts of the barnacle zone, as it is called, a lichen *Lichina pygmaea* is often abundant, forming a black, crisp incrustation after exposure to drying sun and wind.

Resident animal life in these exposed situations is restricted to forms that can either maintain a foothold under the algae or inhabit the area at high tide, as for example, free-swimming fish and crustacea which return from deeper water to feed.

For anyone beginning a study of sea-shore life probably the exposed shore is a very good starting place as the bewildering variety of life associated with more sheltered waters will be absent.

The only common periwinkle on the mussel shore is the tiny *Littorina neritoides* which occurs in vast numbers usually in and above the barnacle zone where they find shelter in between the living barnacles or inside dead shells. Look for these on smooth, damp rocks on which the blue-black shells slowly glide, browsing on algae. The limpet population is dominated by *Patella aspera* and *P. depressa* in the mussel zone but by the common limpet *P. vulgata* higher up in the barnacles, among which it is often extremely difficult to detect. Beneath the mid-shore red algae population of laver and dulse *Rhodymenia* can be found dog whelks *Nucella lapillus* in a variety of brightly banded or

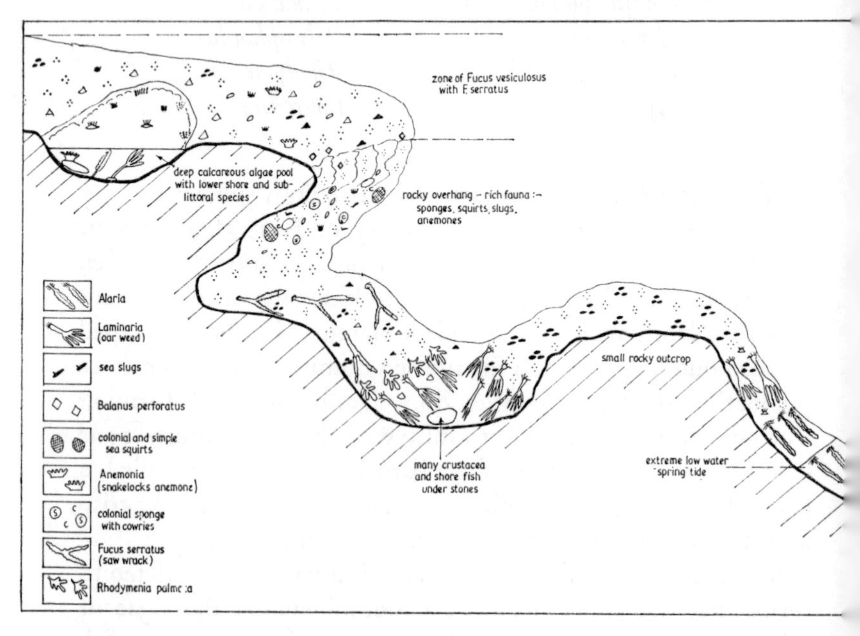

Figure 6 Belt transect diagram of a typical lower shore of an exposed rocky coast showing only the main species of the plant and animal communities (see fig 5 for key to species)

self-coloured forms, and two species of top shell, the grey top *Gibbula cineraria* at low levels and in pools, and a South West shore speciality the purple top shell *G. umbilicalis*. The very small bivalve *Lasaea rubra* is a common inhabitant of *Corallina* and *Lichina* tufts and old barnacle shells, where it can be detected with the aid of a bent back and a hand lens. Many small crustacea will be found beneath tufts of red algae *Ceramium* and *Callithamnion*, although most will scuttle away and seldom allow close observation.

Anemones are common, particularly the blue-eye spotted beadlet *Actinia equina* which is often secreted in rock crevices or gaps between barnacles, while attached to the seaweeds are a wide variety of encrusting animals such as hydroids, mat-like calcareous polyzoans and softer-bodied sponges which the specialist will find of great interest.

Barnacle shores (see figures 5 and 6, pp 98 and 100)

These are probably the most common types of shore in the South West, particularly on the north coasts where exposure to wave action is generally less severe than on mussel (*Mytilus*) shores which may be found on adjacent exposed headlands.

In the area the southern barnacle *Chthamalus stellatus* is dominant, and these shores are therefore known as *Chthamalus* shores. The northern barnacle *Balanus balanoides* may be completely absent from some South Cornwall shores but becomes more common to the north of the region where it is found at lower levels than those occupied by *Chthamalus*. Since World War II an Australian species *Elminius modestus* (with only four white plates covering its body) has in places ousted the native acorn barnacles from their position of dominance. This is particularly true of more sheltered situations and only a few have penetrated the more exposed situations but they may do so and are worthy of note if found.

Three species of limpet are common but not always recognised. As with mussel shores, the common, often massive-shelled, *Patella vulgata* is dominant at higher shore levels but its place is taken lower down by the smaller, flatter southern species *P. depressa*. The third limpet species, *P. aspera* occurs at low-tide levels just above the *Laminaria* zone on open shores but most commonly in deep purple *Lithothamnion*-lined rock pools where it is usually covered by a tuft of green or red algae. The calcareous algae is often unable to grow beneath the limpet and a clear circle of fresh rock will often mark the former site of a limpet's home.

The small periwinkle *L. neritoides* is joined on barnacle shores by the larger rough periwinkle *Littorina saxatilis* which occurs in a variety of colours and stripes. Two other molluscs, both south-western species, also occur: the ear-shaped often purple-shelled *Otina ovata* and the equally small $\frac{1}{8}$in long, banded-shelled snail *Cingula cingillus*, together with a third minute mollusc *Lasaea rubra* which, as we have already seen, is common on the more exposed *Mytilus* shores; all must be hunted inside or between dead barnacle shells which well indicates their diminutive size.

Animals which are locally common include the dog whelk and flat periwinkle *L. littoralis* together with its larger relative the dark blue/brown edible periwinkle *L. littorea.* The beadlet anemone is joined by the much larger green snakelocks *Anemonia sulcata* whose non-retractile purple-tipped tentacles are obvious in many crevices and pools where they sweep the waters for small fish and crustaceans. Tiny blue insects *Lipura maritima* will be found drifting in random wind-blown rafts on the surface film of pools or crawling over barnacle shells into which they retreat with a bubble of air when the tide returns: no insects have mastered the art of breathing oxygen dissolved in sea water.

The less intense wave action allows more seaweed to grow on barnacle shores. Large algae include yards of narrow *Bifurcaria bifurcata*, a southern species replacing thong weed *Himanthalia elongata* which is the common algae at this level further north. *Codium*, a green algae particularly associated with warmer seas, is also fairly common.

Fucus similar to the form appearing on mussel shores again occurs but is more luxuriant and grades into the typical bladdered 'vesiculate' form as the shelter is locally improved. On steep sunny slopes *Lichina* extends right down from the upper shore levels through much of the middle shore.

Page 103 Beer Head, South Devon, one of the most westerly outcrops of Chalk, giving open downland on the cliff top with many calcium-loving plants. In the background the more wooded dissected ground is underlain by Greensand deposits which carry some interesting ash woodlands

Page 104 (*above*) Salcombe, South Devon, a typical drowned valley or ria, but unusual in having now no major stream entering the sea. This unique estuary has many muddy creeks or 'pools' with abundant marine life uncovered at low tide. Sea entrance is steep and rocky (*cf page 154*); (*below*) Redshank—a very common wader which will be seen at most times of the year in muddy estuaries

The following are common algae of barnacle shores:

Catenella repens	*Nemalion* spp
Corallina officinalis	*Porphyra umbilicalis*
Laurencia pinnatifida	*Rhodymenia palmata*

Just above the *Laminaria* there is often a dense red algal community almost forming a short 'turf', sometimes partly covered by the stipes (stalks) of larger algae.

Typical species in the 'turf':

Corallina officinalis—very common on headlands and in damp gullies forming a compact high piled 'carpet' of purple and white calcareous fronds.

Gigartina stellata—replaced locally by Irish moss or caragheen *Chondus crispus* in more sheltered locations.

Also:		
	Laurencia pinnatifida	*Lomentaria articulata*
	Rhodymenia palmata	*Plumaria elegans*
	Ptilota plumosa	*Membranoptera alata*
	Cladophora rupestris	*Leathesia difformis*
	Enteromorpha spp	*Ulva* spp

The bird life of exposed shores is restricted among terrestrial species to rock pipits and jackdaws, but a number of seabirds rest and feed on mussel banks at low tide. Commonest among these are oystercatchers, cormorants, shags, great black-backed gulls and herring gulls with the addition of turnstones, black-headed gulls and ring plover in the autumn and winter.

Occasionally a fox will scavenge along the strand lines but no other mammal is common. Otters make infrequent appearances or leave signs, in the form of droppings or 'spraints', of their presence in the area. On Scilly the white-toothed shrew can sometimes be found among the rocks at high-tide levels, providing a holiday highlight for visiting small-mammal enthusiasts.

Semi-exposed shores (see figure 7, p 106)

Increase in shelter from the waves allows the algae to dominate the rocky shore in the form of members of the family *Fucaceae* (wrack). While some relatively small and often tattered members of this family are found in mussel- and barnacle-dominated shores, it is only in sheltered locations that they attain their full potential size. Walking across such shores can be hazardous and a steadying walking-stick is extremely useful.

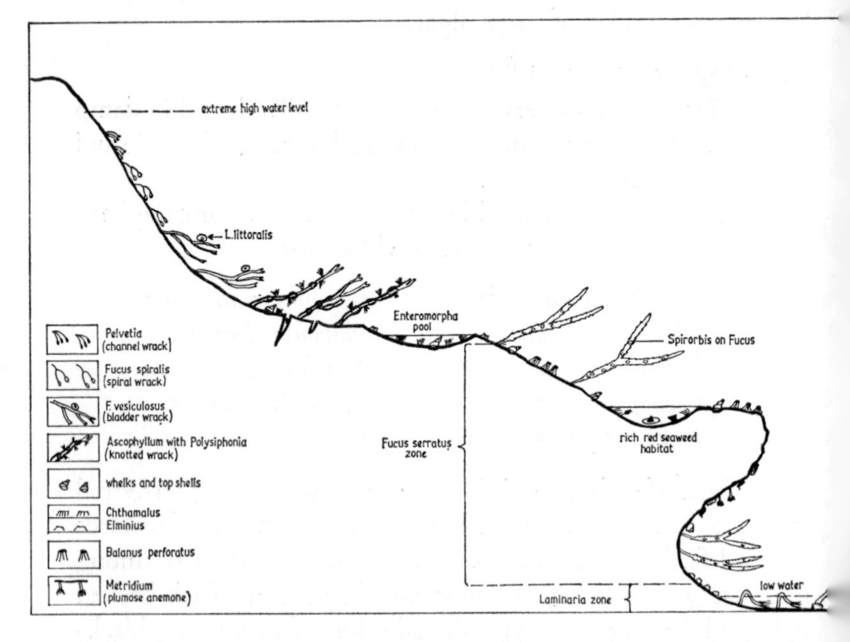

Figure 7 Diagrammatic section of a fairly sheltered *Fucus*-dominated rocky shore showing distribution of the main species. This habitat is common on the south coasts of Devon and Cornwall

Fucus serratus, the serrated or saw wrack, replaces the *Himanthalia* or *Bifurcaria* of more exposed locations, particularly where the lower shore is sandy. The full sequence of seaweeds can often now be seen starting at high-tide level with a band of channel wrack *Pelvetia canaliculata*; often on a hot summer day it takes on a black, crisp, dead-looking habit. Adjoining and intermingling with channel wrack is spiral wrack which has the colour of overcooked cabbage. This algae, with typical rather bubbly inflated reproductive structures at the ends of the fronds, usually forms a thin layer below which the longer, tougher dark green of the knotted wrack *Ascophyllum nodosum* makes a thick and often extensive belt. Locally it is in competition with and even replaced by the very familiar bladder wrack *Fucus vesiculosus* which pops readily and often loudly beneath the feet. Saw wrack *F. serratus* usually occurs just above low-tide mark where on flat shores with a supply of sand it forms a wide zone.

In places where sand movements in summer sometimes partly cover the holdfasts of the algae, *F. serratus* and *F. vesiculosus* are more commonly found than the less sand-tolerant *Ascophyllum* which will, in such cases, be confined to boulders above the sand.

Among other algae, the dark maroon, stain-like growth of *Hildenbrandia* is common on damp rocks and on overhangs, together with tiny-jointed, stemmed, bright red *Catenella repens* which also occurs around the holdfasts of larger algae. The dominance of the larger algae restricts the population of small species in the middle- and lower-shore levels but *Laurencia* and the edible dulse *Rhodymenia* may be present.

Two common seaweeds are *Ulva lactuca*, the sea lettuce, which is well-named and, like its rather flaccid grass-like relative *Enteromorpha*, forms large zones either high up the beach or in lower levels where they tolerate well both running fresh water and sand. Sometimes both species will grow epiphytically on mussels or on the shells of limpets in rock pools. Another epiphyte is the peculiar deflated football-like growth of the brown *Leathesia difformis*.

Two other more attractive seaweeds are the bright green hair-like tufts of *Cladophora*, and the delicate feathery growths of red *Plumaria elegans* which is found in wet spots amongst sponges and on shady overhangs. The jointed-stemmed red *Lomentaria articulata* which grows on rocks and other seaweeds is also common, as are the dark red tufty growths of *Polysiphonia lanosa* on the knotted wrack which acts as host plant.

Many more genera will be found including *Chondrus*, *Rhodo-*

chorton, *Gelidium* and *Ahnfeltia* with fronds like fuse wire, and *Cladostephus* which, like the last genus, is rather rigid and carries in addition stiff hooks in whorls around the dark greenish-brown stem.

Above and within the upper barnacle zone the black tar-like growths of species of lichen *Verrucaria* are common but occupy a more restricted vertical range than they do on more exposed spray-washed cliffs. Removal of a sample with the fingernail may be necessary to differentiate this encrusting algae from tar!

On *Fucus* shores the Australian barnacle *Eliminius* becomes very common on many south coast beaches in sheltered estuaries and on some quiet open coasts where it may replace the other small acorn barnacles, particularly *Balanus balanoides*.

Three species of periwinkle, the rough *Littorina saxatilis*, *L. littoratis* and the edible *L. littorea* are quite common. The pretty, sometimes yellow, flat periwinkle appears on *Fucus* where it is often disguised as an air bladder and *L. littorea* favours bare rock or rock pools, but the tiny *L. neritoides* is rarely seen, preferring as it does more exposed coasts.

Patella vulgata is the most frequent limpet with a few *P. depressa* while *P. aspera* is now only found in the *Laminaria* zone or in pools containing the attractive calcareous algae such as pink-and-white *Corallina* and the purple *Lithophyllum*.

The lack of violent wave action on *Fucus* shores enables a number of top shells to prosper:

Gibbula lineata, the thick top shell
Gibbula umbilicalis, flat topshell
Gibulla cineraria, grey topshell, together with the beautiful red-, green- and purple-painted topshell *Calliostoma*, one of the most exotic-looking British shells.

The top shells will also be seen on more exposed shores with a little algae to shelter them, but the painted top shell *Calliostoma zizyphinum* is usually only found in the more sheltered areas, particularly on the south coast shores.

Dog whelks, which retreat into cracks at low tide, are seldom in very large numbers and although the mussels upon which the whelk preys are larger than on exposed shores their numbers are much reduced. Many empty shells will show the neat round hole drilled by the whelk so that it can suck out the soft parts via its tubular proboscis.

The common beadlet anemone *Actinia equina* comes in a variety of colours and patterns but appears predominantly as dark red and green blobs of jelly at low tide; they reveal their symmetrically-arranged tentacle masses and the bright blue eye spot at the base of each when they are covered with water. The only other really abundant anemone is the green snakelocks, but locally the dahlia anemone *Tealia felina* occurs with its sticky wart-covered crimson or green column protruding from rock cracks. On the lower shore on rocky overhangs the slender tentacles of the feathery plumose anemone often hang in profusion: here they may be accompanied by *Sagartia elegans* and the often dead-white tough colonies of *Alcyonium digitatum* which, in the air, take on a flesh colour and are therefore known commonly as dead men's fingers.

At very low tides the sand and shell debris tubes of the reef building worm *Sabellaria* are exposed on the North Devon coast and also along the south coast east of Beer Head. The worms form honeycomb-like colonies up to 2ft thick on rocks above sand level.

Sedentary worms living in limy, coiled or irregularly squirming tubes are common, forming encrustations over rocks, dead shells and seaweed laminas and occasionally on the backs of degenerate spiny crabs and parasitised shore crabs. The very small clockwise-coiled white tubes of *Spirorbis borealis* are particularly common on the fronds of *Fucus serratus* or they may cover rocks and stones at mid-tide level. Familiar to many students of the new Nuffield biology course will be the worm *Pomatoceros triqueter* which attaches its triangular-shaped, irregularly twisted tube to stones. When placed under water an attractive banded crown of tentacles protrudes and acts as a feeding appendage which filters plankton from the sea water.

Crabs make up an obvious, often fast-moving, element of the fauna with shore crabs, swimming-crabs and the more lethargic crack-dwelling edible crab all being common, as are squat lobsters during the summer. Deep cracks and rocky overhangs are always worth exploring at the lowest state of a spring tide for there will be found a community of light-shy creatures which are mainly in the form of encrustations and will need to be carefully lifted with a strong knife for close observation. Sea squirts, which live singly, are rather off-white objects which seem to do little but squirt water as their name suggests. Much more colourful are the colonial forms, particularly the gold or deep purple colonies of the star ascidian *Botryllus schlosseri* and the more serpent-like colour-banded *Botrylloides leachi* which are very much advanced forms of invertebrate life although they superficially resemble the sponges with which they frequently grow. Again the colonial sponges provide banks of colour—showing the greens, yellows, oranges or sometimes scarlets of the two commonest species, the breadcrumb sponge *Halichondria panicea* and a similarly highly variable species *Hymeniacidion sanguinea.* As with simple sea squirts the free-living sponges are drab but very common, particularly the purse sponge *Grantia compressa* which attaches its flattened body to a variety of small red seaweeds.

Browsing on the sponges are small cowries *Trivia* spp which are but pale shadows of the gigantic tropical forms but are nevertheless an exciting find and one that should be left alone as a number of dead shells can always be found in the fine shingle, particularly on the south coasts.

Sheltered areas

Such habitats are common, particularly within the estuaries where the drowning of the old river valleys has produced many sheltered inlets which, although part of the estuary, are never influenced by fresh water.

The paucity of the fauna in such situations compared with the open coasts and the luxuriance of the blanketing algae are the two dominant features of these habitats. *Ascophyllum*, the knotted wrack, may grow 4–15ft long, and in the middle shore long straps of *Fucus vesiculosus* occur, often thickly covered with flat periwinkles.

Pelvetia and *Fucus spiralis* carpet rocks and the more stable shingle, while lower down, the saw wrack *Fucus serratus* is dominant and often covered with the white-coiled tubes of *Spirorbis* worms.

Two of the most characteristic algal populations of the South West are those of *Bostrychia scopioides* and *Catenella repens* which occur high up the shore in these very sheltered habitats together with the filmy growths of *Calothrix*, *Plectocnema*, *Microcoleus* and *Rivularia*.

Lack of wave action allows the accumulation of silt which often covers the plants and prevents many filter-feeding animals from existing. A few species are, however, plentiful in such situations including small crabs, scavenging isopods and amphipods such as *Ligia* the sea slater; worms appear frequently in rocky cracks where the silt accumulates and under loose stones where eels lurk.

The visiting birds, oystercatchers, turnstones, herons and the scavenging gulls make the most obvious visual impact; these shores require careful scrutiny before the rest of the animal life becomes obvious.

Effects of the 'Torrey Canyon'

The oil disgorged from the shattered hulk of the huge tanker, *Torrey Canyon*, wrecked on the Seven Stones Reef off Land's End, came ashore in thick chocolate mousse-like waves in March 1967. It was deposited on the areas shown in figure 8 (p 112), often inaccessible from land. Many areas shown by arrows on the map were treated with great quantities of detergent, and it was this which destroyed the littoral organisms that it touched rather than the oil. Animal and plantlife, though smothered by the oil, would in most cases have survived had it not been for the detergent: it was the many thousand seabirds, mainly auks, who suffered death as a direct result of the oil discharge.

Many beaches became denuded of all living shore species but even by early summer 1967 there were signs of colonization on the bare rocks. Great stretches of open coast were blanketed in vivid green *Enteromorpha* growths from top to bottom of the

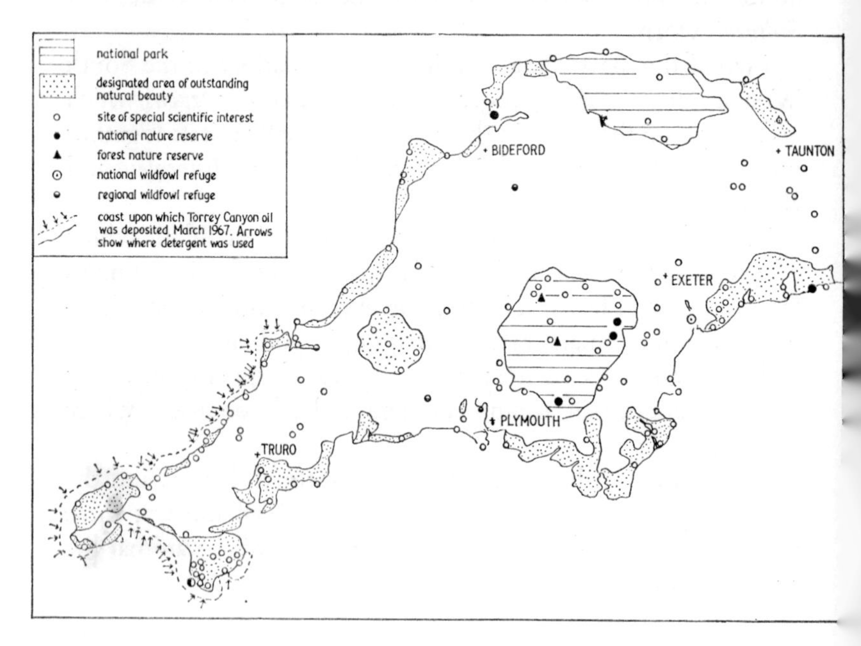

Figure 8 Distribution of areas of particular interest to naturalists in the South West showing position of *Torrey Canyon* oil pollution in 1967

shore. Later, in early winter, the green weed was largely replaced by massive growths of laver *Porphyra umbilicalis*, and then spores of *Fucus* settled down to add slight variety to the scene. By early spring 1968 rocky shores had zones of *Porhyra*, *Enteromorpha* and *Fucus*; some of the latter withstood the oil and regenerated from the tough stipes attached to the rocks.

The most obvious features of the detergent-treated shores

some months later were the luxuriant growths of algae which, in the absence of grazing molluscs such as limpets and periwinkles, were able to flourish. Among the more delicate seaweeds which quite quickly grew up were *Rivularia atra*, *Ulva lactuca*, *Laurencia pinnatifida*, *Cladophora rupestris*, *Corallina officinalis* and *Chondrus crispus*.

Gradually the molluscs returned to the denuded areas, some by migrating round the coast from unpolluted rocks, others no doubt moving from lower shores to colonise the littoral areas. Barnacles were very hard hit by the detergent but during the autumn of 1967 large quantities of *Chthamalus stellatus*, the southern species of acorn barnacle, settled down from the plankton. This species which was formerly the most abundant on South Cornwall rocks, had been decreasing recently in favour of the more northern form *Balanus balanoides*. Conditions now seem to have almost reverted to pre-oil days with *Chthamalus* occupying the upper, more exposed shore areas, and *Balanus* forming a zone lower down the rocks.

An animal that seemed to benefit from the lack of competition was the tube-dwelling worm *Pomatoceros triqueter* which formed massive growths on rock faces. Anemones suffered greatly from the detergent and the worst hit was probably the snakelocks anemone *Anemonia sulcata*, but this, together with *Actinia equina*, has now re-established itself abundantly in most of its former haunts.

However, in the 1970s, effects of the oil are still with us and many beaches have much more *Fucus* cover than formerly; this applies particularly to semi-exposed beaches. In some cases the *Fucus* cover now provides richer habitats for the shore naturalist than in the days of open barnacle- and mussel-covered rocks before the oil. Gradually, however, the limpets are restoring the balance and will probably eventually convert the beaches to their old appearance although the process will take many years. Marked differences were originally visible between beaches on which detergent was used and those not so treated, and it is to be hoped that should such disasters happen again, much more use will be made of mechanical methods for clearing oil; many shore animals can cope with crude oil in small quantities but even a trace of detergent is lethal. Investigations as to the long-term effects of the oil and detergents are being carried out by the Marine Biological Association and recent work suggests that the shell fish population off Marazion and Porthleven is increasing again, in particular the bivalves *Lutraria* and *Ensis*.

The birds are the group most susceptible to long-term damage by disasters such as the *Torrey Canyon*, and the decline in the auk population continues, accelerated recently by man-made ocean pollutants such as polythene derivatives, and the scourge of West Country beaches, oil.

Shingle beaches

Such areas of rounded, often highly polished pebbles of various sizes and often attractive colour are probably best explored by the well-shod 'rock hound' looking for semi-precious stones or by botanists investigating the sparse vegetation, for progress is slow in such a yielding medium and can be uncomfortable in the extreme as many bathers will testify.

Pure shingle beaches are not abundant in the South West except locally along parts of the Exmoor coast and parts of North Cornwall; there are also some attractive serpentine pebble beaches on the Lizard peninsula. Often a fringing shingle bank occurs above the sand of the lower shore area which is only covered by spring tides, and sometimes the strand lines so formed will contain a few sparse plant growths. Unfortunately every year more polythene containers and lumps of crude oil, frequently attached either to the feathers of an auk victim or to pieces of drift wood and old fishing net, are washed in and the products of 'homo contaminens' are much more likely to be found than natural organic objects. Despite the rubbish, however, cuttle fish bone, and the empty egg cases of dogfish and skate which form familiar mermaid's purse are frequently stranded together with the bubbly collections of whelk egg cases.

It is with shingle shores of greater extent, however, that we are most concerned, particularly the spits and barriers. Where the currents roll the pebbles parallel with the coast line, banks of shingle are built up above sea level; one end is attached to the mainland and the other is open to the tide. Such spits are not very common but a famous example is built northwards from Westward Ho! in Devon, forming a pebble ridge locally known as the Popple which bounds the seaward approaches to the sand-dune complex of Northam Burrows.

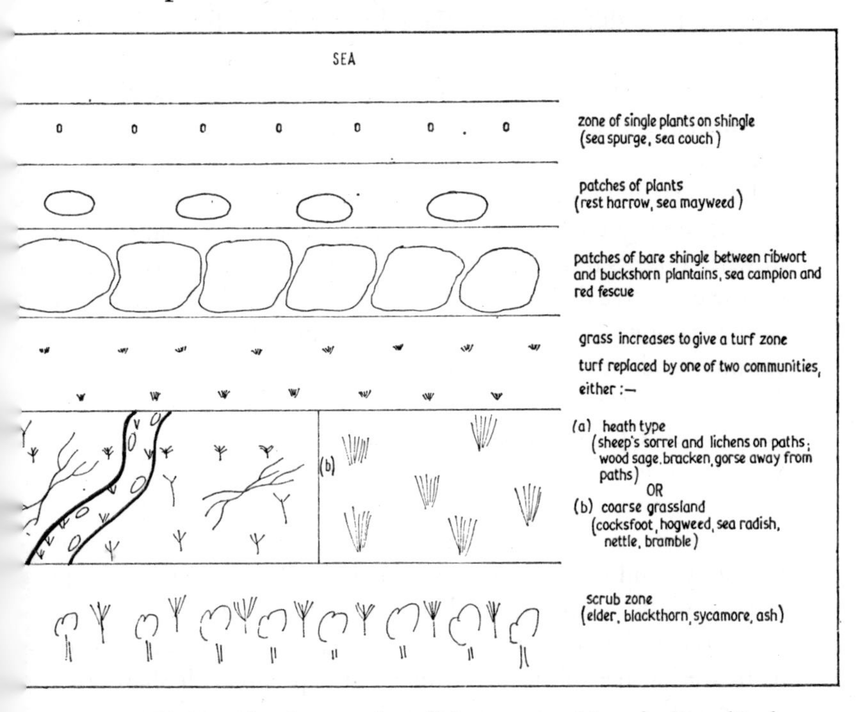

Figure 9 Diagram showing zonation of plant communities colonising shingle beaches based on published information on the Slapton shingle ridge, South Devon

A second coastal feature is the barrier which, unlike the shingle spit, is closed at both ends. At Loe Pool near Helston the barrier impounded the water flowing to the sea via the River Cober which now empties into a freshwater lagoon between shingle and the land, a position known as the 'back' of the ridge. Other shingle barriers can sometimes be formed with an admixture of sand, as happened at Slapton ridge, with the ley on the landward side. The South Devon coast offers other similar examples, and in Cornwall there is a barrier at Swanpool near Falmouth.

Strangely, many of these south coast beaches are composed of flint pebbles, the origin of which is a mystery for chalk (from which flints are derived) is now only found locally in South-east Devon. It is difficult to explain how pebbles from this area could move west against the trend of the longshore drift: some have suggested an outcrop of chalk on the bed of the English Channel as a possible source, but much more investigation seems necessary.

For the general naturalist, pebble beaches can be barren places but, at the right season, even the few plant species that survive in what appears to be a hostile medium produce attractive shows of flowers above their typical mat-like growths. The sea campion *Silene maritima* makes carpets of large white flowers during the summer and, at the same time, the handsome purplish sea pea *Lathyrus japonicus* produces blooms which fade to blue when cut. Another prostrate form is sea sandwort *Honkenya peploides* which is one of the first plants to colonise mobile shingle. It has been used as a pickle in Yorkshire, due to its reputedly pungent taste, but its green-white flowers have little to commend them to the eye and only open in bright sunlight. The delicate large flower of the yellow-horned poppy *Glaucium flavum* is not as common on the mainland as it is on Scilly, but can be seen during its flowering period between June and September. It shares this season with bittersweet *Solanum dulcamara*, a form of nightshade with poisonous red berries and yellow-anthered purple flowers: it is similar to the normal woodland and hedge variety but has prostrate angular stems and fleshy heart-shaped leaves. Equally typical as a shingle plant is sea kale *Crambe maritima* which could only be called an attractive plant if considered gastronomically: it can be eaten, when cooked, like asparagus. A similar rather untidy plant with dull green flowers is the orache *Atriplex* with a number of species of this genus commonly found. Curled dock *Rumex crispus triangulatus* is another common seaside version of a very familiar inland plant.

Few plants can exist on constantly moving shingle, and the plants which have been mentioned help to bind the unstable pebbles, a function for which they are well adapted. Particularly efficient are those with long creeping rhizomes, such as sea campion and sea sandwort, which are also able to send up new shoots very quickly should the plant be covered with a new deposit of loose shingle. In this respect they are like the marram grass which performs similarly in loose sand.

Once partly stabilised, shrubby seablight *Suaeda fruticosa* is well able to cope with shingle life. This Mediterranean species is only locally common as a wild plant but it has been introduced together with tamarisk in a number of places such as Northam to help further stabilise shingle. When conditions are not too salty, seablight forms a 3–4ft high shrub with thick woody stems which for most of the year is clothed in foliage which shades from dark purple to green. Another plant, more typical of South-west Europe but occurring in Devon and Cornwall, is the shore dock *Rumex rupestris* which is rather like a slender version of the more common curled dock.

Plants of shingle banks have a reasonably good supply of fresh water and so are not true halophytes as are the salt marsh plants which occasionally invade the backs of shingle ridges. Although most shingle plants have fleshy leaves and a prostrate habit, they grow best when sheltered from the direct salt winds at the backs of the ridges; from these they may creep to the top and during favourable growing spells sweep down the seaward side. Both the attractive but rare little robin *Geranium purpureum* and the common larger-flowered herb Robert *G. robertianum* can be found on stable shingle. Brilliant gold patches of stonecrop cover large areas on some beaches and when joined by the sea bindweed *Calystegia soldanella* with its large trumpet-shaped pink-and-white striped flowers, this habitat can hardly be described as dull. Of more specialist interest will be the slender sea knot grass *Polygonum raii*, the sea couch grass *Agropyron pungens* and a Mediterranean species, the sea hard grass *Parapholic stringosa* which is like a small version of the common rye grass. Less common is the related recurved sea grass *P. incurva* which is largely restricted to the south-western counties.

All the plants mentioned form relatively open communities with one species rarely dominant over more than a few square yards. Despite the fact that the shingle beaches in winter are desolate, windy places with grinding pebbles chattering in the backwash, they can be pleasant places to botanise in summer—particularly in the lee of the ridges, where fortunately plant life is at its best.

Of the bird species frequenting shingle beaches in the South West, only a very few now breed on the mainland, but Scilly is better off. Ring plover, which formerly bred on many beaches, are now scarce: very few nest in Cornwall, although Devon can claim rather more breeding pairs. Disturbance of nesting sites is mainly to blame, although probably predation of rats and gulls has added to the decline in numbers. Terns still have breeding colonies on Scilly, where the arctic tern is at one of its most southerly breeding stations in Europe, with only the colonies in Brittany further south. In Cornwall, the arctic tern was formerly more common than the common tern, but it seems the tables were turned at the beginning of this century; even so, the numbers of common terns on Scilly is small. This species formerly nested in Devon also and would probably still do so at Dawlish Warren were it not for disturbances. If the 'comic terns' have declined in the area, the roseate tern has increased as a breeding species on Scilly from a position of near extinction in the late nineteenth century. A few oystercatchers nest on almost all the islands which form the Scillies but very few do so on the mainland, and then they use cliff ledges rather than the shore. In Devon about fifty pairs breed, mostly on Lundy and the north coast.

Sandy beaches

High tide on much of the north coast and many parts of the south coast completely covers the wide areas of sand that are such a feature at low tide. The sandy beaches below the cliffs are much disturbed by wave action and hold little permanent animal or plant life. During the winter, vast tonnages of sand are taken out to sea during gales by the tremendous backwash created by the waves and this often exposes the rocky foundations of what are to the summer visitor, typical sandy coves. The sand comes in again, usually in the spring, covering any young stages of species that had managed to establish themselves. Many young barnacles and seaweed sporlings are killed by the engulfing sand, and often a bare zone of rock can be seen below the lowest barnacles which indicates the region of sand scouring.

In winter gales the sand is moved about in great quantities and some burrowing animals are washed out and eventually deposited on the beach, as sometimes happens with the burrowing sea urchin *Echinocardium caudatum* on the south coast. The unstable sand is of temporary use as shelter for shoals of the lesser sand eel *Ammodytes lancea* which is caught by the local fishermen by means of a 'sprat hook', a curved blade fitted into a wooden handle. This is drawn in zigzag fashion into the surface layers of the sand and if sand eels are lying concealed they soon wriggle out on to the surface. Another typical dweller on these barren sands is the weaver fish *Trachinus vipera* which buries itself except for the projecting tip of its dorsal fin, which it raises when disturbed; this carries a painful poison which is injected into the foot of the unshod bather.

The strand line is worthy of attention and in the summer the small transparent floats of the warm water jellyfish, by-the-wind-sailor *Velella spirans* and the remains of *Chrysaora isosceles* can be found together with the more common jellyfish *Aurelia aurita*. The former two species tend to occur after a spell of south-west wind, as does driftwood bearing the goose barnacle *Lepas fascicularis* and *L. anatifera* from the South Atlantic. Many seaweeds are washed in, usually showing the brilliant red of the partly decomposed red seaweeds together with the holdfasts of *Sacchoriza* and *Laminaria.* In among the stranded weed, cuttle-fish 'bones' are common at times.

Where the beaches are sheltered by headlands or face away from the prevailing westerly and south-westerly winds, a much richer invertebrate fauna can be found, particularly where a certain amount of silty material is incorporated, as in sandy estuaries. Here flourish the lug worm *Arenicola marina,* the sand lance *Lanice conchilega* and a number of burrowing molluscs, *Ensis,* the razor shell; also *Cardium edule, Spisula, Venus gallina, Dosinia lupinus, Tellina, Donax, Gari, Natica* and the echinoderms *Astropecten irregularis* and *Echinocardium cordatum.*

Fish are common on the sandy bottom, particularly plaice, dab, flounder, and the greater and lesser sand eels; the common topknot *Zeugopterus punctatus,* is fairly common in the South West, although it is rare in the rest of the British Isles. At high tide the bass come in with other fish to feed under the surf as it breaks on the beach, but as many beach fishermen know, not every tide will bring reward although just standing facing a thundering surf provides many with sufficient satisfaction.

CHAPTER SIX

Lower shore and sub-littoral

Plantlife – Animals: invertebrates, fish, mammals and birds – Rock pools

SINCE THE LAST century, this has been the habitat par excellence for the naturalist in the South West. The rocky shores of this area provided abundant material for the books of Gosse and other Victorian naturalists such as J. Couch and C. W. Peach, after whom a sand-burrowing anemone was named, *Peachia hastata*. The Victorian fashion for sea-shore study largely disappeared until it was revived in post World War II years, mainly by a re-emphasis on biology as an outdoor pursuit rather than a museum study of pickled specimens. This surge of new interest in the sea shore was aided by the formation of the Field Studies Council who established a number of residential centres as at Slapton and Nettlecombe Court, offering weekly courses for amateur naturalists and students, the latter mainly from sixth forms and universities. If the emphasis in Victorian times was on collecting and naming, it is now mainly on observing behaviour and working out relationships of plants and animals as part of a living community. The visitor to the South West is still able to enjoy many habitats that have been little affected by man and it is to be hoped that very little collecting of specimens will be attempted.

Fortunately, at present, there is little obvious pollution from the land mass except in the St Austell Bay region where between Dodman Point and Gribben Head about fourteen square miles of sea bed are affected by china clay waste which is disgorged into the sea as a milky suspension. This material covers the surrounding beaches with slime and converts the sea into a turquoise suspension of clay. Near the shore the china clay waste produces an almost sterile sea bed, but a little off-shore, where less silt is deposited, a rich community including many echinoderms is present. Groups that seem to flourish in the silt are the sedentary polychaete worms and the deposit-feeding bivalves. These have the surprising effect of improving the area locally as feeding grounds for some fish, but others are no doubt deterred by the cloudy water.

A scheme to pump the clay waste out into the English Channel some distance off Gerrans Point was proposed but was looked upon with great suspicion by the local fisherman who felt that the residues would later be washed in and destroy their off-shore fishing grounds. Tests were carried out by the English China Clay Company to ensure that the scheme, if tried, would not adversely affect the environment. In 1971 it was decided to find alternative land-based methods for silt disposal.

Plantlife

For our purposes the *Laminaria* (oarweed) zone will be taken as the top sublittoral zone as it is only uncovered properly for a few days a year at the spring and autumn equinoxes. The shallow sea life below the oarweed, the sublittoral proper, is now becoming increasingly popular with the aqua-lung divers and we shall probably learn a great deal about this area when hunting for buried treasure and collecting sea urchins for tourists give way to scientific exploration rather than exploitation.

The large algae are the most obvious feature of the lower zones of the shore, particularly species of the genus *Laminaria*, but they are joined by other species depending on the degree of wave action and type of sea floor (see figure 10). On very exposed shores the frilled-edged laminas of *Alaria* are exposed at very low spring tides. Despite its apparent flimsy appearance the central mid-rib of the frond enables tremendous wave pressure to be resisted. So-called *Alaria* shores are common on the north coasts of Devon and Cornwall below the mussel zone. Two other species are present here, calcium carbonate-secreting *Corallina*, and *Lithothamnion*; the latter forms purple encrustation or thin attractive films on the rocks. The *Alaria* zone is widest on gently sloping shores.

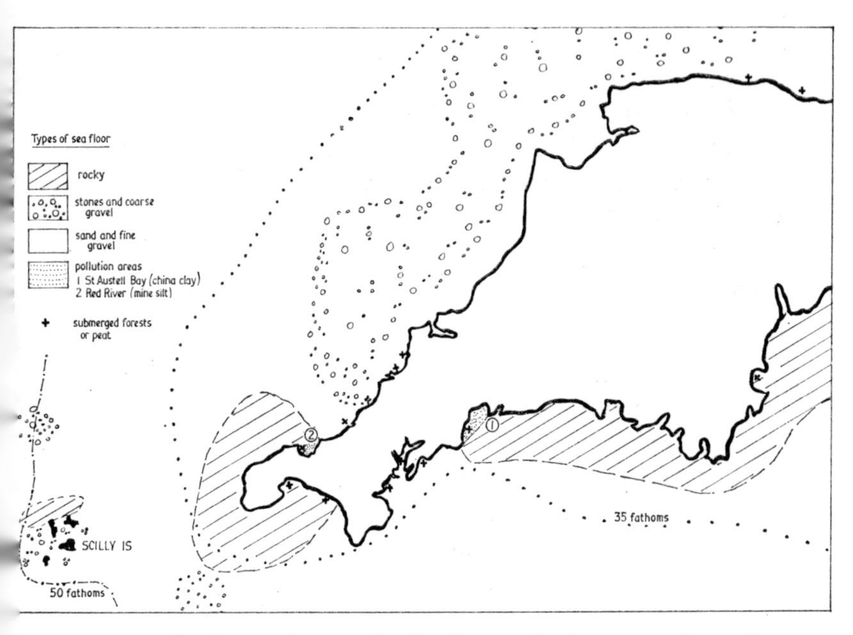

Figure 10 Sketch map showing the distribution of sediments on the sea floor and indicating the positions of submerged forests and peat deposits along the coast

On more sheltered coasts but still open to the Atlantic in slightly less exposed conditions, *Alaria* is replaced as the dominant species by *Laminaria*, although a few *Alaria* plants may still be intermingled. Two species of oarweed are common in the South West, *Laminaria digitata* and *L. hyperborea*, the latter a southern species occupying a slightly lower zone than the former. They are often joined by another southern species, the frilly fronded, bulbous-based *Saccorhiza polyschides* (= *S. bulbosa*). This algae, which is a summer annual, locally dominates the lower shore below a thin fringe of *L. digitata*, and its swollen base is often cast up on the strand line.

Although thong weed *Himanthalia* usually occurs in the middle shore, in the South West it often appears well below this level. Three other algae are common in this zone—*Bifurcaria*, *Cystoseira* and *Codium*. A typical zonation would be: *Alaria/Laminaria digitata* or *L. digitata* alone, followed by *Saccorhiza* or *Himanthalia* below.

Of the smaller algae *Laurencia pinnatifida* and *Lomentaria articulata* occur in the *Laminaria* zone and extend further down the beach on south-west shores than elsewhere; this feature they share with *Himanthalia*.

Lewis (*Ecology of Rocky Shores*) lists a number of algae from this zone and most can be collected, many from the strand lines, or in pools at very low water.

Ceramium rubrum
Chondrus crispus
Corallina officinalis
Cladophora rupestris
Cryptopleura ramosa
Cystoclonium purpureum
Delesseria sanguinea
Dilsea carnosa
Dictyota dichotoma
Desmarestia spp
Gigartina stellata
Membranoptera alata
Nitophyllum punctatum
Odonthalia dentata
Phycodrys rubens
Plocamium coccineum
Plumaria elegans
Polyneura spp
Polysiphonia spp
Porphyra umbilicalis
Ptilota plumosa
Rhodymenia palmata

Animals: invertebrates, fish, mammals and birds

If the number of species of algae is large in this zone the fauna is also rich, yielding by far the greatest number of species, both true shore forms and sublittoral species visiting the shore for breeding or while in their juvenile stages. Animals will have to be looked for beneath the luxuriant algal growths, on overhangs, and particularly in shaded clefts. Here will be found many encrusting sponges and anemones including the beautiful plumose anemone *Metridium senile*, together with *Sagartia elegans* and less commonly the Devon cup coral *Caryophyllia smithii* which is found also in rock pools (see p 134).

On open damp rocks the limpets *Patella depressa* and *P. aspera* may be found with a few mussels. Most of the animals, however, are either attached to the fronds of the algae or shelter among the holdfasts and in the dense turf-like *Corallina* growths. Anemones, polyzoans, compound sea squirts and some polychaete worms can be found between *Laminaria* holdfasts. Beneath the *Corallina* tufts lurk amphipods and isopods, crustaceans, small bivalves and snails. Various encrusting polyzoans such as *Membranipora pilosa* and *Flustrella hispida*, and hydroids, eg *Dynamena pumila* attach themselves to rocks and seaweeds. Molluscs in the oarweed zone include some from higher levels such as the purple-top shell and among holdfasts the delicate tiny blue-ray limpet *Patina pellucida*.

Shallow sea forms occur including the cowries which browse on the rock-encrusting sponges, while the painted-top shell is common on some beaches among stones.

Other common species include the rather amorphous-brown mollusc, the sea hare *Aplysia* which migrates up the beach often in company with an equally curious worm, *Aphrodite*, the sea mouse, to lay eggs in spring. Simple sponges *Sycon* and *Grantia* occur with colonial breadcrumb sponge *Halichondria*, which cover all but the aperture of barnacles *Verruca stroemia*, *Balanus crenatus* and *B. perforatus*. Tube worms are abundant, particularly *Pomatoceros*, *Hydroides* and *Spirorbis*, the latter usually found smothering *Fucus serratus*.

There are, of course, many other species too numerous to mention here. Reference should be made to Collins *Pocket Guide to the Seashore* for illustrations of the species mentioned.

Larger invertebrates make up an obvious element in the community. Here can be found edible crabs, occasional lobsters and, more commonly, squat lobsters, and small hermit crabs, some complete with the anemone *Calliactis* forming a living cloak for the shell. Starfish are only locally common, under stones; the most usual species is the little cushion star *Asterina gibbosa*. Common starfish *Asterias rubens* are joined in shallow water by the splendid star *Marthasterias glacialis*. Edible sea urchins *Echinus esculentus* come into shallower water to breed, often in large numbers, where unfortunately they fall prey to the skin divers who sell them for table-lamp manufacture and other trinkets. There are still large numbers in deeper water round the coast but the very shallow water is almost denuded and they are seldom seen on the beach proper.

Of course, the vertebrate element in shallow-water communities is important and at times very obvious, for many fish occur in the shallow warm waters which are nutritionally so rich with abundant plankton. In recent years the temperature of the surface waters seems to have been increasing as has the number of small fish, and it is possible that the larger fish will again become prolific in the area as they were in the early part of the century when large fishing-boat fleets were stationed at Newlyn and St Ives.

Many shore fish can be caught with a shrimp net at low water. Both the three- and five-bearded rocklings can be found, particularly in the lower pools and among *Laminaria*. The shanny *Blennius pholis* is very common indeed and is sometimes found in wet crevices as the tide retreats. The pretty wrasse appear in summer, particularly the gold-sinny wrasse *Ctenolabrus rupestris*, but other species occur. The long-spined sea scorpion *Cottus bubalis* is a common species as is the butterfish *Centronotus gunnellus*. Attached to stones and sides of rock pools are the little Cornish sucker fish *Lepadogaster gouanii*. Lesser sand eels and young forms of open-sea fish such as pollack, whiting and mullet sometimes appear in large shoals, but often prove difficult to capture with a small net.

The waters of the South West, although warm, are not suitable for the sea horse so typical of southern European coasts, but members of the same family, *Syngnathidae*, are not uncommon, particularly the worm of snake pipe-fish *Nerophis lumbriciformis* and the greater pipe-fish *Syngnathus acus* among *Zostera* (eel grass).

Zostera beds form one of the most interesting and unusual habitats for study. They are rarely extensively developed but do seem to be extending, locally at least. Disease wiped out many areas of eel grass early this century and with its loss many animal species declined locally. Perhaps we shall see recolonisation of former areas which will greatly add to the interest of a locality for the naturalist. Eel grass occurs mainly in sheltered waters little affected by wave action and in Cornwall such conditions are common just within the estuaries as at Helford and near St Mawes where good colonies exist. Species to be found among *Zostera* are indicated by figure 21 (p 173), but of special interest are the two species of hermit crab. Mention has already been made of *Eupagurus bernhardus*, the soldier crab which sometimes carries an anemone on its borrowed shell; in deeper water, however, lives *E. prideauxi* which is often associated with a second species of anemone, *Adamsia palliata*.

Of the larger animals to be seen off the south-west coast, 30ft basking sharks sometimes cruise slowly close to shore, showing dorsal fin and tip of the caudal fin above the water. They are, of course, harmless, and plankton feeders. The same cannot be said for the blue sharks often caught some miles off Looe, but as the shark fishing is done well away from the coast they are not likely to be encountered in shallow water. Occasional basking sharks are washed up on the beaches but the flesh-eating sharks only commonly make their appearance as deck cargo when the fishing boats return to the south coast ports. See figure 11 (page 128) for a diagram of other fish present.

Sea mammals in the form of the grey seal *Halichoreus grypus* breed in small numbers on the Scillies and the North Cornish coast, mainly around Portreath and the surrounding stretches of cave-indented cliffs. During the summer, seals are common, either fishing close inshore or just 'bottling' beyond the breakers watching visitors watching seals. The pups are born in November or early December and each year some are washed up on north coast beaches, mostly suffering either from starvation or pneumonia. Some of these pups are cared for at a 'seal sanctuary' at St

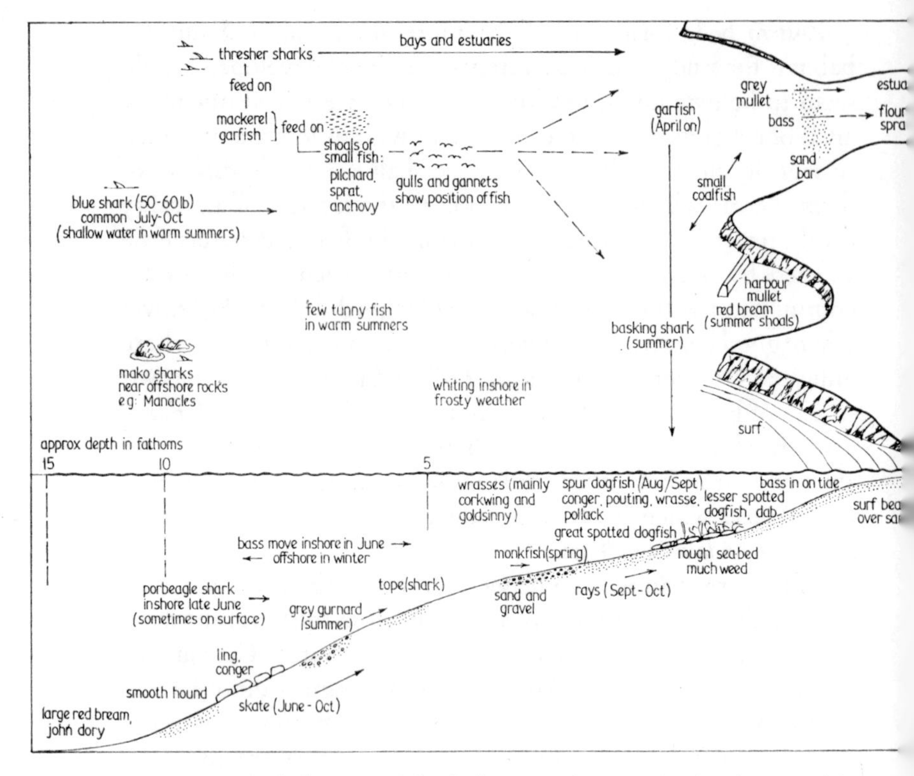

Figure 11 Block diagram of the shallow area showing the distribution of the common fish

Agnes, Cornwall, where a small observation pool is provided for them, and for some transatlantic imports, sea lions, who disport themselves with the seals. It should be the aim to return storm-washed pups to the sea, but this is rarely possible.

In 1969 this species seemed to suffer more than usual from pup deaths in autumn. There is normally a high infant mortality rate on the Cornish coast with a number washing in on to the rocks, but in 1969, thirty-six baby seals are known to have died instead of the more usual dozen or so. The National Environment Research Council have now concluded that the young seals starved and were not poisoned, as had been suggested, by organophosphorous effluent from the Ministry of Defence Establishment at Nancekuke near Portreath which is, as it happens, right in the middle of the main breeding grounds for the grey seal in Cornwall. Despite the finding, there is still much local comment about possible pollution from Nancekuke. It should be remembered, however, that natural infant mortality is necessary along the Cornish coast as suitable breeding areas are small and could easily be subject to overcrowding. Other marine mammals, mainly porpoises and common dolphin, are seen on occasions and some are washed up dead each year. In August 1970 a rare dolphin was washed ashore injured at Gwithian near Hayle in Cornwall but subsequently died. The common dolphin is at the northern limit of its range and not so abundant as the porpoise often seen making acrobatic leaps some way out at sea, particularly off the south coast. Occasionally turtles are washed inshore but these are rare indeed.

Bird life is abundant over the rich waters off the coast with large populations of sea birds breeding around the cliffs of the north coast and offshore stacks on the north and, to a lesser extent, on the south coast (see figures 14, 15, 16, 17 and 18). While gannets are very frequently seen fishing and on passage they do not now breed in the South West, having left their last site, Lundy, some years ago; now the nearest breeding colony is in South Wales at Skokholm. Kittiwakes are, however, a very common breeding species, particularly on the North Cornish coast around St Agnes Head. Other breeding birds include puffins, guillemots, razorbills and fulmars. These will be further discussed in the chapter on cliffs.

Sea watches are particularly rewarding in the autumn and spring during the passage of thousands of birds along the Channel and Atlantic coasts. Many headlands provide excellent viewpoints but probably the best in Cornwall is the Headland at St Ives, especially after some days of north-west gales. Numerous sea birds are then blown into St Ives' bay and pass very close to the 'Island'. This combination of wind direction and geography provides ornithologists with sightings of many rare gulls and skuas. Sea birds can also be seen to advantage during the sea crossings from the mainland to the Isles of Scilly, and to Lundy Island. Probably the best season for this is between August and September when shearwaters, gannets and great skuas are commonly seen; less frequent are sightings of divers, petrels, sea ducks, rarer gulls and terns. For the boat travellers both dolphins and porpoise make frequent appearances.

However, many areas along the coasts such as Carrick Roads off Falmouth and the shallow sea around the Lizard are, because of their clear water, becoming increasingly popular with skin-divers; consequently, the need for some form of protection for our undersea life is essential. Furthermore, large quantities of edible sea urchins are being collected each year as souvenirs and for sale in local shops, not to mention the crawfish, lobsters and crabs taken for the table. It would seem that some underwater nature reserve or national park is necessary if the plentiful and diverse life is not to be destroyed. The decimation is unnoticed by those on the surface but to the visiting skin-diver the effects of man on the sea bed are becoming more apparent each year. Examples have already been set elsewhere, for instance by the underwater parks off Florida and the east coast of Africa: and these are examples which the South West must follow if policies of nature conservation are to succeed.

Rock pools

Gently shelving rocky beaches provide an abundance of pools of various shapes and sizes along the shores. Many are very shallow, narrow, water-filled cracks excavated by the sea along bedding planes in the slaty rock. These typically occur high up the beach and are filled to choking point with the green string-like growths of *Enteromorpha* seaweed which bleaches white when the pools dry out on hot summer days. The warm water in these pools contain little animal life although a few small crustaceans including an 'overgrown woodlouse' called the sea slater *Ligia oceanica* make at least temporary use.

Lower down the beach wave action has a smoothing effect on the rocks and, as a result, the pools are often almost circular or oval albeit in an irregular fashion. Such mid-tide pools are thickly lined by a crusty, smooth or at times foliaceous growth of bright purple/pink algae *Lithophyllum/Lithothamnion* which are both capable of taking calcium from sea water and using it to build up their rough 'skeletons' which bleach when exposed to sun. Another algae with a calcareous thallus is the stiffly branched *Corallina officinalis* which again dies and bleaches when exposed to drying air and sun.

Both *Corallina* and *Lithophyllum* seem to exert a stifling influence on other organisms particularly those which need to be attached directly to rock. The limpet *P. aspera* is a characteristic feature of these calcareous algae pools and is sometimes covered by bright purple patches of algae which share the limpet shell with tufts of green and red algae forming a topknot. Barnacles do not penetrate into such pools neither do the common limpets *P. vulgata* which cluster above water mark at low tide. Other molluscs will be found, mainly top shells *Gibbula* spp and a few chitons beneath loose stones. Around the sides of the pool a variety of delicate red and brown algae gain a foothold and these are best studied by collecting a small quantity and floating them out on white paper in a shallow bowl of water. Some are extremely beautiful such as the blue-green iridescent *Cystoseira tamariscifolia* which, unfortunately, turns almost black when out of water so the plant has to be observed while in its natural habitat (which is by far the best way for the naturalist to see things, anyway). Another brown seaweed which is far from delicate and has a leathery twiggy growth is *Halidrys siliquosa* which inhabits the lower pools but is most likely to be found cast up on the beach. In large middle-shore pools another large brown seaweed which is characteristic of south-western shores *Bifurcaria* produces long-branched, rounded, strap-like growths from a brown toadstool growth on the rocks.

It is the red seaweeds which will probably give the greatest pleasure, such as cockscomb *Plocamium*, one of the few seaweeds with a common name; also occurring are the bead-like hollow stems of *Lomentaria articulata*, many species of *Ceramium* and a host of others. A few green algae will also be found in the deeper pools including the attractive *Bryopsis hypnoides* and *Cladophora* spp.

Deep pools, often formed like potholes by wave action whirling round stones which grind like a rock drill into the bedrock of the beach, are shaded from the sun and have cool water. In such pools live animals and plants more typical of the sublittoral but able to move up the beach by using the pools. *Laminaria*, *Alaria* and *Saccorhiza* will all be found together with *Fucus serratus* which does well in the sheltered conditions. Many of us no doubt were introduced to rock pools such as just described in search of sport in the form of shore fish.

The shanny, or common blenny, *Blennius pholis* is the commonest fish of rocky pools where one can find fish of all ages. Some are even large enough to be taken with a piece of limpet on a hook, while others, with their large pectoral fins which seem almost too big for the body, are even lost in a seaside bucket. The impressive long-spined sea scorpion *Cottus bubalis* and its relative the father lasher *C. scorpius* are both common, sometimes reaching a foot in length. Two shore fish withstand the sea's movements by clinging to rocks with modified fins: one is the Cornish sucker *Lepadogaster gouanii*, with two blue false eye spots contrasting with its rather pinky-red body, which is only about two inches long; this is just half the size of the common rock goby *Gobius paganellus* with its high-set bulbous, rather protruding, eyes.

Free-swimming rocklings *Onos* spp and the rather similar looking butterfish *Centronotus gunellus* can both be captured with a shrimp net pushed beneath weeds at the edges of shallow pools. However, more skill will be needed to capture the elusive brightly coloured wrasse and fifteen-spined sticklebacks which are usually found in small shoals in large pools or at very low tide in temporary lagoons. The only occurring member of the sea horse family of fishes in rock pools is the pipe-fish *Nerophis lumbriciformis* which is usually represented by young specimens only an inch or so long.

The warm water of rock pools during the summer and the oxygen shortage during periods of low tide make unsuitable conditions for many shallow-sea fish which, although they probably feed over rocky shores at high tide, rapidly retreat to the more uniform environment of the sublittoral regions when the tide turns. Crustaceans are common in pools, particularly free-swimming prawns *Leander* spp and bottom-dwelling crabs. The green shore crab *Carcinus maenas* shares the pools with much more attractive fiddler crab *Portunus* spp which has the disadvantage of being extremely pugnacious despite its decorous shell. A few small edible crabs lurk under stones or wedge themselves in cracks but seldom show themselves. In lower pools under stones the squat lobster *Galathea* spp is not uncommon and makes a rapid tail-flicking retreat when disturbed.

A number of molluscs are found, particularly in the lower-shore pools. Top shells are of three main types: the largest is the thick-top which has purplish-black zigzag streaks on its spire and attractive mother-of-pearl near the aperture; this typical south-western species is joined by the flat- or purple-top; and lower down the beach by the very common grey-top. The edible periwinkle is the only common member of its genus to be found in pools, and on south coast beaches it is joined by the predatory whelks including not only the common dog whelk but the netted *Nassarius reticulatus* and the heavy-shelled sting-whelk *Ocenebra erinacea*. Under the root-like holdfasts of the oar weed in the deeper pools will sometimes be found the tiny blue-ray limpet *Patina pellucida* whose three vivid blue stripes across the shell unfortunately quickly fade when it is lifted out of water. On stones and inside old shells, coat-of-mail shells or chitons are common, particularly *Chiton cinereus*, looking more like a legless woodlouse than a mollusc.

There are a few bivalves in the pools, mostly small mussels in the shallows but an occasional saddle oyster *Anomia ephippium* occurs welded firmly inside a dead shell while small variegated scallops *Chlamys* attach themselves by coarse threads, like guy-ropes, underneath rocks. If stones are overturned they should, of course, be replaced in the original position so that the delicate life beneath is not destroyed.

During the spring rather peculiar molluscs with reduced shells enclosed within the soft body come into the pools to spawn. These are the sea slugs, of which the brown, rather amorphous-looking sea hare is the most common; but they are also joined by the sea slugs with no shell at all, such as the sea lemon *Archidoris pseudoargus*. This latter group of molluscs contains some of the most beautiful of the littoral animals, but patience and a keen eye will be needed to detect the smaller, well-concealed forms which blend so cleverly with their prey—often the colonial sponges or sea squirts.

Anemones add great beauty to the rock pool habitat: dahlia *Tealia felina*, snakelocks *Anemonia sulcata*, beadlet *Actinia equina*, plumose *Metridium senile* and the wartlet *Bunodactis verrucosa* are all fairly common, but the latter mainly on Scilly. Their related animals, the corals, are rare, but two of these more tropical water animals do occur in the South West. The more common is the Devonshire cup coral *Caryophyllia smithii*, but much more local and rare is the scarlet and gold star coral *Balanophyllia regia*. Both would provide a rare treat indeed and should be left in situ if found so that others can enjoy them also.

Of the spiny-skinned animals or echinoderms only the cushion star *Asterina gibbosa* and the writhing brittle stars are common beneath stones in pools low down the beach. Occasionally an edible sea urchin will make its way to a shore pool to spawn but usually fall prey to predators (mainly human, but they also provide a welcome meal for the marauding gulls).

CHAPTER SEVEN

Sand dunes

Cornish dunes–Braunton burrows

AN ABUNDANT SUPPLY of light, small sand grains produced by erosion of cliffs, onshore wind of considerable strength, and a low-lying coast, are the requirements for the development of sand dunes. In the South West their appearance seems to have been rapid on the north and west coasts of Devon and Cornwall, at least since the early centuries AD. There are many local stories and evidence to prove that once flourishing communities were engulfed in the sands: the lost church of St Piran at Perranporth, St Enodoc's church, and the discovery of old farm buildings buried under feet of sand, are proof enough of the mobility of the local sand dunes.

One of the reasons for the shifting nature of the north coast sands, and a factor that makes them of great interest to the naturalist, is the high calcium carbonate content due to the presence of much shell sand. This enables calcium-loving plants to occur in places where a glance at the geological map would indicate highly acidic rocks, and hence potentially highly acid soil. Sand dunes in the South West are therefore habitats to be closely studied, but the only ones on which much work seems to have been done are those at Braunton in North Devon, and the dunes of the Camel estuary in Cornwall.

In Cornwall, sand dunes are known as towans, and the name frequently crops up along the coastal strip on the north side of the peninsula, as at Gwithian Towans and Hayle Towans. Further north in Cornwall there are the extensive Penhale sands rising to about 270ft north of Perranporth forming the highest dunes in Britain. Smaller dunes occur at Bude, Widemouth and south of Rock, and also near Trevose at Constantine Bay. The National Trust property at Crantock and the nearby Holywell also consist of dune lands, while in the Land's End area they occur at Lelant and Sennen.

If the north coast is well supplied, the south coast has but few areas of sand—at Par, and on the Lizard at Kennack Sands and Church Cove, while to the west is Prah sands. The elongated dunes between Marazion and Penzance are much disturbed but still manage to produce some interesting plants. Granite sand is heavier than that with high shell debris content so the quartz sands of the Scilly Isles are less mobile but still fairly extensive on Tresco, with small areas on the other islands.

In Devon dunes are signified on the map by the name 'burrows' and this part of the country can boast one of the largest and most famous sand-dune systems in Great Britain, at Braunton.

Cornish dunes

The most striking features of the Cornish dunes are their height and mobility. An extremely high proportion of light shell sand is typical and at Harlyn Bay in North Cornwall the dunes contain over 80 per cent calcium carbonate. The average lime content for north coast dunes is about 60 per cent, falling to around 25 per cent of the smaller dunes of the south coast.

Near Hayle, over 200ft of sand has accumulated along the course of the river, but this is surpassed by dunes at Perranporth which are another 70ft thick and form the highest dunes in Britain. Sand blown in by dry north-west winds are stabilised by marram grass (see plate, p 71) and sand sedge, with locally the pale blue/green lyme grass and stout sea couch roots acting as sand binders.

A succession of plants can be traced from the Atlantic, washed foreshore where saltwort, common and Babbington's arache, sea rocket, spurge and sea beet make up a rather sprawling, untidy plant community. Just inland, the fore-dunes are stabilised by tough-leaved marram between the stems of which gay pink and white trumpets of sea bindweed, and the attractive prickly bluish leaved sea holly are still commonly found. Increasing stability of the sand allows a more diverse plant community to flourish, conspicuous among which are storksbill, curled dock, sea spurge, coltsfoot, sea mayweed and scarlet pimpernel.

Behind this community, mosses such as yellowish *Camptothecium lutescens* bind the sand and also provide attractive patches of colour. Moss also grows amongst the sand-tolerant red fescue grass which produces a thick, springy sward, attractive to rabbits. The grass in places acts as host for the parasitic dodder which produces blazes of tangled red thread-like stems, along which are the pink flowers.

Older dunes inland have a varied collection of plants with many species which flourish on limestone soils and are therefore rare generally in Cornwall. Lime-rich dunes have yellow wort, rest harrow, carline thistle, hounds-tongue, fairy flax weld, roast beef plant and, very commonly in late spring, the cowslip.

Even when rainwater and accumulated acid humus reduce the lime content of the sand, calcium carbonate is added due to the breakdown of shells from the abundant land snails which are such an obvious feature of the dunes. Characteristic snails, all of which are typically white with dark bands, are the heath snail *Helicella itala* and a variety of sandhill snails, wrinkled *H. caperata*, striped *H. virgata*, and the elongated spire shells of the pointed sandhill snail *Cochlicella acuta*. These small shells are supplemented by those of the large common garden snail and the variably coloured brown-lipped snail which are locally very common indeed.

Much stabilising vegetation at Perranporth was removed after the last war when mine clearance operations were under way. This was followed by large-scale movement of the dunes, a feature still very obvious on a windy day. The local council together with the Cornwall Naturalists' Trust is experimenting with marram planting to begin the stabilisation of the sand, but so far the results are not encouraging.

Braunton Burrows

Braunton Burrows is the most important sand-dune system in the South West, and one that has become internationally famous since the descriptions of the rich flora and fauna to be found there were given by the seventeenth-century naturalist John Ray.

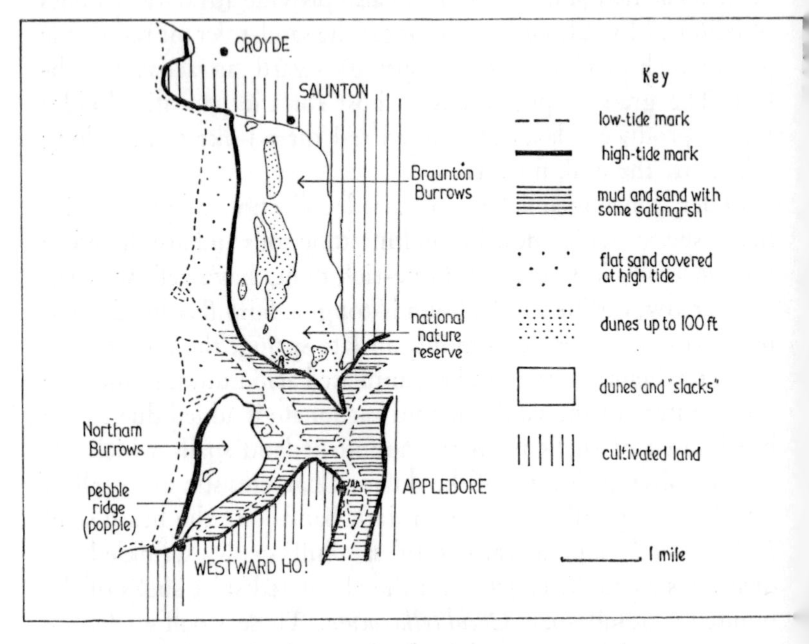

Figure 12 Sketch map of Braunton Burrows, North Devon

At present the dunes on the north side of the Taw/Torridge estuary (see figures 12 and 13) have a National Nature Reserve of 560 acres in the south. There is a military firing and training range at the northern end and this means that much of the dune system (932 acres) is not available, except by permission, for scientific research. There is an interesting nature trail over the dunes but this again may be closed, due to military operations at which time a red flag will be flying. Notice of closure can be seen in local newspapers.

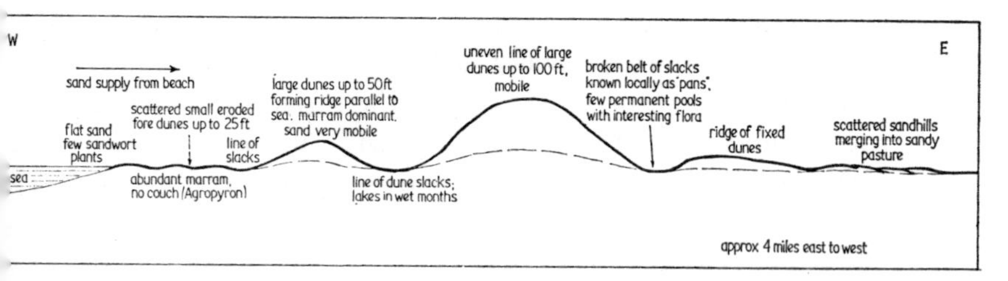

Figure 13 Diagrammatic section of Braunton Burrows National Nature Reserve (not to scale)

Due to their position between the open sea and the estuary, the dunes are unstable, and natural erosion has for many years had a modifying influence on the form of the dunes which, on the seaward side, are highly mobile and dominated by marram grass. Mine clearance activities at the end of the last war, as at Perranporth, destroyed much of the stabilising vegetation on the foredunes. Marram is now re-establishing itself but only after planting measures have been taken.

The dunes themselves are arranged in two parallel groups: the landward ridge of mobile sand is the highest, rising to 100ft and forming one of the highest dune systems in the British Isles. The sand composing the dunes is supplied from the beach to the west, and is a mixture of shell and rock sands. The calcium carbonate content of 2·86 per cent is roughly the same for both the older fixed and the younger mobile dune areas.

Calcareous sands provide habitats for species of mosses otherwise scarce in the South West. One of these *Tortula ruraliformis* takes on a golden-green colour when wet, and is typical of the unstable sand areas which it helps to bind, as do the dense tufty growths of *Tortella flavovirens* and the common *Bryum pendulum* which is most often found on the lee slopes of the dune. Where banks of broken shell sand accumulate due to the winnowing effect of the wind, the yellowish calcium-loving moss *Camptothecium lutescens* covers sunny slopes. In more acid soil conditions, however, the latter moss is replaced by the silky tufts of *Brachythecium albicans*.

Between the two sand ridges are flatter areas known locally as pans but more generally called dune slacks in which the water table is at, or very close to, the surface so allowing the development of swamp vegetation with, in places, thickets of creeping willow *Salix repens*. *S. repens*, subspecies *argentea*, is characteristic of dunes in the west as it is in North France and Belgium. The damp ground beneath the willow supports a wide variety of marsh and damp grassland species including many bryophytes. (See Watson, 1918, for list.)

The vegetation of the slacks is the most diverse, mainly due to the availability of water and the more stable nature of the sand. Here the most common grass is *Agrostis stolonifera*—white bent, with sea pearlwort *Sagina maritima* abundant. Also prolific is the marsh helleborine *Epipactis palustris* which is unique among British orchids in having purplish-brown-and-white flowers which it produces in July and August. In moist places in the slacks, patches of lichen carpet the sand including *Arthopyrenia arseniseda*, *Collema glaucescens*, *C. pulposum* and *Riccia crystellina*. Two species of green filamentous algae can be found, *Vaucheria dichotoma* and *V. sessilis*.

Strangely, the commonest member of the violet family at Braunton is the rare seaside pansy *Viola curtisii* which grows with the more common hairy violet *Viola hirta*, the blue flowers of which contrast with the yellow of the pansy petals in early summer. The two plants of unstable sand, sea rocket and prickly saltwort, are joined by the characteristic green upright spikes of Portland spurge, a plant mostly confined to the western seaboard and a typical west European species. Liverworts and mosses are typical of dune slacks, and the association is commonly one of the delicate, pale green, patch-forming liverwort *Leiocolea turbinata*, and the mosses *Dicranella varia Drepanocladus aduncus* and *D. sendtneri*, all of which grow well in calcareous dunes; the last two are typical also of the pools which collect in the slacks during wet weather. Such water is often rich in reddish-brown oxide of iron. The rainfall of 26in per annum over the dunes at Braunton is very low compared with that for the county of Devon as a whole. Slightly more rain falls on the northern sands and at night the temperature over the dunes falls quickly, so the resulting heavy dew supplements the low rainfall.

While of pre-eminent interest to the botanist, the fauna of sand dunes is of no less interest and almost anything can turn up in the autumn as this is a stopping place for migrant birds. In winter, these include merlin, harriers and a few short-eared owls. Several species of ground-nesting birds are found including shelduck and wheatear which breed in old rabbit holes, but the black-headed gull colony that existed until the early 60s is no longer in existence. Lizards are common and so are snails which make use of the calcium carbonate in the sand for shell construction; snakes, however, are rare. Rabbit and fox trails will commonly be seen in the sand and smaller mammals include woodmice, field voles and shrews, particularly among the low mixed scrub of privet, hawthorn and sallow on the landward side of the dunes.

North and east winds in the spring have a desiccating effect on the vegetation causing the death of many seedlings on the dunes. The dry conditions of summer are reflected in the greater hairiness of plants such as woodsage, fleabane and horehound. Shelter and water supply are the two dominant environmental features in determining the distribution of plants on the dunes which show marked vegetation zones (see diagram of cross-section, figure 13, p 139). The sea rush *Juncus maritimus* is common in the wetter areas of the dune slacks where, with the dwarf yellow sedge *Carex serotina*, it colonises the ground beneath the creeping willow. Probably the water germander *Teucrium scordium* which occurs commonly at Braunton in the slacks will cause most excitement, for the pale purple flowers of this sprawling, grey, downy plant are now very rare in other parts of the British Isles: under less waterlogged ground conditions, clustered club rush *Juncus acutus* flourishes, with the club rush *Scirpus holoschoenus*, another Braunton special, to delight the botanist in search of the unusual.

On the exposed mobile sand, only marram will be commonly

found but it has difficulty in stabilising the higher dunes. It is aided by sand sedge *Carex arenaria* which produces upright shoots at regular intervals from its extensive roots; these creep in straight lines across the sand just a few inches below the surface. With increase in shelter on the landward slopes, rest harrow, many small annuals, and the mat-forming moss *Tortula ruraliformis*, are common. Here among the more stable sand, marram is far less vigorous. On the dry, stable dune areas, short turf pasture has been produced, but bracken has now invaded this, and it seems to have been modified by the decline in rabbit populations locally following myxomatosis.

Once a thin grass sward is established this can be colonised by the sea storksbill *Erodium maritimum* which is an Atlantic plant confined largely to the west coasts. It is smaller than the common storksbill with which it grows, and has rather sticky, undivided leaves. Both plants produce pale pink flowers right through the summer. In very dry turf the slender centaury *Centaurium pulchellum* makes its appearance as a minute plant; it is, however, very variable, and grows much taller under more moist conditions.

The lesser hawkbit *Leontodon taraxacoides* is common at Braunton as it is in many dry grassy places in the South West, with its bright yellow, dandelion-like solitary flower heads blooming from early summer to late autumn.

The area also offers some unusual, alien plants which do well locally, including the Argentine dock *Rumex cuneifolius* and French toadflax *Linaria arenaria* which was introduced to the dunes in the last century and is now well established. Other native rarities include shore dock, sea knot grass, and shore weed *Littorella uniflora* which is a declining species yet still plentiful at Braunton where, of course, it is protected. Other plants that one would expect are, however, absent; this applies to the Burnet rose *Rosa pimpinellifolia* which is abundant nearby at Croyde, Woolacombe and Instow.

Insect life is often common on dunes particularly in July and August when at dusk the common and smoky wainscot moths are flying; while on warm days a large flying insect population includes the small tortoishell, peacock (particularly on hemp agrimony), painted lady, common blue, small copper, red admiral and fritillary butterflies. Of the day-flying moths, the six-spot burnet and the cinnabar are common and the larvae of the cinnabar can be seen especially frequently on the ragwort in August. Damp, cold evenings in summer can be particularly rewarding, when species of moth rest on marram flower heads where they can be studied easily by torchlight.

Many members of the grasshopper family of insects, the *Orthoptera*, make their presence heard, particularly the great green bush cricket, but others are also common, including the common ground hopper, mottled grasshopper, meadow grasshopper and the common field grasshopper. The dragonfly family *Odonata* is represented by the golden-ringed dragonfly which is very common from June onwards, as is the ruddy sympetrum.

Braunton was, until recent years, a breeding place for black-headed gulls. These are common enough in the winter but are at their southern limits for breeding, with Cornwall outside their normal range. There are now no large colonies in the South West but a few pairs do manage to breed in undisturbed sites.

Sand dunes are probably the most vulnerable habitat in the area; both natural and man induced changes are taking place rapidly. Feet, cars and litter, together with physical cover of the sands by holiday chalets, bungalows and caravan sites, are rapidly destroying many dune areas. (See plate p 171 of Hayle Towans.)

Other physical pressures come from sand-dune use by the army as training areas, and removal of vast quantities of sand for the building industry as at Gwithian and Perranporth.

A policy of controlled access would seem to be necessary if the destruction of the dunes is not to be made irreversible, but as the area's major source of revenue is tourists who are the chief reason and often direct cause of the destruction, it is difficult to see how 'mere' conservation arguments can protect these important habitats. Their destruction would remove one of the tourist attractions to the regions as well as presenting grave 'blow-out' problems for local councils to face, while in at least one area, for example at Gwithian, serious flood risks may be brought about by too much removal of sand and gravel.

We have already lost the last large breeding colony of black-headed gulls in the area, due mainly to human disturbance; now the outlook is also bleak for many of the remaining dune species, particularly the plants.

CHAPTER EIGHT

Cliffs

Birds–Insects–Other animals–Cliff vegetation

CLIFFS IN THE South West mean spectacular scenery, long sea views, wild flowers in abundance, nesting sea birds, and in spring, and particularly autumn, vantage points for watching sea bird movements and migration.

Cornwall, with its 326 miles, has more coastline than any other county while Devon, with 160 miles, is also well blessed. Access is good along almost the whole length with the proposed South West Peninsula Coastal Footpath running for 515 miles between Minehead in Somerset and Studland Bay in Dorset. Not all of the latter path is yet passable but much is already well used.

Many miles of the coasts in both counties have cliffs, some of spectacular proportions (see plate p 85) east of Combe Martin, with Holdstone Barrows and the Great Hangman in North Devon both rising over 1,000ft. The North Cornwall coast can claim cliffs along almost its whole length, though whilst these are majestic they are not as high as those in Devon; and though both South Cornwall and South Devon are also rich in cliff scenery it does not compete with the massive scale of the north coast as the cliffs are lower and more luxuriantly covered with vegetation which gives a softer, gentler appearance to the coast (see plate p 85, near St Austell Bay). The cliffs are, of course, not continuous; rocky and sandy coves or 'porths' provide breaks, and in some cases wide beaches backed by low sand areas occur, forming Woolacombe Sand, the Taw/Torridge estuary, Perranporth and Crantock dunes in Cornwall and further south still, a low-lying coastal area near Hayle.

If the north coast cliffs house a greater population of breeding

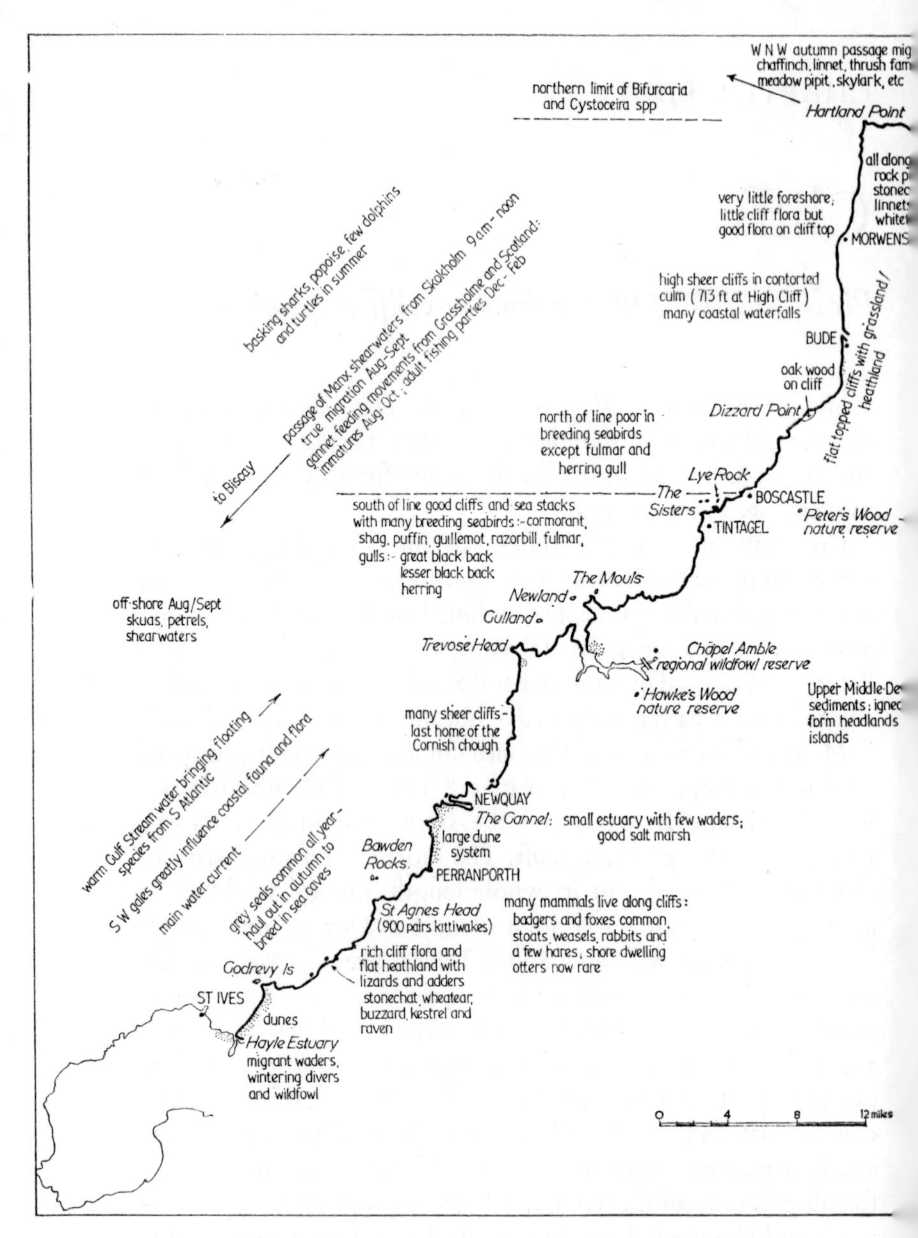

Figure 14 The coast line of north-west Cornwall showing plant habitats and indicating bird migration routes and animal distribution

sea birds than the south, the latter, with the larger area of foreshore, shallower sea, and numerous sheltered inlets, bays and estuaries, attracts more wildfowl, waders and terns, and provides rich habitats for the marine biologist. The accompanying sketch maps (see figures 14–18) indicate the main breeding sea bird colonies around the coast.

Particularly in spring and early summer, when the birds are nesting, the cliff-top ornithologist will be rewarded with a wide variety of species as shown on the maps. The type of rock forming the cliffs is often of great importance in determining plant and animal communities. For example, the easily excavated sandstone cliffs of Ladrum Bay in South Devon allow an interesting colony of house martins to live there. Cliffs in North Cornwall on the Culm measures are less rewarding than elsewhere, both for plants and birds; probably the best results are obtained on the more stable cliffs provided by the Devonian killas, particularly in West Cornwall between St Ives and Tintagel.

Granite of the Land's End peninsula (see plate p 86 of Lamorna Cove) tends to provide less cliff flora than the killas, and most breeding birds occur on sea stacks rather than on the mainland. At Porthgwarra, however, an important bird-ringing and observation site is run by the Cornwall Bird Watching and Preservation Society. Migration studies are undertaken and a list of birds likely to be seen there is given on page 252.

Further influence of geology on vegetation is seen at Beer Head (see plate p 103) in South-east Devon where an interesting calcareous flora with short turf downland is developed over an outcrop of chalk.

The serpentine cliffs forming part of the Lizard, although having many features of geological interest, are also botanically noteworthy for their very rich bryophyte flora. But the dark, slowly weathering rock seems to provide few holds for higher plants; for possibly similar reasons the cliffs here are poorly colonised by birds except for the small island at Mullion which is popular with breeding sea birds. An important feature of Lizard Head is its position for bird-migration studies, par-

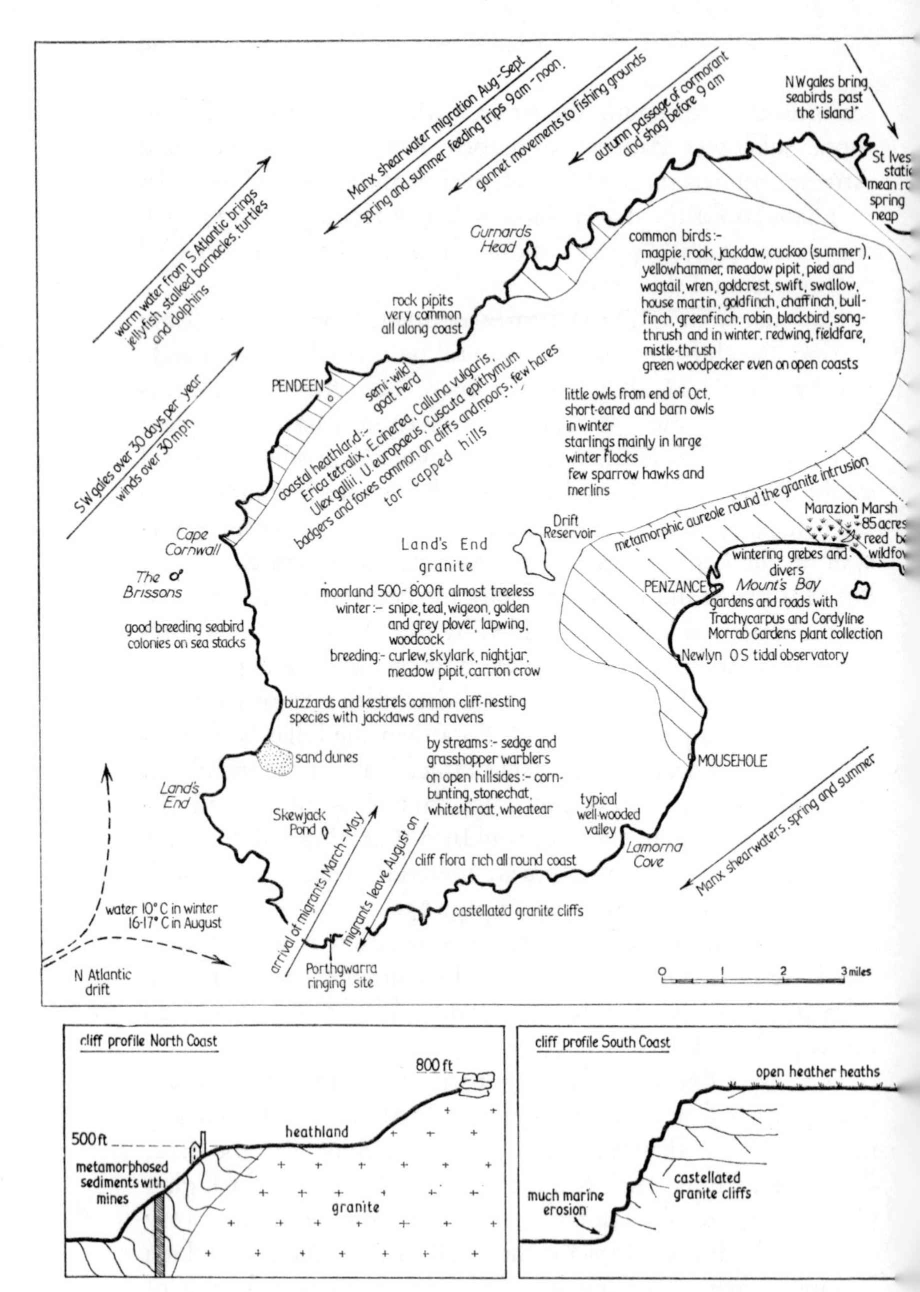

Figure 15 Sketch map of the Land's End peninsula showing main items of interest with inset sketches of typical cliff profiles (see also plate p 86 of Lamorna Cove for a general impression of the area)

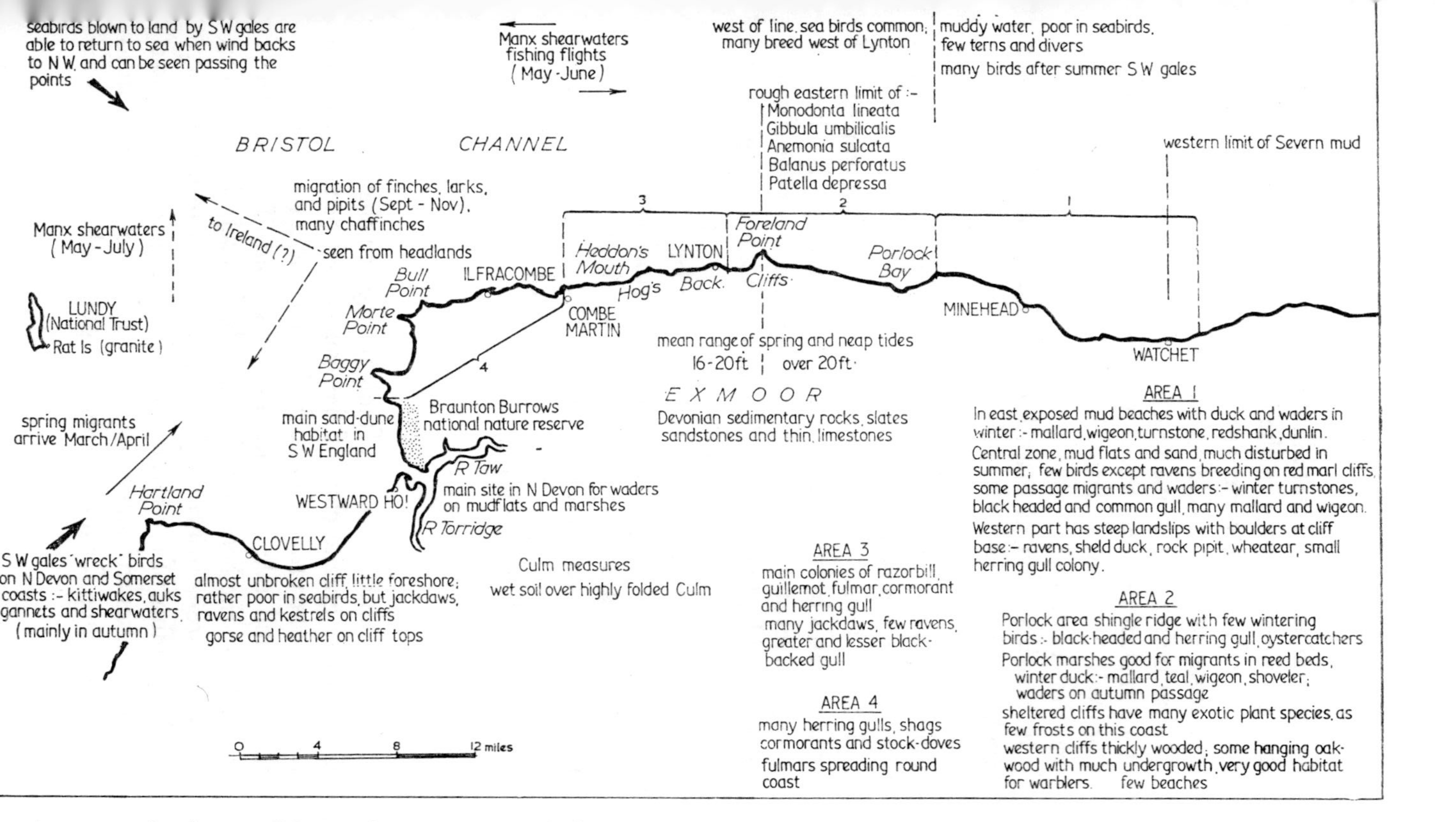
seabirds blown to land by S W gales are able to return to sea when wind backs to N W. and can be seen passing the points
Manx shearwaters fishing flights (May - June)
west of line, sea birds common; many breed west of Lynton
muddy water, poor in seabirds, few terns and divers
many birds after summer S W gales
rough eastern limit of :-
Monodonta lineata
Gibbula umbilicalis
Anemonia sulcata
Balanus perforatus
Patella depressa
BRISTOL
CHANNEL
western limit of Severn mud
migration of finches, larks, and pipits (Sept - Nov), many chaffinches
seen from headlands
to Ireland (?)
Manx shearwaters (May - July)
LUNDY (National Trust)
Rat Is (granite)
3
2
1
Heddon's Mouth
LYNTON
Foreland Point
Porlock Bay
Bull Point
ILFRACOMBE
Hog's Back
Cliffs
Morte Point
COMBE MARTIN
MINEHEAD
WATCHET
mean range of spring and neap tides
16-20ft
over 20ft
Baggy Point
4
E X M O O R
Devonian sedimentary rocks, slates sandstones and thin limestones
Braunton Burrows national nature reserve
main sand-dune habitat in S W England
spring migrants arrive March/April
R Taw
Hartland Point
WESTWARD HO!
main site in N Devon for waders on mudflats and marshes
R Torridge
CLOVELLY
S W gales 'wreck' birds on N Devon and Somerset coasts :- kittiwakes, auks gannets and shearwaters (mainly in autumn)
almost unbroken cliff, little foreshore; rather poor in seabirds, but jackdaws, ravens and kestrels on cliffs
gorse and heather on cliff tops
Culm measures
wet soil over highly folded Culm
AREA 1
In east, exposed mud beaches with duck and waders in winter :- mallard, wigeon, turnstone, redshank, dunlin.
Central zone, mud flats and sand, much disturbed in summer; few birds except ravens breeding on red marl cliffs, some passage migrants and waders :- winter turnstones, black headed and common gull, many mallard and wigeon.
Western part has steep landslips with boulders at cliff base :- ravens, sheld duck, rock pipit, wheatear, small herring gull colony.
AREA 3
main colonies of razorbill, guillemot, fulmar, cormorant and herring gull
many jackdaws, few ravens, greater and lesser black-backed gull
AREA 2
Porlock area shingle ridge with few wintering birds :- black-headed and herring gull, oystercatchers
Porlock marshes good for migrants in reed beds, winter duck :- mallard, teal, wigeon, shoveler; waders on autumn passage
sheltered cliffs have many exotic plant species, as few frosts on this coast
western cliffs thickly wooded; some hanging oak-wood with much undergrowth, very good habitat for warblers. few beaches
AREA 4
many herring gulls, shags cormorants and stock-doves
fulmars spreading round coast
0
4
8
12 miles

Figure 16 Sketch map of the North Devon coast and adjacent Somerset coast showing the types of habitats with their associated bird life and also migration routes

ticularly in autumn. Lizard heathland backing and topping the cliffs is of great interest to the botanist, containing as it does a number of extremely rare species, many with a Lusitanian or Mediterranean affinity. Here, in abundance, grows the rare Cornish heath *Erica vagans*, and in spring and summer a wide variety of heath plants. Predannack Downs, now a nature reserve of the Cornwall Naturalists' Trust, is of European importance as a maritime heathland.

In South Devon at Start Point and Bolt Head are rocks similar to the schists and gneisses forming Lizard Head. These cliffs also provide excellent observation points for land migrants and sea bird movements (see list of birds in Appendix, p 247). Similar watch-points are found in North Devon at Bull, Morte and Baggy Points where coastal migrations and movements of birds towards Ireland occur, mainly in the autumn. Further east along the Devon coast the cliffs have some fine stretches of woodland backed by Exmoor. Much of this coast is inaccessible, however, except to the rock climber.

Most of the coast is unspoilt, except near large holiday resorts; but where tin and copper mining activities took place in the past, the old spoil heaps and engine houses provide interesting habitats for lichens, flowers and many invertebrates together with the sun-loving vertebrates such as the lizard and adder, which utilise the cracks in the walls.

Birds

Casual acquaintance with cliffs might suggest a changeless scene. The massive granite cliffs of the Land's End peninsula give a feeling of permanence despite the lashing seas at their base. Like the wind and tide, gulls are always around. The permanent residents are the herring and greater black-backed gulls whose population seems to increase yearly. During the late summer there is a large influx of the smaller black-headed gull which winters in the estuaries and along the coasts before returning north to breed in spring, for no black-headed gulls' colonies exist in the

South West although a few pairs do manage to breed sporadically on reservoirs. The short-legged, dark-eyed kittiwake breeds in large numbers along the cliffs with probably the largest colony of over 1,000 pairs on the killas cliffs at St Agnes Head. Despite being a pelagic species which spends only the breeding season on land, this small gull occurs in often vast numbers close to the cliffs, particularly during gales. In severe gales, quite large flocks of kittiwakes are sometimes 'wrecked' inland, but this is probably the only time they will be seen away from the sea.

Like the kittiwake, the gannet does not appear over the cliffs but is a common sight about a mile off shore at all times of the

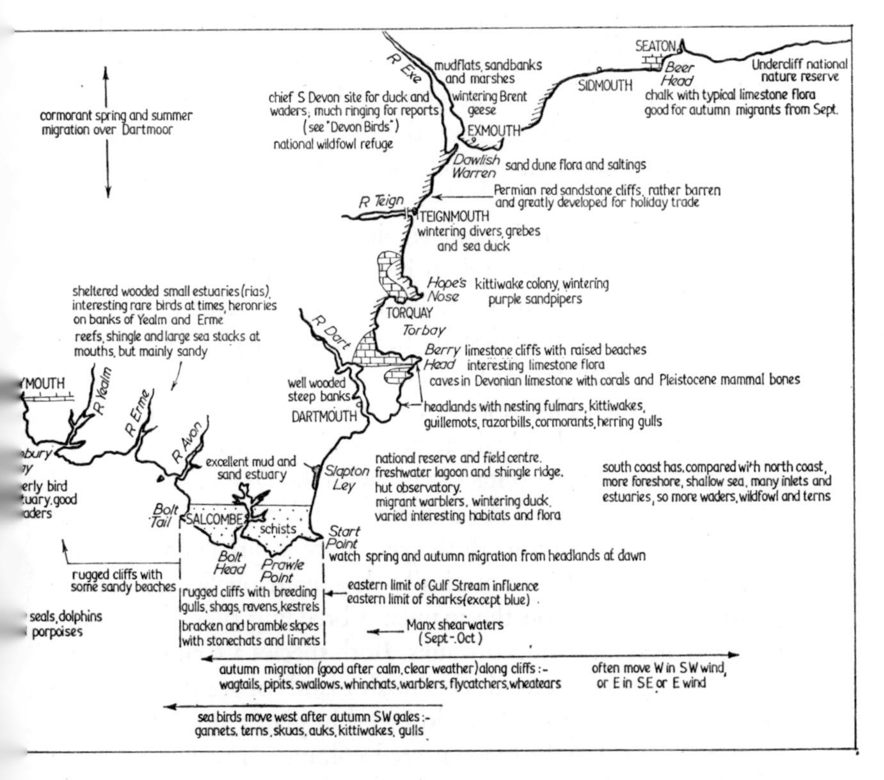

Figure 17 Part of the South Devon coast showing areas of interest and indicating the main regions in which birds are to be found

year. Lundy was the last breeding colony in the South West, where the last known eggs to be laid were removed in 1903. The depopulation of Lundy which took place throughout the nineteenth century coincided with the colonisation of Grassholm (nearly fifty miles away, off the Pembrokeshire coast) which is now the nearest colony. Frequently it is possible to watch from a cliff-top seat the spectacular diving of this bird with its 6ft wing span.

If the gannets and black-headed gulls have declined as breeding species, the fulmar has been added to the avifauna of the area during this century, and is now a relatively common breeding bird. It is again a pelagic bird, spending the winter out at sea where its straight, knife-like wings are perfectly adapted for stiff-winged gliding between the swells. In early February, pairs of fulmars appear along the cliffs, and after selecting a suitable precariously placed ledge, start their highly vocal but rather unmusical courtship with much neck-stretching and growling grunts.

Like the fulmar and gannets, the auks are mainly offshore birds, only coming to land to breed or, unfortunately all too frequently now, when oiled. Even a slight smear of light oil seems to be sufficient to destroy the auk's ability to fly and dive, so it makes for the nearest beach to preen, and in many cases, die. There is an oiled-bird rescue system which operates largely on the initiative of individuals at present, but casualties should be taken to the RSPCA or contact made with the Devon or Cornwall Naturalists Trusts. It is the guillemots and razorbills that suffer most from oil pollution. Both species are at present very common; the razorbill is numerically dominant on Scilly, but the position is reversed on the mainland breeding sites, for reasons probably best known to the auks. Both species are cliff breeders, mainly siting their activities on small islands or sea stacks off the north and west coasts. Both do breed in places along the south coast also, and Lundy has scattered colonies. There is evidence of a decline in breeding strength of both species, but great rafts of the birds sometimes assemble offshore in the late autumn and

Page 153 (*above*) Slapton Ley, Devon, looking south with Start Point in the left background. The Ley forms the largest stretch of natural freshwater in Devon and the shingle bank which impounds the water carries an interesting flora. There is a nature reserve, field centre and bird-watching cabin. Much of the northern part of the Ley is choked with vegetation through which a small stream winds; (*below*) a party of resting common and roseate terns on Porth Kidney sands near St Ives. Migrant terns are a feature of the autumn migration in the South West

Plate 154 (*above*) Dawlish Warren, South Devon. A degenerate, double sand spit across the mouth of the river Exe, now much influenced by holiday trade, and subject to severe natural erosion. Behind the spit upstream are wide expanses of mud and sand forming a National Wildfowl Refuge. The low-lying coast with sand dunes is in marked contrast to the rocky entrance to Salcombe estuary; (*below*) the Helford estuary, Cornwall. A typical south coast estuary with extensive mud and sand areas at low tide and many creeks rich in marine life and waders. Good *Zostera* beds exposed at low tide

during stormy weather; small groups fly low over the water into the wind, and with the aid of a good pair of binoculars, can be watched for hour after hour from the cliff tops.

The third auk to breed in the South West is the puffin, but again the numbers of this species, which is the emblem for the Cornwall Bird Watching and Preservation Society, are going down rapidly. In 1939 there were about 3,500 breeding pairs on Lundy, an island with many traditional connections with this rather comic bird, but in the last few years the numbers have fallen to about sixty pairs. Much the same story can be told for Scilly. In Cornwall the largest puffin colony is at Lye Rock off the north coast at Tintagel with about 200 pairs; but the future seems bleak, and the species is rapidly becoming extinct locally.

The best time to see the sea birds is during gales, particularly the north-westerly kind which drive the birds towards the shore. St Ives 'Island' in Cornwall is one excellent watch-point not only for common species such as kittiwakes, passing at the rate of about 20,000 per day, together with large numbers of gannets and auks, but for rarities which are also blown in. Arctic skuas, for instance, are regularly reported flying west off St Ives and other West Cornwall headlands between mid-August and early October. The great skua, the largest of this airborne pirate family which forces other birds to disgorge food to escape attack, is regularly seen off Land's End and Wolf Rock, particularly in September and October. Terns can also be watched from cliff-top vantage-points, mainly during passage migrations in spring and autumn; parties of several hundred common terns are not unusual autumn sights in St Ives Bay (see plate p 153).

A constant feature of the cliff avifauna is the rather ungainly shag which builds its untidy, often stinking nest on many rocky cliffs. Its larger cousin, the cormorant, is far less common as an open sea bird, but is more abundant in estuaries and reservoirs where its visits are hardly welcomed by local fishermen.

Autumn gales provide the possibility of seeing storm petrels on their southerly migration, being driven close into the rocky headlands. September and October are the best months for petrels and manx shearwaters; the latter, moving west on migration, pass St Ives 'Island' at up to 9,000 per hour, and this census only covered those visible from land, and took no account of the birds moving further out to sea. The shearwaters no longer nest on the mainland but do so on Scilly. A few petrels manage to breed on the mainland, or rather just off-shore on an island near Padstow, but again the bird nests commonly on the Scillies.

A number of waders frequent the lower cliffs and the mussel-covered rocks which are exposed at low tide. Oystercatchers are very common, although the breeding population which is scattered mainly along the north coasts of Devon and Cornwall and on Lundy, can be counted in hundreds rather than thousands. Non-breeding birds are always probing their way along the coast, and the numbers are considerably supplemented in winter when over 2,000 birds converge on the Exe estuary.

Turnstones are also common in small numbers, mainly in winter, for this attractive wader does not breed in Britain. The dark plumage and flitting movements of the rock pipit must be familiar to holiday visitors on rocky shores, but many no doubt mistake it for a sparrow. This resident bird breeds probably in quite large numbers along the coasts, but few breeding statistics are available although in Devon one stretch of coast 150yd long had four nests. Kestrels frequently appear above the cliffs and the peregrine falcon takes advantage of the wind to move efficiently and effortlessly on straight wings away from the attentions of mobbing gulls and jackdaws. This falcon which was, in the early part of the century, a fairly common breeding bird, has declined, and will now be seen mostly in the winter months. Some pairs do still breed, and there is no shortage of nest sites along the north and west coasts.

The demise of the chough is now complete with the last Cornish bird failing to survive the winter of 1970–1. Plans are in hand to reintroduce this small red-billed crow, using Irish birds, but it would seem to be a vain hope as we do not know the reason for the decline of the native stock, a decline which

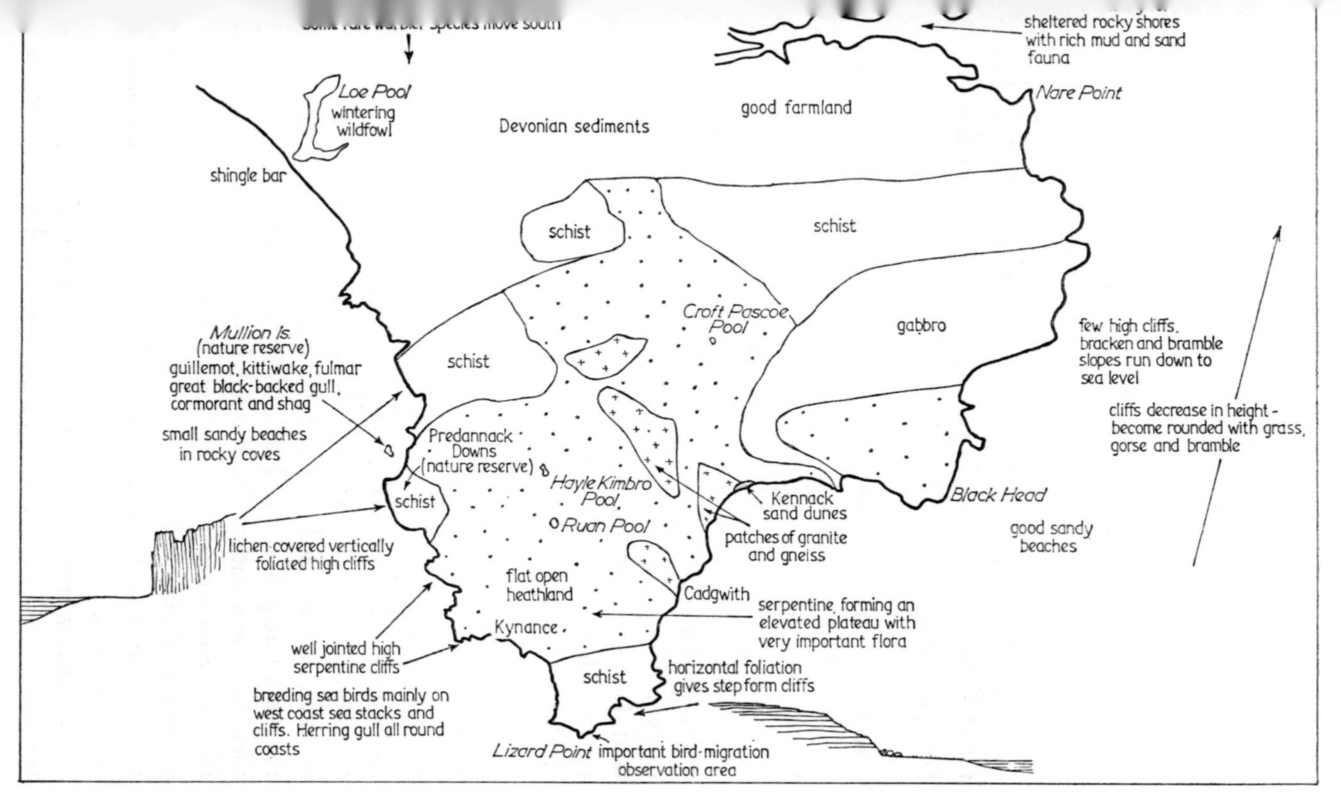

Figure 18 Sketch map of the Lizard peninsula showing the main geological boundaries and indicating points of interest for the naturalist

started many years ago and is not only confined to the British sub-species. The chough, which forms part of the emblem for the county of Cornwall, has probably gone for good, due perhaps to climatic fluctuations.

The jackdaw, however, has not followed the decline of its long-billed cousin, but is on the contrary an extremely successful and common cliff-nesting bird. In winter, large foraging parties, over a hundred strong, visit inland pasture land to feed, and on the cliffs they have filled, in part, the nesting niches left by the choughs. Magpies and jays shun the cliffs, but the largest member of the crow family, the raven, is a common bird, breeding along inaccessible stretches and croaking, 'belling', and performing high aerial acrobatics, vying with the weekend glider pilots for the thermal elevators rising up the cliff face.

Cliff-top breeding birds are well represented in areas of gorse and bramble with stonechats, wrens, whitethroats and meadow pipits, the latter acting as host for the abundant cuckoos sometimes seen in groups of six or more on the open cliff-top heathland. Late summer sees even more activity, with the wheatears moving along the cliffs. Still later, black redstarts arrive for the winter, together with a variety of wagtails.

Insects

Cornwall and Devon are well placed for the visiting naturalist to be reasonably sure of seeing some of the more common migratory insects. The most likely species are painted lady, red admiral, and clouded yellow butterflies with the possibility of the more rare pale clouded yellow. For the extremely fortunate there may be a Bath white or even a North American vagrant, the milkweed butterfly. Moths are numerous also and the common silver Y can usually be seen; the convolvulus hawkmoth is a regular visitor to the South West and a few striped hawkmoths occur at times.

Two sites which find themselves in the path of insect migration routes are Chapel Porth near St Agnes, and Mawgan Porth in the vale of Lanherne, both in Cornwall; the Victoria County History mentions that at these coves insects have been spotted on occasions passing in steady streams, or sometimes in small groups, out to sea. It is worth looking at the strand line on the beaches for the remains of insects on migration drowned en route and washed up by the tide, sometimes in great quantities.

Dragonflies can be sighted over much of the area, and in particular the golden-ringed dragonfly *Cordulegaster boltoni* is very common from June onwards. The large red damselfly *Pyrrhosoma nymphula* and the common ischnura *Ischnura elegans* are also likely to be seen, but much more observation of this group is needed.

A third animal which is used as an emblem in the South West, and is in danger of rapid extinction, is the large blue butterfly used as a motif by the Cornwall Naturalists Trust. This now very rare butterfly, with its peculiar ant-dependent life history, is confined to a few well-protected cliff sites in North Cornwall and the adjacent Devon coast. The decline of this once common and attractive insect is probably climatic, and although considerable conservation efforts are underway, it would seem to be likely to meet the same fate as the chough—though perhaps only locally for there is still a flourishing continental race.

If the large blue is rare, the common blue butterfly lives up to its name on the cliffs and is by far the most likely species to be seen. The grayling butterfly with large eye-spotted wings is locally common in grassy places and, with patience, its interesting courtship behaviour is easily watched. Ragwort is an extremely common and colourful cliff-top plant, and where it occurs so will cinnabar and six-spot burnet moths, both of which are day fliers. The larvae of the cinnabar in their yellow-and-black hooped skins sometimes occur in great numbers and reduce the ragwort to only a tattered main stalk, providing an excellent example of local biological control. Other commonly occurring species are:

Butterflies	*Moths*
painted lady	garden tiger

green-veined white	oak eggar
large skipper	drinker
small tortoiseshell	small elephant hawk
meadow brown	fox
speckled wood	
wall	
small heath	

For a full account of the insects of the North Cornish coast, the reader is referred to the special issue of the *Bulletin of the Amateur Entomological Society*, no 268, August 1965. Any record of interest should be sent to G. B. Trebilcock, 42 Normandy Avenue, Barnet, Hertfordshire.

Other animals

Small mammals are common, particularly wood mice *Apodemus sylvaticus*, and the short-tailed vole *Microtus agrestis* whose excavations are seen when the gorse and heather cover is removed by burning. This swayling used to be practised regularly but is now mainly an accidental occurrence as the result of visitors dropping matches or cigarettes in the dead undergrowth. During the summer, dangerously extensive fires can take place as a result of similar carelessness and control of cliff-top vegetation is one of the conservation problems that will have to be solved. A balance must be maintained: if the gorse and heather are left to grow they become 'leggy' and impenetrable. After burning, if the fire has not been too hot, a variety of plants quickly colonises the ground. Too much burning, however, will reduce plant varieties leaving mainly gorse and heather.

Threats to the cliffs come in the form of housing development, and visitors with their attendant cars. The cliff vegetation at Kynance in Cornwall would seem to be doomed by the constant passage of feet visiting the cove, and much of the approach has already been destroyed. This is a very real threat to much of the heathland adjacent to towns and popular beaches but fortunately much is only accessible on foot and should remain so if these important habitats are to be allowed to survive.

Animals living on the cliff tops include the badger, and very frequently the fox, both finding shelter among the rocks, and tunnelling into the relatively soft raised-beach deposits so commonly found around the coast.

Where a little soil can accumulate, lichens are dominant on the cliff faces and on walls adjacent to the cliffs, particularly the old mine buildings. Ancient mine adits and pits in West Cornwall provide good habitats for mosses and the shade-loving ferns, including sea spleenwort; sometimes bats use the old buildings and caves along the coast as roosts.

The land-slip areas between Seaton and Lyme Regis, now a National Nature Reserve, are of great interest both botanically and ornithologically, with breeding nightingales in the ash wood. This bird, so well known further east and north, is a rare breeder in the two south-western counties.

From the cliffs excellent views can often be had in spring and summer of basking sharks, seals, dolphins, porpoise, and even shoals of fish, particularly young herring or 'whitebait', that break surface, presumably to escape from predators beneath. Old look-out huts for the prolific mackerel shoals still stand, for example the hewers' hut at Newquay in North Cornwall, but low prices mean that fishermen are not encouraged to catch too many.

Whales are, unfortunately, seldom recorded but must often pass along our coast, and more regularly systematic watching may reveal that they are more common than hitherto supposed. Strandings are few, although it took a bomb-disposal squad to remove the bodies of two pilot whales, 18ft and 9ft long respectively, from a beach on the tiny island of Gugh (Scilly).

Much of the *Torrey Canyon* oil was deposited on inaccessible cliff bases, particularly in the Land's End region. Their remoteness has probably helped to save many of the original shore animals and plants as the harsh detergents could not be used in such places; however, it must be left to the cliff climber, of whom there seem to be an increasing number in the Land's End area, to investigate the effects of the oil, and to see just how successful were the natural biological agents in removing the crude oil.

Locally blown sand has influenced the flora of the cliffs, particularly on north-west facing slopes where calcareous species can be found side by side with acid-loving plants. The juxtaposition is due to the high calcium carbonate content of the blown sand which consists in large part of shell debris. Here will be found a multitude of snails, so lacking on the leached, dominantly acidic soils of the south-west cliffs where only shell-less slugs flourish.

Grasshoppers and crickets are well represented on the cliffs, and again little work seems to have been done on this group which is most 'vocal' in high summer.

Cliff vegetation

The coastal-strip heathlands may represent the original vegetation cover, for in such regions of high wind and salty spray it would not be possible for the deciduous trees to dominate the vegetation. In the absence of trees the dominant types of plant are the woody shrubs such as ling, or heaths, or the dwarf western gorse. This latter plant produces a typically hummocky vegetation cover with the gorse supplying the hummocks and the ling and heaths in the depressions. Most cliff plants have a mat-forming or rosette habit which is well suited to protect them from the scything winds.

It is difficult to describe the beauty and variety of cliff plants in Devon and Cornwall, but these are probably among the most exciting and varied habitats in the area.

Despite the great visual attraction of the cliff flora, very little observational work seems to have been done on the actual plants or their ecology. The naturalist in Cornwall and Devon would therefore have abundant opportunity to rectify this gap in our knowledge by making observations on the vast areas of cliff available for study. All that will be done in this section is to indicate the broad zonation observable on cliffs subject to direct salt spray, and list some of the typical species that may be found (see figure 19).

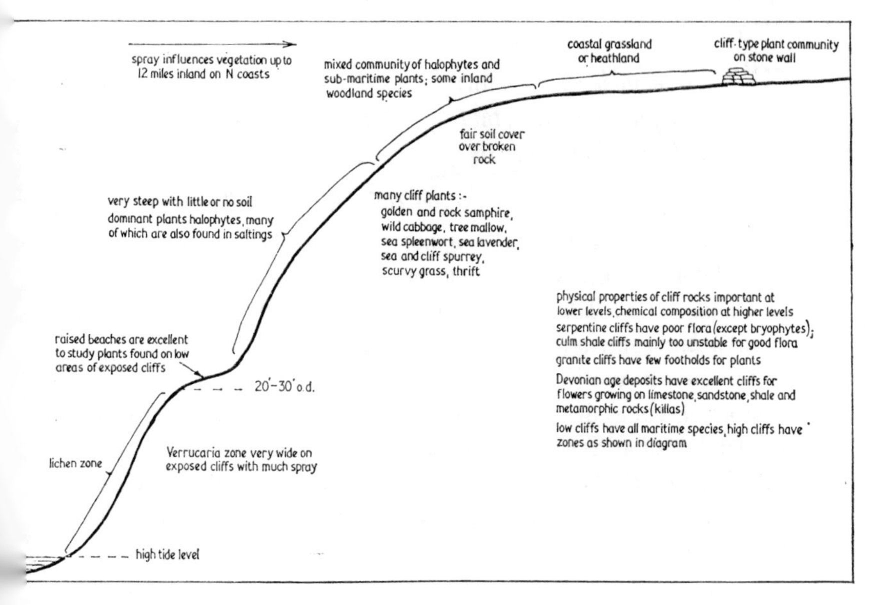

Figure 19 Vertical zonation on cliffs with main species mentioned

Splash zone plants. At the base of the cliffs live the true marine algae with above them a zone of varying width, dependent mainly upon the degree of exposure, where lichens are dominant to the virtual exclusion of all other forms. Here the encrusting, tar-like growths of *Verrucaria maura*, and the tufted *Lichina pygmaea* give a black appearance to many of the exposed cliffs where often the warmer colours of the fresh rock are exposed by rock falls during winter gales or after frosts. Above the black lichen is the orange zone of *Xanthoria* and *Caloplaca*, together with the green tuft-like growths of *Ramalina* and encrusting white lichen *Ochroleuca* (*Lecanora*). On the west coasts in particular the maritime moss *Grimmia maritima* grows just above high-tide level, and more rarely are found *Ulota phyllantha* and *Trichostomum mutabile*. Also growing near high-water level on the cliffs are *Pottia heimlii* and *Tortella flavovirens*.

The cliff bryophyte flora of the Lizard is outstandingly rich with many rare species, but the following are widespread on many soils and rock types around the coasts:

Desmatodon convolutus	*Trichostomum brachydontium*
Scorpiurium circinatum	*Pottia erinita*
Scleropodium tourretii	*Eurhynchium megapolitanum*

Cliffs with sandy soil support tufts of *Pottia lanceolata* and *P. commutata*, *P. recta*, *Trichostomun crispulum*, *Neckera crispa* and *Ctenidium molluscum*. On wet or damp cliffs, *Barbula tophacea*, *Eucladium verticillatum*, *Funaria attenuata*, *Epipterygium tozeri* and *Eurhynchium speciosum*, can be found.

The first flowering plants appear at varying stages above high-tide level, their situation again dependent mainly on exposure. On sheltered cliffs away from the blasting south-westerly winds, the flowering plants grow much closer to the water than on exposed cliffs where twenty or thirty feet may separate high tides from land plants.

Lower cliff plants. The species found on the lower parts of the cliff where soil is often very sparse are salt-loving plants or halophytes, some of which also occur on salt marshes, while other species are confined to cliffs. Here are included the common south-west cliff forms, the golden samphire *Inula crithmoides* and the ordinary samphire *Crithmum maritimum*, together with the beautiful rock sea lavender *Limonium binervosum*. Two species of white-flowered scurvy grass occur, the early scurvy grass *Cochlearia danica* which is one of the first cliff flowers to bloom, often in February, and the common scurvy grass *C. officinalis*, flowering in April and May. May and June are probably the most beautiful months as far as cliff flora is concerned, for then the very common thrift *Armeria maritima* and the sea campion *Silene maritima* add great patches of pink and white to the cliff face. Other common plants in this lower zone include rock sea spurrey, sea beet, orache, sea spleenwort (the only true maritime fern), bucks horn and sea plantain, sea mayweed, wild cabbage, and in the South West, tree mallow, of up to six feet high, which occurs frequently. The lower cliff flora can of course be studied on easily climbed cliffs but many are inaccessible; however, it may be possible to study the community on one of the raised beaches in the South West. These occur in many cases just above present high-tide level where conditions for plant life are similar to those experienced on the lower slopes of exposed cliffs.

Cliff-top plants. Above the zone of true halophytes and often on deeper soil, developed on broken bedrock towards the top of the cliffs, is another plant community, this time including with the halophytes a number of submaritime forms and alien plants which are considered to be woodland species further inland. Among this invading group and apparently right out of their natural habitat, are wood sage, slender false brome, male fern, royal fern, bluebells, primroses and wood spurge. The most commonly occurring shrubs are blackthorn and bramble which between them often form impenetrable thorn thickets, but provide useful habitats for birds, particularly migrant warblers in autumn and spring. Some of the upper cliff forms are crevice-growers such as wall pennywort, wall pellitory and ivy. Damp clefts harbour other more usually woodland forms such as honeysuckle, angelica and the butterfly-attracting dark red flowers of hemp agrimony.

Much of the cliff-top vegetation is heathland dominated by the yellow-flowered gorse *Ulex europaeus* and the western gorse *Ulex gallii*, the latter forming a colourful carpet of flowers when mixed, as it usually is, with purple heaths and ling. Very few trees exist on the coasts exposed to west or south-west winds, mainly because of the salt-laden, moist, strong winds that blow over the open Atlantic and burn up the leading shoots on the seaward side of shrub vegetation. When viewed from the sea looking inland, much of the heathland appears dead, but in the lee of the dead shrub, fresh growth is able to flourish, and the impression looking seawards is one of a green carpet in winter, and a yellow and pink mass in summer and early autumn.

Despite the high rainfall and the humidity, the soils are usually fairly dry and very acid due to the high run-off rate and quick evaporation. On hot summer days the lizard and adder population bask under hedges or gorse bushes, but are ready to flee silently upon the sound of approaching human footsteps, which of course the snakes detect through ground vibrations.

Ragwort is a very common cliff-top plant, and in more grassy places, carpets of bluebells and pink campion occur. The sea storksbill, common in the west, occurs with English stonecrop and sea pearl wort and other submaritime species such as buck's horn plantain, already met lower down the cliff. The dominant grass on the cliff top is either sheep's fescue *Festuca ovina* or bristle bent *Agrostis setacea*. Thrift is again a dominant flower found alongside rib-wort plantain, golden birdsfoot trefoil, the yellow, red-tipped flowers of kidney vetch, and purple wild thyme.

In spring large patches of yellow-flowered prostrate broom *Sarothamnus scoparius* sub sp *prostratus*, are locally abundant on the North Cornish coast, and at the same time a blue haze may be given to the cliff vegetation by the presence of the beautiful tiny vernal squill *Scilla verna*. Its larger relative the autumn squill is unfortunately much less commonly found. Some alien species also appear on cliffs, particularly in South Cornwall and the Isles of Scilly; one of these is Hottentot's or Kaffir fig which forms dense, cascading, straggling growths down cliff faces to the exclusion of other species. A particularly good example occurs on the red cliffs near Teignmouth in South Devon.

On cliffs and stacks where sea birds congregate, the droppings they produce lead to a luxuriant growth of scurvy grass and sea beet, with coarse specimens of rock sea-spurry, orache, and sea mayweed, together with nitrogen-loving land plants such as chickweed, white campion, goose grass, nettles, sorrel, and annual meadow grass. Plant species commonly present on the cliff top also spill out over the edge and here the white-flowered sea carrot *Daucus carotus* and English stonecrop *Sedum anglicum* occur, together with much thicker growths of sea campion than those found at lower levels. Kidney vetch, mouse-eared chickweed, sea pearlwort, birds foot trefoil, silverweed, coltsfoot and curled dock, are common among many other plants in a very complex community.

The salt-laden winds allow cliff plants to live at some distance from their normal habitat on stone walls and broken-down old cottages. Here, particularly in exposed places, grow thick blankets of thrift, sea campion, scurvy grass, sea beet and sea spurry, but not samphire which only grows on the cliffs. Stone hedges make attractive natural rock gardens, particularly in spring.

The cliffs therefore provide something for all naturalists whatever their particular interest; much work remains to be done on the flora, and also the insect life of these regions. The coastal footpath runs with few breaks, from North Devon right round the peninsula; this needs to be used to establish it fully, as it provides access to some of the best cliff habitats in the British Isles and those which are probably second to none in their botanical variety.

As will be seen from the map of conservation areas (figure 8, p 112), many parts of the cliffed coast of the peninsula are designated as areas of outstanding natural beauty and a number of Sites of Special Scientific Interest (SSSIs) are scattered along the coast, which for much of its length is fortunately now protected by the National Trust.

CHAPTER NINE

Estuaries

Types of estuary–The Fal–The Exe–Animal life The Tamar

THE SOUTH WEST is well supplied with estuaries, mainly because of past geological events rather than as the result of river action, although a typical feature of the area is the ria or drowned river valley. During the last Ice Age, the Pleistocene, the sea level was much lower at times than it is now and this resulted in over-deepening of the existing river valleys which produced gorges in their lower reaches, eg the Hamoaze channel, Plymouth, which is minus 60–150ft OD, deepening seawards. At the close of the Pleistocene period the sea level began to rise with the resultant drowning of the old river courses which in some places gradually became silted to a considerable depth (120ft), producing large expanses of mud and sometimes sand at low water; between 1698 and 1855 12–18ft of silt was built up and closed many inland ports. Evidence of the drowning can be seen in the numerous submerged forests around the coast, as at Marazion and Polperro (see map, figure 8, p 112) and on the Exmoor coast; the deposits of peat are now found just at and below high-tide mark.

Some of the South Devon and Cornish rias have only small rivers emptying into them, eg the Fal estuary, or no real river at all, as at Salcombe. The 'drowned' valleys contain many delightful creeks, often wooded right down to high-tide level on the South Cornish coast as along the Fal, Truro and Tresillian rivers. The overhanging woodland, mainly of scrub oak, clothing the often steeply-sloping rocky banks, is trimmed by salt water (see plate p 154) making a very obvious, neat, clipped line at high-tide level.

Salt marshes (or saltings) are characteristic of the south coast and are developed locally in the estuaries of the Tresillian, Helford and Fal rivers and extensively in the Hamoaze and Exe. On the north coast there are tidal marshes in the Camel estuary and Taw/Torridge, with smaller areas in the Gannel south of Newquay, and at Hayle.

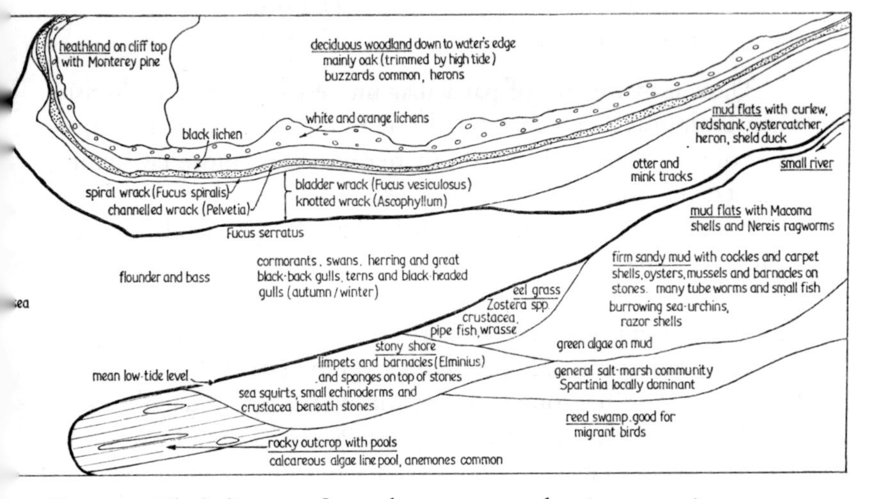

Figure 20 Block diagram of a south coast estuary showing vegetation zones and the distribution of common animals

South coast estuaries in the area have long been famous for the wealth of animal life that they contain both living in and on the sand and mud. Salcombe, although perhaps not an estuary in the true sense of the word, is probably best known to the marine biologist as an area of outstanding interest, while another area of similar importance is the Fal estuary in Cornwall.

The estuaries can be divided up into nine major and ten minor ones.

Major	*Minor*
Exe	Axe
Teign	Otter
Dart	Avon (South Devon)

Major	*Minor*
Salcombe	Erme
Hamoaze (Tamar, Tavy, Lynher)	Yealm
	Plym
Fal, Truro and Tresillian	Looe
Hayle	Fowey
Camel	Helford
Taw/Torridge	Gannel

These estuaries are of particular interest to marine biologists, ornithologists and botanists. Although the salt restricts the number of species in a salt marsh, there can be few more fascinating habitats to study.

Botanically, the estuaries can be broadly grouped into two different types:

(a) Those on the north coast with a dominance of sand or sand and mud, give rise to fairly typical west coast, salt marsh plant communities. Slightly higher up the beach than the maritime algae is often found an area dominated by annual glasswort *Salicornia* spp and sea meadow grass *Puccinella* spp. Two species of *Puccinella* occur in the South West but the sea meadow grass *P. maritima* grows in greater abundance than the reflexed form *P. distans*: the latter is more characteristic of muddy habitats. Glasswort turns deep reddy brown in autumn and is an obvious feature of the Hayle estuary, well seen from the Causeway.

Above the glasswort is the area usually described as 'saltings' which is extensively developed and carries what is known as a 'general salt marsh community'; here will be found a variety of plants none of which is really dominant:

scurvy grass
sea aster, characteristic and obvious in July/August
sea spurries, both common and greater
sea plantain, also very well developed
annual glasswort
thrift
sea purslane, just above low-water mark commonly

Page 171 (*above*) Part of the Perranporth sand dune complex, Cornwall. Stable dunes in background, but evidence of recent human and wind erosion in foreground, with isolated clumps of marram grass surviving; (*below*) Hayle Towans. An example of the extreme pressure which the dune systems in the South West suffer due to over use in the holiday season. Erosion of the sand-holding vegetation of marram, sea holly and sea bindweed, is taking place rapidly, and the size of sand 'blow-outs' increases annually

Page 172 (*above*) Base of 'killas' cliffs bounding a typical rocky, exposed beach. St Agnes, Cornwall. This is the realm of the marine algae; (*below*) upper cliffs and cliff tops have a varied flora including samphire, thrift, sea carrot, kidney vetch and vernal squill, forming natural rock gardens at their best in spring and early summer

sea arrow grass
sea milkwort
common seablite

Sea rush is another common plant higher up the marsh and this in places gives way to reed swamp with *Phragmites* as at the head of the small valleys in North and West Cornwall from which

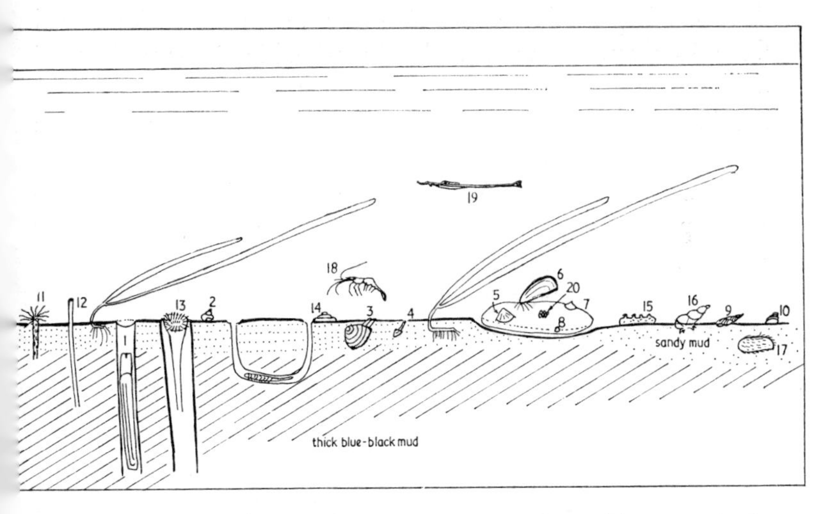

Figure 21 Diagram showing the common species of a muddy estuary in the *Zostera* zone which is exposed at very low tide only. Key to species:

1. razor shell
2. edible periwinkle *Littorina littorea*
3. common cockle *Cardium edule*
4. northern lucina *Lucinoma borealis*
5. limpet *Patella vulgata*
6. mussel *Mytilus edulis* and *Modiolus modiolus*
7. chinaman's hat *Calyptraea chinensis*
8. small scallop *Chlamys* spp.
9. sting and netted dog whelks and tower shells
10. slipper limpet *Crepidula*
11. sand lance *Lanice conchilega*
12. peacock worm *Sabella*
13. *Myxicola infundibulum*
14. lug worm *Arenicola marina*
15. sponge *Halichondria*
16. hermit crab *Eupagurus bernhardus*
17. sea potato *Echinocardium cordatum*
18. Crustacea, many shrimps and prawns
19. shore fish: pipe fish, wrasse, gobies, spined stickleback
20. sea squirts, compound and simple, under stones

the sea was excluded by silting within the last thousand years or so.

(b) On the more muddy estuaries characteristic of the south coast, particularly where younger more easily eroded rocks provide the source of the transported silt, a green algal community will sometimes colonise the mud just above or in the *Fucus serratus* zone; particularly common here is the tangled green thread-like *Enteromorpha*. Above the algal community is a region dominated by cord grass *Spartina townsendi*. This species spread from Southampton water and only arrived in Cornwall in 1956 but it is now widespread in the Tamar and Lynher, and also occurs in north coast estuaries as at Hayle and Wadebridge. The cord grass found on the northern side of the Exe spit at Dawlish was introduced in 1935 by the golf club to stabilise the silt (see figure 22 p 180 and plate p 154). Above the cord grass zone the slender salt marsh rush *Juncus gerardi* is widespread on the south coast mainland and Scilly, together with or often slightly higher up than the sea club rush *Scirpus maritimus*.

The Fal

The Fal and Truro river complex, which eventually meets the open sea of the English channel below Falmouth between the twin headlands of St Anthony on the east and Pendennis Point on the west, produces a typical south coast estuary.

The high, steeply sloping banks end usually in a low rocky cliff which then shelves away quickly to deep water and such conditions are not suitable for the extensive development of mud flats or sandbanks. Where muddy shores do exist they are in side creeks away from the general, often fairly rapid flow of the main channel. The thickly wooded banks provide sheltered backwaters in the calm of which generous supplies of fine silt are deposited to form a black tenacious mud, often a yard deep and showing both by its colour and characteristic smell that very little oxygen is available; in such stagnant, reducing conditions there is little animal life. Where the mud is built up above low-tide mark it is firmer and quite stony in places, and such conditions suit at least small sand-hopper-type crustaceans of the genus *Gammarus* and the common ragworm *Nereis*. Almost every overturned stone will reveal a horde of springing crustaceans, and very frequently, a rapidly moving eel. (All overturned stones should of course be placed with the seaweed side uppermost after observations have been made.)

The water in the upper parts of the estuary is usually full of suspended silt which not only spoils underwater visibility but clogs up the delicate feeding mechanisms of many animal species which would otherwise be able to tolerate salinity changes. The silt is deposited on the growths of bladder wrack and channel wrack which usually festoon the low, black boundary cliffs of the river; colour of the rock is determined by the adjoining colonies of *Verrucaria* which flourish in the damp and shade of the overhanging sessile oak trees. The lower branches of the oaks are covered and killed by the high spring tide salt water and the river edge has a neatly trimmed appearance as a result.

Where an area of mud is built up just below high-tide mark, a salt-marsh in miniature is often developed. Here will be found the usual collection of salt-tolerating halophytes such as the curious fleshy glassworts *Salicornia* spp with their red or green cylindrical branches joined into segments. Intergrowing with the glasswort is a plant similar in colour but with alternate cylindrical leaves, the annual seablite *Suaeda maritima*.

Lower plants such as the green algae sometimes form a thin coating on the mud below the zone of the flowering plants, and this is the region most frequented by waders and duck when human disturbance has gone. Most characteristic is the bobbing, well-named redshank which can be seen throughout the year although it does not breed locally; neither does the larger, curved-billed curlew whose bubbling calls of alarm can be heard at their best across water in the early morning or on still evenings.

A resident duck which also breeds if it can find a suitable rabbit hole locally, is the gaudy shelduck. Kingfishers are frequently seen although the number of breeding pairs is probably not great. Often gliding above the trees and nesting in them is a characteristic bird of prey, the buzzard; this is much more common than the peregrine which, however, one can expect to see especially during the autumn and winter months when it causes panic among the wintering waders and wildfowl.

Just off the main channel of the Fal river where the tidal waters make a great sweep round wooded hills, there is an excellent place for autumn and spring waterbird watching; this is the Cornwall Naturalists Trust reserve at Ardevora and Trelonk. China clay waste brought down from the St Austell region by the river is deposited at this point where stream pace slackens and the salt water causes the flocculation of the suspended clay. The pale yellow-white clay is built up above normal tide level, and has been colonised by a variety of plants; otters' footprints and slides can be seen, but it is the birds that come to feed on these unconsolidated squelchy saltings that are the major attraction, and lack of disturbance means that almost anything can turn up. Wigeon, teal, red-breasted merganser, snipe, black-tailed godwits, redshanks, spotted redshanks and greenshanks can all be expected, together with the ubiquitous grey heron and the mute swan.

The main river channels are not as productive in bird species although the numbers of curlew, redshank and buoy-squatting cormorant compensate, at least in volume. During the late summer, terns and black-headed gulls arrive, the latter staying all winter but not remaining to breed. Of the gulls, herring and great black-backed are the most common with an occasional common gull at the 'back end' of the year.

Further down, the Fal, after flowing in a narrow deep channel past the picturesque King Harry Ferry, opens out and eventually forms the wide expanse of relatively sheltered water known as Carrick Roads. One or two small creeks join the main estuary, but one running up to Devoran on the west bank is larger and has at low tide a great expanse of often wader-covered mud. Here again salt marsh vegetation is only found in a limited belt at the head of the creek on either side of a meandering small stream. At low tide the small freshwater runnels flow in deep muddy valleys across the mud flats and it is along these drainage channels that most of the birds will be feeding, retreating near to dry land as the salt water, once it has filled in the channels, rapidly covers the flat expanses of mud.

Returning to the main estuary, little evidence of brackish water will be found now along its low rocky shores; these show all the typical features of a sheltered rocky coast, for there is little fresh water to dilute the incoming tide. The Fal which is a ria, can be compared in its animal and plant communities with so-called typical estuaries further east; there, freshwater inflow is great and produces decidedly brackish water conditions for some miles inland.

The Exe

If a marked gradient cannot easily be demonstrated in the Fal, studies carried out by Mary Gillham, now of the University of Wales at Cardiff, show that there are marked changes in the vegetation of the wide mudflat and sandbank bordered Exe estuary when traced from above Countess Wear to Dawlish. This is a distance of about nine miles and in the upper reaches the bur reed *Sparganium*, the great reed mace *Typha latifolia*, the naturalised sweet flag *Acorus calamus*, and another highly attractive flower, Himalayan balsam *Impatiens gladulifera*, point to fresh-water conditions. The river here is often flanked by reed grass *Phalaris arundinacea* and common reed *Phragmites communis* which, however, is more abundant lower down stream where it forms extensive beds between Countess Wear and Topsham.

Red fescue *Festuca rubra*, and bent *Agrostis stolonifera* show their ability to tolerate a wide range of habitats from dry land to salt marsh by occurring in the upstream mud flats all the way down to the sandy mud and gravel shores near the coast. Below the A38 road bridge, the long-leaved scurvy grass *Cochlearia anglica*, which is typical of muddy estuarine shores and has fleshy leaves, gives the first indication of salt content in the water

—a point which is abundantly made in the area between Topsham and the mouth of the river Clyst. Here, a host of brackish water species clothe the mud and sand flats where they are observed each year in passing by train-travelling visitors, some of whom have no doubt noticed not only the plant life, but have looked with greater interest at the many species of wading birds and ducks that, at high tide, are pushed right up against the sea wall, along the top of which the main railway line runs.

The Exe is famous as an overwintering place for many thousands of water birds, and for its variety of migrant waders passing through in spring and, more abundantly, in autumn. It is now a National Wildfowl Refuge and attracts bird watchers from many parts of the country; they can easily watch the feeding birds from the cover of the railway bank and the levies which were built up to prevent flooding of surrounding low-lying pasture land. These also provide feed in winter for wild swans such as Bewicks and whoopers, and an important wintering flock of brent geese. Up to 5,000 wigeon occur in winter together with a wide variety of other wildfowl, waders and terns.

The brackish water flora is dominated by the sea club rush, the attractive Michaelmas daisy-like flowers of the sea aster *Aster tripolium*, and in the upper parts of the salt marsh, the mud-loving rush *Juncus gerardi*. The sea arrow grass *Triglochin maritima*, and sea meadow grass *Puccinellia* Spp form salt marsh turf in which the common samphire *Crithmum maritimum* provides yellowish splashes of colour.

Between the mouth of the Clyst and Exton Turf, a newcomer to the plant community is cord grass *Spartina townsendi*, which plays an important role in stabilising the silt deposited by the Exe, so leading to the formation of more salt marsh and eventually low-lying pasture land; silt is trapped by the network of roots, resulting in the land level rising above high-tide mark. In the latter position grows the second new plant, the sea rush *Juncus maritimus*.

As the influence of less diluted sea water increases, so the vegetation becomes more adapted to coastal conditions, and glasswort and thrift form open colonies, the latter appearing as masses of pink pin-cushion clumps in the spring and early summer. Sea purslane *Halimione portulacoides* is joined by the much more beautiful sea lavender *Limonium vulgare* which unfortunately is not as common as its specific name suggests, but does add attractive purple flower heads to the salt marsh.

Below and just above low-tide mark the eel grass *Zostera* makes the only attempt of land plants to recolonise the sea completely and successfully, for the flowers are pollinated beneath the waves, and the seeds produced are carried away by salt water. Amongst the *Zostera*, mute swans are frequent feeders at low tide; but this is the realm of the marine organisms for there is now little influence of fresh water. The mouth of the Exe is bounded by extensive sand deposits which form a double spit at Dawlish Warren. Such sand spits are not common in South West England, and that at Dawlish seems to have an uncertain future unless urgent conservation work is undertaken to prevent the sea washing away most of this sand and pebble feature, and with it a major tourist area in South Devon.

Natural processes are causing the major problem for in 1743 the sandhill area was 250yd wide but by 1949 it was less than 50yd at its widest. Most of the damage occurs when south-easterly gales coincide with high spring tides, and much erosion is still taking place in the outer warren. The inner warren is now a low ridge of sand used mainly as a golf course together with an area that before drainage was known as Greenland Lake. This former lake divided the spit into two, but it now appears as only one. (See plate p 154, and figure 22, p 180.) The distribution of the major habitats can be seen on the sketch map, and an excellent impression of the actual structure is given by the aerial photograph.

For a naturalist it still has plenty of interest although to a geographer the area may be described as a degenerate sand feature.

As with so many habitats in the South West, very little has

been published on salt marshes and most of the above comments are based on personal observations, and Hepburn's useful account in *Flowers of the Coast*.

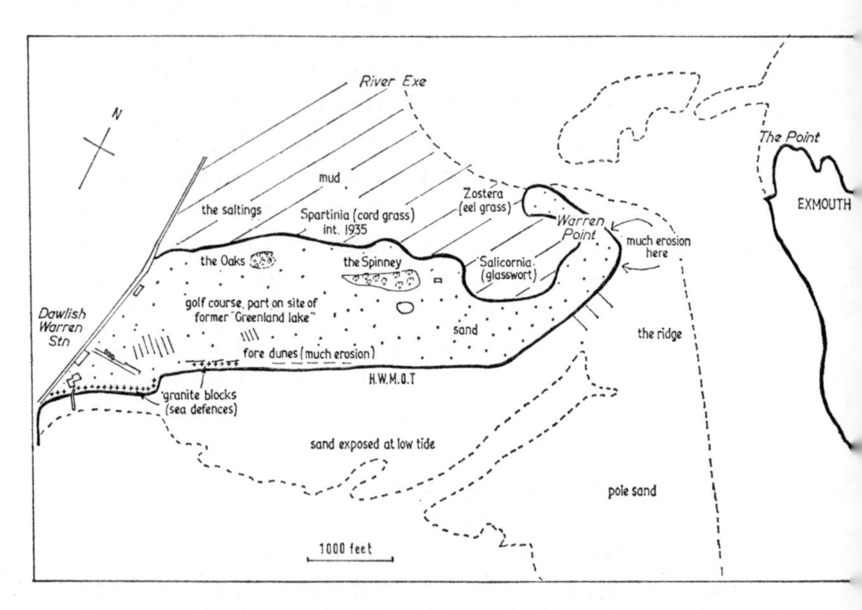

Figure 22 Sketch map of Dawlish Warren double sand spit at the mouth of the River Exe, South Devon. See also plate p 154 for an aerial view of this rapidly changing and largely destroyed sand dune area

The mosses and liverworts (bryophytes) found on the salt marshes, particularly in Cornwall, are not very extensive as far as species are concerned. Jean Paton records that *Drepanocladus aduncus* and *Acrocladium cuspidatum* are frequent with *Pottia heimii* on rocky banks bordering the estuaries.

Not all the estuaries of the South West have extensive mud or sand deposits; some have stony shores flanked by steep, well-wooded banks with the river flowing to the sea through deep channels, eg the Dart in Devon and the Helford in Cornwall, although in the latter, good muddy creeks occur further up-stream away from the sea.

Animal life

Bivalve molluscs are common with *Mya arenaria* in sandy mud and *M. truncata* in good stiff mud. Others include razor shells *Ensis* spp; cockles *Cardium edule*; and mussels on stones above the mud, the large *Mytilus edulis* edible mussel, and *Modiolus modiolus* the horse mussel. Two species of carpet shell *Venerupis decussata* and *Venerupis pullastra* are very common, as are the Baltic tellin *Macoma balthica*, the large otter shell *Lutraria lutraria*, and the predatory whelks *Nassarius reticulatus* and *Ocenebra erinacea*.

Burrowing forms are of course common on muddy shores, none more so perhaps than the annelids such as the fan or peacock worms *Sabella pavonina*, *Branchiomma vesiculosum*, *Myxicola infundibulum* and *Lanica conchilega*, while the catworm *Nepthys hombergi* can be very common indeed (see diagram based on Helford, figure 21, p 173). Peacock worms can be stalked at low tide but quickly retreat into their mud-encased tube if disturbed suddenly.

Two anemones, *Cereus pedunculatus* and the burrowing form *Peachia hastata* may be found, the latter occurring less frequently and usually in deep water. Colonising stones in the mud are the sponges *Halichondria bowerbanki*, and often brilliant orange or scarlet masses of *Hymeniacidon sanguinea*, together with colonial and simple sea squirts *Botrylloides leachi* and *Clavelina lepadiformis*, and *Sycon* spp, as for example in St Just-in-Roseland, South Cornwall.

Probably of all the sandy and muddy shores in the peninsula, that at Salcombe has been most closely studied and here a number of apparent rarities are common, eg *Callianassa subterranea*, *Upogebia stellata* and *U. deltaura*, all three burrowing shrimps.

Estuaries would seem to offer a very suitable and undisturbed habitat for mammals such as the otter: indeed, otters used to take advantage of their shelter in large numbers, but are now found only rarely. If otters have declined, however, the mink has increased and is now widespread in the rivers of the South West, as far west as Hayle. Grey seals sometimes come up an estuary for a short distance and an occasional whale is stranded, but this is a rare event.

For the ornithologist, the estuaries are of outstanding interest containing as they do a wealth of resident birds and, in the spring and particularly autumn, a feast of migrant waders and duck. The most important estuary habitats for the birdwatcher are the Fal, Hayle and Camel in Cornwall, and the Exe and Taw/Torridge in Devon, with the Hamoaze forming extensive area between the two counties.

Autumn and winter are the best times for the bird watcher but along the banks in summer there will always be resident species such as herons which are common and have many nesting sites in the wooded areas along the south coast estuaries. Most of the ten main heronries in Devon are on estuaries where they have been since at least the nineteenth century. The largest, boasting twenty-three nests which were occupied in 1967, is at Powderham on the Exe. In Cornwall heronries do not seem to have been reported until the last century and those now in existence in about fourteen places are small, of no more than fifteen nests.

Cormorants are common, often sitting with wings outstretched on mooring buoys, great black-backed gulls and herring gulls commonly feed together, and there are always curlew to break the silence with their bubbling calls.

Shelduck are fairly common throughout the year, while kingfishers are typical, but rarely observed unless one is prepared to sit and wait.

The Tamar

In a paradoxical way, planning for the future appearance of our surroundings, so lacking generally, seemed to be offering a real threat to the solitude and wildlife of one of the most important estuaries in the area, that of the Tamar. A development study carried out by the Dartington Amenity Research Trust for the Countryside Commission, was looked upon with alarm by local natural history organisations and preservation societies as it was felt wrong to attract to an area, which is at present still quiet and relatively unspoilt, the type of recreation and amenity development which the plan suggested. The recommendations of the Research Trust will not now be implemented. Estuary developments in the form of marinas and water sports centres are already developing along the south coast estuaries further east; must all estuaries be looked upon as suitable for multi-purpose use or cannot we retain as wild places of peace those at present unspoiled?

A second more traditional threat comes to the Tamar in the proposed construction of a huge electricity generating station on the estuary near Plymouth. This is to be oil burning and will necessitate unloading large tankers in the tidal waters. The memories of *Torrey Canyon* and other less spectacular but no less serious oil damage, such as that on the north Cornish coast in the spring of 1970, point to the obvious fact that accidents do happen sometimes, and their results are in many cases devastating to wildlife. Water intake from the river for cooling purposes will also no doubt influence wildlife in the Tamar estuary, as will the discharge of heated water. A further threat is the discharge into the atmosphere of many tons of sulphur dioxide which could well destroy much of the important bryophyte flora of Dartmoor.

Although much water is extracted from the Tamar tributaries the first results of an ecological survey carried out by the Marine Biological Association shows little change in the salinity of the lower estuary waters, and very few changes since 1928 in the populations of intertidal sessile (stationary or attached) animals on rocks along the banks.

The Association is also at present investigating the possible effects of Plymouth City Corporation's proposal to dump sewage from barges in the sea off Plymouth. This involves hydrographic measurements, chemical analyses and a phytoplankton survey, a very necessary investigation as little seems to be known of the effects of sewage effluent on offshore life.

The Cornwall Naturalists' Trust have two reserves on their side of the river which is reckoned to be the best for birds, particularly around the Lynher river and St John's Lake. The Trust reserves are at Cargreen where there is a wintering flock of avocets, and Kingsmill lake where the mudflats and salt marshes are important feeding grounds for a wide variety of birds. Natural history excursions are made by boat during the summer and winter to study the wildlife of the estuary; there is always plenty to see, not least is the winter when a number of wintering birds are present, including golden plover, black-tailed godwits and wigeon.

CHAPTER TEN

Freshwater Habitats

Streams and rivers–Weirs and leats–Marshes–Lagoons–Reservoirs

So MUCH RAIN falls in the uplands of the South West that it would seem reasonable to expect an area scattered with lakes, ponds and large rivers. Yet Dozmary Pool, on Bodmin Moor, and a few other small stretches of water are the only inland lakes in the peninsula, for reasons which can be traced in recent geological history.

The South West was probably free from sheet ice during the last Ice Age, but formed a periglacial region, affected by permo-frost and snow. Running water in the short summers formed alluvial and 'head' deposits on the lower ground: and the lack of glacial action meant that no suitable depressions or dammed-up valleys were produced to form lakes when the northerly glaciers finally melted. Permofrost and chemical weathering, together with decomposition of the granite with superheated gases and liquids (pneumatolysis), probably in Permian times, produced a rotted granite or 'growan' bedrock. Highly porous and jointed, it has the effect of draining away surface water—and so denying the South West of its lakes.

But if glacial action directly failed to provide high-level freshwater habitats, it indirectly produced some of the most impressive and lively wildlife habitats: the estuaries, which were considered in the last chapter.

High rainfall on Exmoor, Dartmoor and Bodmin Moor does, however, give rise after storms, to many small streams, often fast-flowing with brown, peat-stained water. But the shape of the peninsula does not allow the streams to flow any significant distance before reaching the sea, and so they result in no really grand rivers. Two of the largest rivers in the area, the Exe and the Tamar, both rise near the north coast and collect innumerable small waterways before they finally discharge into the English Channel.

The largest river system on the north coast is the Taw/Torridge: the Taw flows almost due north from Dartmoor but the Torridge follows a U-shaped course, rising and having its estuary on the North Devon coast. In the northern parts of both Devon and Cornwall, many small streams find their way quickly down to the sea (some near Hartland Quay in North Devon give rise to spectacular cliff waterfalls) for as the watershed in both counties runs only a few miles inland from the north coast, north-flowing streams are short and rapid.

Although hardly more than trickles, some of the very short rivulets flowing directly down the cliffs provide wet flushes with an interesting community of plants, with some species more typical of damp woodlands than exposed cliffs. In Cornwall, such habitats contain bog rush *Schoenus nigricans*, tussocky purple moor grass, hemp agrimony, purple loosestrife, and probably strangest of all, the royal fern *Osmunda regalis*, albeit in a very stunted form due to the salty wind which cuts down the potentially handsome foliage to a rather scruffy collection of brown-tinged fronds.

In North Devon and North Cornwall there are many small streams flowing quickly down to the sea; some near Hartland Quay in North Devon give rise to spectacular cliff waterfalls. The watershed in both counties runs only a few miles inland from the north coast so that north-flowing streams are very short and rapid.

Streams and rivers

All the main rivers of the area arise either from Dartmoor, Exmoor and Bodmin Moor, or from the high ground between Hartland and Bude; they are shown on the sketch map, figure 23.

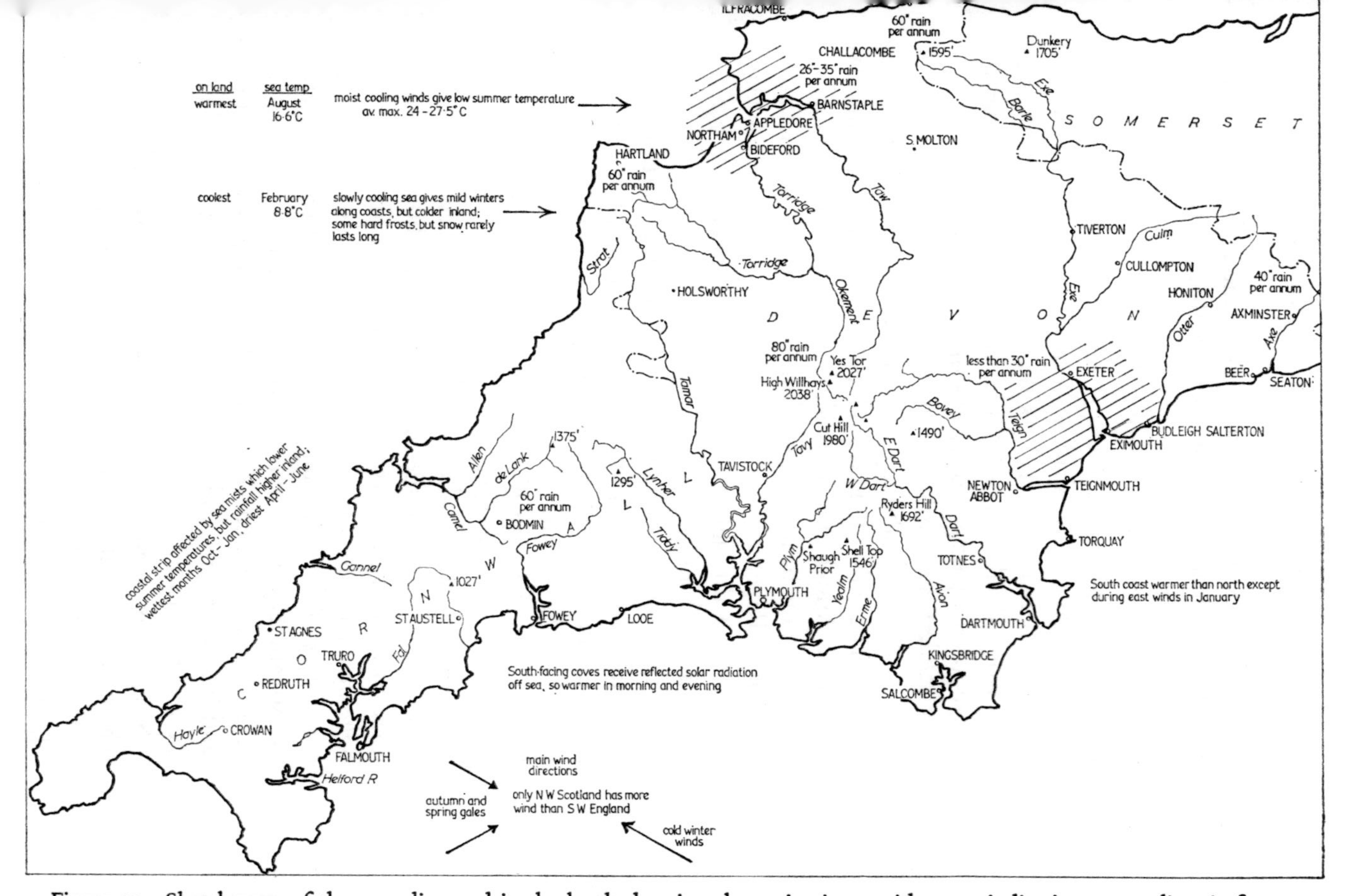

Figure 23 Sketch map of the area discussed in the book showing the main rivers with notes indicating some climatic factors

The Isles of Scilly have almost no streams and the Land's End peninsula, while having a few, lacks anything that could be called a river. In Cornwall the largest rivers are in the south and east but Devon is better supplied; it claims thirteen main rivers with a combined length of about 400 miles of which about 60 are tidal. Some rivers have shallow muddy estuaries flanked by salt marshes and mud flats such as the Exe. Others flow through steep wooded hills and enter the sea by a deep, often narrow rock-bordered passage, as for example the Dart.

By modern standards the running water in the South West is relatively clean although sewage effluent is an increasing menace. The only obvious pollution appears in the china clay area of St Austell in Cornwall (see p 121). Other industrial waste, this time from mine workings, colours the stream known as the Red River which enters the sea at Gwithian near Hayle after flowing through old copper and tin mine areas between Redruth and Camborne.

For the visiting naturalist the small streams starting on the high moorland will be of great interest. Figure 24, p 190, shows a profile of a typical Dartmoor stream, indicating the most important species and microhabitats that are present. Most streams begin life in the high plateau region of open moorland, bog, and an almost ever-present wind which whips low cloud across the tor-dominated skyline. Skylark and curlew provide the dawn chorus to which the stream water adds little background noise as it emerges quietly from among the green carpets of *Sphagnum* and filters through the clumps of rushes, sedges and coarse grass. After collecting itself from the restricting vegetation the stream begins to live up to its name and, gaining side-streams on its way, curves through low heather-covered moorland banks which are blanketed with vegetation concealing all the rocks beneath.

Stream flow is quite rapid at this stage, especially after storms when, for the walker, the high level of swirling, peat-stained water rapidly turns a negotiable stream into a major obstacle. The flood water quickly passes to low ground, a fact that should be remembered by anyone lost while walking on the moorland. When low cloud or mist obscures the way, the water courses should be followed away from the high ground and will provide a safe, if at times soggy, escape route. It will not be long before the stream cuts a road, or meets an old clapper bridge built of large flat stones set on rounded boulders of granite. The stream is probably the source of the bridge building material as it is well supplied with roughly rounded rocks between which the water scours into the bedrock. There is little deposition of silt and fine stone in these higher reaches of the stream and consequently the aquatic insect life is sparse. Rocky bottoms provide few opportunities for plants to get a foothold but the lower plants are well able to cope and diatoms cover rocks which are constantly wet with a slippery olive-brown film. The aquatic moss *Fontinalis* produces almost black trailing growths on the downstream side of boulders and shelters predatory caddis larvae.

In pools where the stream pace slackens, the undersides of flattish stones conceal from both predator and snatching current the rapidly moving twin-tailed larvae of stone flies and the small houses of tiny stones or sandgrains in which caddis larvae spend their lives. Other caddis species, looking like off-white brown-jawed caterpillars, spin a fine silken net-like tunnel which is open upstream; the animal remains in the blind end waiting to eat any small organism, either plant or animal, which is swept in. Figure 24 (p 190) shows other insect larvae which can be found in stream waters.

The stream flow rate decreases as it meets the almost level benches which were cut into the hillside by ancient waves. Conditions here are more suitable for the growth of higher plants that can root themselves amongst the finer silt and pebbles which can accumulate. Flowing through rough pasture and cutting through drystone fences, where the stream plugs the gap and prevents grazing animals from straying, large areas of bracken dip their aromatic fronds into the water. Plants which have permanently submerged or floating leaves are white-flowered

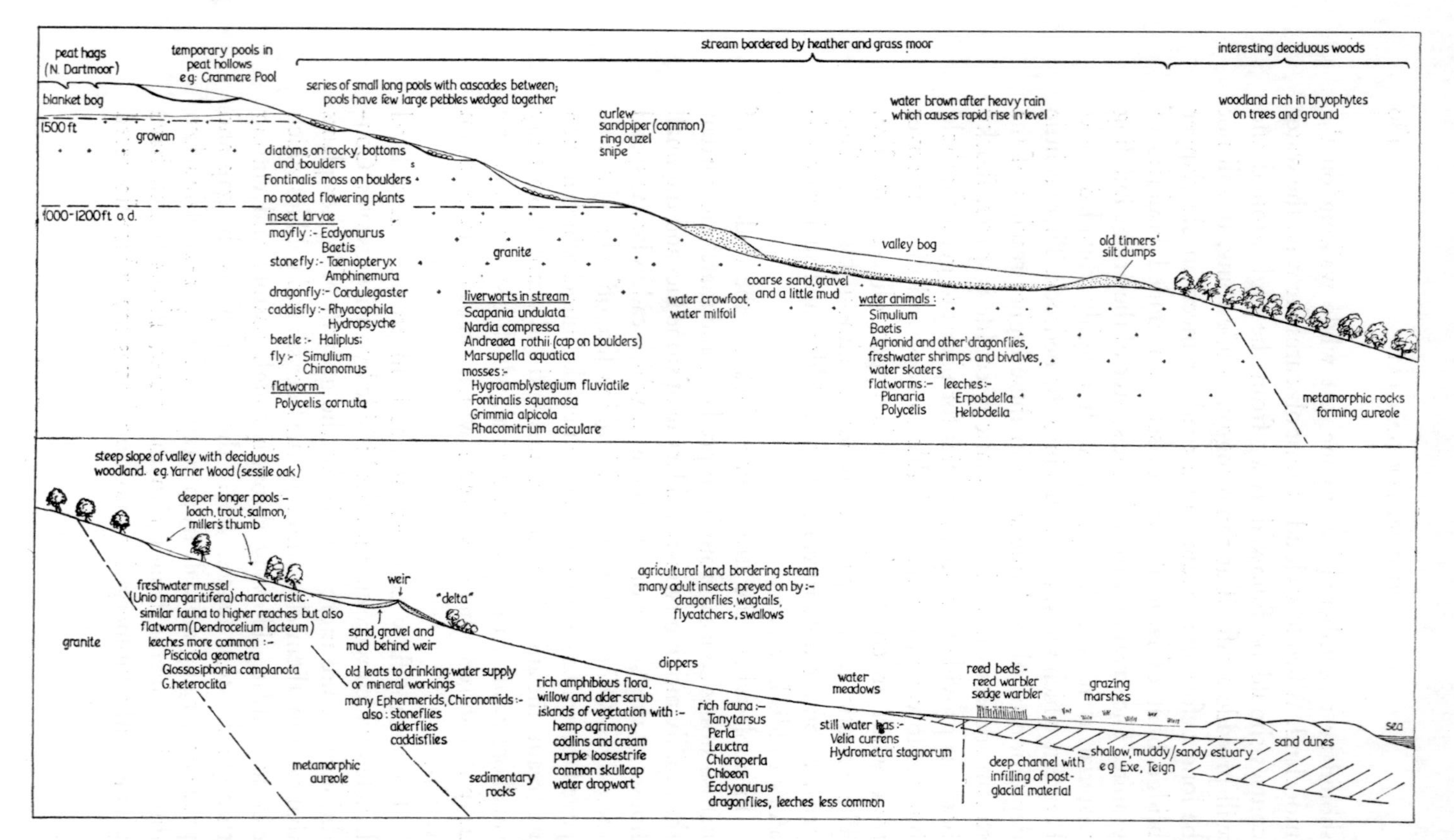

Figure 24 Diagrammatic section down the length of a typical Dartmoor stream with the distribution of the main habitats and species

water crowfoot *Ranunculus aquatilus* and water milfoil *Myriophyllum spicatum.* An incautious approach to the stream bank will disturb a multitude of small trout which hide among the aquatic vegetation. Vegetation also shelters a large number of insect larvae, a variety of crustaceans, hordes of slowly gliding flatworms and even less rapidly progressing molluscs which live almost a sedentary life amongst the silt.

Where willow scrub occurs along the bank, sedge and willow warblers are commonly heard, the rather harsh babbling of the former contrasting with the liquid tumbling song of the willow warbler. In tall gorse the visitor may be lucky enough to catch sight of the whinchat which is a typical if none too common breeding bird in such habitats.

We now reach the richest habitat for the general naturalist and one of the most visually and aurally attractive habitats in the South West, where the stream plunges into wooded valleys or combes as they are locally called on Exmoor. The stream flows more deeply and often darkly for only sunlight filtered by a leaf mosaic of oak, beech, willow and alder, reaches the water, which swirls around the numerous liverwort and moss-crowned boulders.

Careful search may show up the spraints (droppings) of an otter which typically decorate a favourite boulder, and so indicate some territorial claim. Less welcome are the footprints of the mink which are now commonly found in patches of wet sand at the edges of most of the streams. The mink which escaped from local farms now breed far too well and cause havoc with the indigenous wild life, particularly with fish and water birds.

Trout, which enjoy the deep long shady pools, are not, however, now the only fish; their larger cousins the salmon come upstream to breed, but permanently resident are loach, Miller's thumb and grayling. The great variety of insect and other invertebrate life under stones, or in the fine silt, provides excellent food for the fish; but despite the feast available the adult salmon returning from the sea do not partake even though they may take an occasional flick at a cast fly.

A peculiar feature of the salmon is that each river seems to have a different race, the individuals of which will only return to the stream of their birth when they migrate upstream after their years of feeding and growing in the sea. Different races return to their natal rivers at quite specific seasons; some run upstream in late autumn to spawn in November and December, others arrive in the spring but rest in the river all summer until they spawn in the late autumn. Rivers are said to have either spring or autumn runs of salmon; the Dart has a spring and early summer run, but the Plym is a sanctuary for the run here is during December and January. It is only in these months that sufficient water comes down to enable the large fish to reach the small headstreams in which they breed. As the fish run, spawn and return to the sea during the close season for fishing, they are, or at least should be, immune from capture. Man has complicated the position by introducing fertilised salmon eggs into the streams to increase the fish stocks and this results in some rivers, for example the Teign and the Taw/Torridge, having both spring and autumn runs: one for the native race and the other due to the foreigners.

In Exmoor streams the salmon adults are found from March onwards throughout the spring and summer with the largest runs taking place after the fishing season closes in late summer and early autumn when the fish can be easily observed from bridges. The resident brown trout and the salmon spawn during winter months. The salmon eggs, having been laid in a stony shallow excavation (known as a redd) in the floor of the stream, hatch from between the protecting stones; then, the young black-marked parr spend from one to three years in freshwater before changing into silvery coats and going to sea as smolts. They return three to five years later and the cycle is repeated.

The brown trout is a resident but the sea trout is migratory and splits its life between fresh and salt water. Young sea trout, known as school peal, come up the Exmoor rivers in July. The adults may reach a length of 10–14in when mature. Although the streams of the South West have, at least in their higher reaches, beautifully clear, cold, acid water, with a substantial invertebrate population, Cornwall, has at present a very restricted range of fish species. A general feature of the natural history of the area is that as one moves further west, some common species tend to become less common, and this is well exemplified by the Cornish fish. There are some perch and dace but these have been introduced and are not native; neither are the chub, bleak, gudgeon, roach, tench, bream and rudd. Even minnows and sticklebacks are by no means plentiful due partly, no doubt, to the large population of smallish brown trout which prey on the smaller fish and are even cannibalistic at times. Nor is man helping the situation: one of the most attractive upper reaches of a Cornish stream, the Fowey, begins life on Bodmin Moor, but will soon flow into a new reservoir that is to be constructed at Lamelgate, so destroying a very important natural history area.

Exmoor rivers are richer in species including grayling, eel, brook lamprey and occasional sea lamprey, miller's thumb, stickleback and loach; to which must be added the North American rainbow trout which is raised at Exbridge and used to stock the local reservoirs and rivers.

If fish life is more abundant in the streams flowing through the wooded combes, the same is true of the birdlife, with the dipper, like an overgrown, white-chested black wren providing one of the star attractions. It frequently perches on midstream boulders to devour fat caddis fly grubs, secured by a daring underwater walk which must have as many hazards for a small bird as lunar walking has for man. Another constant boulder percher is the insect-eating grey wagtail which darts after the emerging mayflies and caddis, who have a limited enough natural lifespan even in the absence of predators. They have to contend also with flying insects of their own class in the form of darting dragonflies which are still fortunately common.

Kingfishers are not uncommon but more obvious are the sedge and willow warblers, and where there is larger vegetation surrounding pools, heron can be found fishing, and the moorhens and mallards breed.

Weirs and leats

Man again showed his influence on the river by the construction in the past of stone weirs across the streams; this usually results in a diversification of the habitat. On the upstream side, there is now a deep pool where tranquil waters allow more silt to be deposited; the water then spills over between the stones and produces a minor rapid before making a final uninterrupted drop as a small, white waterfall. Both along the weir, and more commonly below, islands of vegetation grow up which frequently have a scrub covering of willow or alder. The stream below the weir follows a rather tortuous path between the small islands of vegetation bright with the hemp agrimony *Eupatorium cannabinum*, long spikes of purple loosestrife *Lythrum salicaria*, skullcap *Scutellaria galericulata* and hemlock water dropwort *Oenanthe crocata*. This last is a stout parsley-smelling herb with umbels of attractive white flowers during the summer; also to be seen is the greater willow herb *Epilobium hirsutum*, more pleasantly known as 'codlins and cream'.

Some of the islands of semi-floating vegetation are very transitory and quickly swept away by flood water which, however, is more constructive at times, providing tree trunks, branches and plant debris from upstream which act as a focus for new amphibious growths; the dead trunks are soon coated with festoons of moss and colourful patches of fungi in the autumn. Trees which fall across the stream may provide a bridge to be used by badgers which drink from and cross the streams at night. No doubt the agile fox uses the natural bridge and the local squirrels make its prostrate trunk a feeding place, leaving evidence in the form of split acorn and hazel nut shells among the moss covering. During the winter months a variety of small birds of the tit family frequent the waterside woodland, often in flocks that can be heard more easily than seen.

Below the wooded combe, the stream opens out into a broader valley bordered either by farmland or settlements, and it is here that stream pollution begins. Run-off from farmland

and drainage from roads, houses and industrial areas bring organic solids and inorganic nitrates and phosphates which result in a lowering of oxygen content in the water and therefore the death of all but the hardiest animal life. It is not long, however, before the small streams and larger rivers find their way to the sea where the contaminated fresh water is quickly swallowed up by the salt water of the estuaries. Many small stream valleys were highly industrialised during the last century and hide beneath a blanket of gorse, heather and bracken, a strange collection of old building foundations and tin ore dressing floors. This is the realm of the industrial archaeologist, but for the naturalist the leats, flooded buddles and locally dammed streams form intriguing habitats. The weirs, which in their pools provide such good habitats for semi-aquatic plants and invertebrate life, were constructed to raise the water level so that water would flow into the leats. These were channels dug to take water slowly down hill, skirting hillsides and so distributing the water over many miles of country to feed either domestic water supplies or to provide water power to turn machinery. In Cornwall and Devon many leats were dug to work the stamps which were used to crush tin ore before it went to be concentrated and then smelted. Due to weathering, lack of maintenance and the scramblings of animals, many of the retaining walls of the leats have been breached and most have long ago ceased to carry flowing water. There are some short stretches that do retain water, and some which become temporary pools in wet weather and do contribute, particularly on Dartmoor, some important habitats for aquatic vegetation which is generally rather sparsely developed. Due to silt accumulation, some of the leats have degenerated into marsh, the mud of which is colonised by water crowfoot *Ranunculus aquatilis*, starwort *Callitriche* spp water blinks *Montia fontana*, and pondweed, *Potamogeton polygonifolius*.

Some of the leats which have flowing water are rich in small trout that thrive on the abundant insect, worm and crustacean mud life. The old leats to tin stamps in Cornwall are often rich in mosses, liverworts and ferns and shelter newts and frogs which breed in the pools that form locally along their length. Where high retaining banks were thrown up, these have been colonised by rabbits and foxes which, by their tunnelling, helped to destroy the leats as watercourses. Canals were never constructed in great quantities in the South West and few are still used for shipping in Devon. In Cornwall some old partly-infilled waterways occur in the south-east and provide local ponds and marshes with vegetation similar to that of the leats. They are usually difficult to locate and, although of interest to the local naturalist, have no great attraction for the visitor.

Marshes

High rainfall and the presence of slow-draining soils means that marshes of various types are frequent on the resulting waterlogged ground. The marshes may be small areas of poorly drained pasture land, or have developed round the margins of pools of various size or along stream courses and at the sides of roadways where water lies for much of the year in ditches. In places where drainage of waterlogged fields has taken place, a marshy flora often develops on the bottom and sides of the ditches.

On heathland areas small pools, which form during the winter, drain away or evaporate in the wind and sun later in the year, but the clayey waterlogged soil provides the correct conditions for plants typical of wet heaths, rather than marshes. Marsh water is neutral rather than acidic and the plants forming the fresh water community are quite different from those of bogs.

Marsh plants, although not truly aquatic, always exist in soil which is damp for most of the year. These waterlogged soils are deficient in oxygen but rich in dissolved mineral salts unlike the bog habitats, so the marsh vegetation is lush and typically has large-leaved species and a spongy texture for the storage and transport of air.

A very typical plant is the marsh marigold producing showy

golden-yellow flowers as early as March in Cornwall. The great heart-shaped leaves of butterbur cover many damp places and in April it is joined by lady's smock *Cardamine pratensis* with lilac or sometimes white flowers. The small white flowers of blinks *Montia fontana* is common, as are the cone-producing rather primitive horsetails. The giant horsetail is not common but the marsh form *Equisetum palustre* is widespread. The huge tussocks of the sedge of that name *Carex paniculata* makes an obvious visual impact, but the smaller members of the genus, although common, will be of main interest to the specialist. However, all can appreciate *Iris pseudacorus*, the yellow flag, and with it the southern marsh orchid which is classed as common, at least in Cornwall. Also in flower from the end of May are ragged robin *Lychnis flos-cuculi* and creeping water forget-me-not *Myosotis secunda*. The wet ground between the marsh plants is often covered with the rounded leaves of marsh pennywort *Hydrocotyle vulgaris*.

Purple loosestrife *Lythrum salicaria*, common valerian *Valeriana officinalis*, marsh thistle *Circium palustre*, and a variety of willow herbs produce a dominantly pink, red and purple background to the marshes in June. Against this, the tall yellow sweet pea-like flowers of greater birdsfoot trefoil *Lotus uliginosus* and the paler yellow of lesser spearwort *Ranunculus flammula* are contrasted. Hard rush is confined to more basic soils but the soft rush *Juncus effusus* and the compact rush *J. conglomeratus* are both very common. South-west Britain is the home of the so called Cornish moneywort *Sibthorpia europaea* which despite its common name is not confined to the Duchy; and branched bur reed *Sparganium erectum* with its spiky pompom-like heads of fruits is common by the side of streams, as is the conspicuous reed grass *Phalaris arundinacea*.

July is a good month for marsh flowers with a number of large plants producing a showy community which often includes meadowsweet *Filipendula ulmaria*, hemp agrimony *Eupatorium cannabinum*, great willow herb *Epilobium hirsutum*, wild angelica *Angelica sylvestris*; and also the yellow daisy flowers of common fleabane *Pulicaria dysenterica*. Bruised stems of water mint *Mentha aquatica* will give a characteristic smell, but the equally common water pepper *Polygonum hydropiper* has a decidedly hot taste and is not recommended. A marsh plant almost restricted to Devon and Cornwall is wavy St John's wort *Hypericum undulatum* which grows with yellow loosestrife *Lysimachia vulgaris* and marsh woundwort *Stachys palustris*. Blue flowers are not obvious in marshes but common skullcap *Scutellaria galericulata* is at least locally common, as is the creamy-white flowered sneezewort *Achillea ptarmica*.

Extensive reed beds much frequented by small warblers have developed around many of the freshwater pools, but *Phragmites communis* also tolerate brackish water and form extensive warbler-sheltering beds along estuaries such as the Exe, which have mud and sand banks. During the summer nesting, reed-warblers are relatively common in reed beds. Less obvious is the smaller population of sedge warblers and reed buntings although the latter species, which is a resident, is widely distributed from estuary marshes to upland bogs and marshes. The sedge and reed warblers are summer visitors, arriving in April and leaving by early autumn. There is an interesting autumn passage of both species in August and September.

The rather bleached dead stems of the reeds harbour great numbers of common migrants such as swallows, and gradually as winter approaches the numbers of waterfowl which find shelter in reed beds increases rapidly. Mallard, which are breeding residents, increase, as do the coot and little grebe. The great-crested, and less commonly, the slavonian grebe, are winter visitors, but although the former species is common over most of the British Isles, it is a very sporadic breeder in the South West. Moorhens are rather rare as a breeding species in Cornwall but are more abundant in Devon.

Cornwall possesses a reasonably high population of skulking reed-breeding water rails which can sometimes be spied upon from small bridges in areas of reedswamp near the coast. They formerly bred in Devon but now occur chiefly in coastal marshes bordering estuaries from late summer to spring, as winter visitors and passage migrants. The Exe estuary reed beds hold a good number of rails in November and December, and during autumn passage the species also visits Lundy.

Unusual reedswamps are often developed on soils derived from Devonian slates and a number of these are found in Cornwall. The interested reader is referred to Tansley, p 637, but reference must be briefly made to an interesting plant association occurring at Polzeath and Mennic Bay in North Cornwall: a plant which is generally regarded as a rare species, the galingale *Cyperus longus*, a sedge which has a graceful spray of red-brown flowers in large forked clusters, is here co-dominant with the branched bur reed.

Reed swamps and marshes form fringes around the standing water areas and are developing locally at the margins of the reservoirs which, as we shall see, leave the naturalist in a peculiar dilemma over the pros and cons of their construction.

Lagoons

It may appear rather odd that the sea should have provided the best and, Dozmary excepted, the only large natural open freshwater habitats in the South West. So-called pools on Dartmoor such as Cranmere are purely temporary structures which for most of the year are boggy areas of *Sphagnum*. Although Dozmary is quite extensive it is shallow and this rather uninviting stretch of water on Bodmin Moor is liable to dry out during very dry summers to reveal many Stone Age implements of worked flints (though never a trace of Excalibur).

The sea is responsible for the construction of natural barriers of shingle along the coasts. Some of these formed dams across the mouths of rivers or streams whose waters were impounded and formed freshwater lagoons. The freshwater percolates through the shingle to the sea in winter but during dry weather the lagoon level falls and exposes a wide shore on the landward side of the shingle ridge which is quickly colonised by annual plants. This fluctuation in water level is vital to this plant community and any artificial stabilisation will quickly destroy it.

At Loe Bar near Helston in Cornwall the damming of the river Cober created the very important habitat known as Loe Pool. This is excellent for bird watching and is a good hunting ground for the botanist. At Slapton in South Devon the largest natural stretch of freshwater in the South West was formed by a bar composed mainly of flint pebbles but in this case no major stream was impounded. There were formerly four of these so called 'leys' in this area of South Devon, but apart from the one at Slapton the others have been much affected by drainage and are no longer open water areas. Much the same sort of fate has occurred to the once important plant habitat at Swanpool, Falmouth. This stretch of freshwater was again formed by a shingle ridge, but at the beginning of the present century dumping began to shrink the area of open water, then swans were introduced. The birds quickly consumed most of the interesting shallow water plants, and now the pool is predominantly a boating area with thick reed beds in places. A similar area to those mentioned above, but this time relatively unspoilt, is Marazion marsh, separated from the sea by the usual shingle ridge along which run the main railway line and coast road. While now having little open water, there are considerable reed beds and swampy ground which provides one of the most important wetlands for birds and annually produces its rarities, some from North America. Slapton Ley provides a good example of these natural freshwater habitats and the following description is based mainly on articles by Ian Mercer formerly warden of the Field Centre at Slapton, and now County Conservation Officer for Devon.

The ley is one of the largest sheets of freshwater in the British Isles which exists so close to the sea, and is over two miles long and about 400yd wide. The lagoon covers 248 acres which are impounded by the shingle and sand ridge about 60 per cent of which is composed of flint pebbles, as are the other barriers in the South West. The shallow water is only about 10ft at its deepest which makes it ideal for abundant vegetation rooted in the shallow water, and hence provides plenty of food for wild-fowl (see plate p 153).

Slapton bridge which will be seen in the aerial photograph running east-west, cuts off a northern area of the ley which is heavily silted by material transported by the river Gara; this now winds its way through emergent vegetation mainly of common reed with a few areas of willow carr, and an occasional bur reed, reedmace, yellow flag, watermint and waterplantain. These species, joined by the true bullrush *Schoenoplectus lacustris*, form a discontinuous fringe down the seaward edge of the open water, forming the Lower Ley. There are also some areas of reed swamp in the lateral valleys.

The water level falls in dry summers by about four feet and so exposes a wide shore zone which quickly becomes colonised by annual plants. Shore weed *Littorella uniflora*, spikerush *Eleocharis palustris*, and the very rare strapwort *Corrigiola litoralis* occur as do water lily patches particularly at the southern end, and many forms of diatoms, with over fifty species identified. Of the freshwater algae *Nitella* is particularly abundant at times forming banks on the bottom of the ley. Other flowering plants include water crowfoot *Ranunculus aquatilis*, water millfoil *Myriophyllum* spp, Canadian pondweed *Elodea canadensis*, and curled pondweed *Potamogeton crispus*.

The region is very attractive to both migrant and resident birds. It is on the main line of coastal migration and at a point at which many birds probably make their first landfall after leaving northern France on their northbound spring migration. Insect food, particularly midges and gnats, provide abundant fuel for many migrant warblers together with other insect-eating birds such as swallows, martins and wagtails. Seventeen of the forty-one species of British dragonflies have been recorded at Slapton and they too feast on the small semi-aquatic insects.

During the winter the abundant freshwater plants rooted in the shallow marginal water provide plenty of food for wintering wildfowl. At this time it is the best place in Devon to see freshwater duck; every common species has been recorded here in recent years. Particularly abundant are tufted duck and pochard but only the mallard is a regular breeding species.

Scaup are regular and shovelers rather erratic visitors but the pintail is found nearly every year together with teal and garganey, the latter of which, although mainly passage migrants, have bred; two or three thousand wigeon overwinter.

The population of resident breeding coots is supplemented later in the year by overwintering birds and while the population is normally 200–500 birds this can rise to over 3,000 as it did in the severe winter of 1963. The moorhen which also breeds is not much supplemented by winter visitors as this species seems to be more sedentary.

Slapton is the main breeding ground in the South West for reed warblers, a species which flourishes now that reed cutting has almost ceased, but the sedge warbler is the commonest species of warbler to be ringed at the Devon Bird Watching and Preservation Society's station at Slapton. Between 1961–7 nearly 2,000 were handled. The reed warbler ringed as a juvenile on 1 August 1965 and recovered in Spanish West Africa on 15 September of that year, must, however, take the prize for speed of migration. The considerable autumn passage of warblers occurs during August and September. This is the time, too, for spectacular migrations of sand martins which pass through, sometimes in thousands, on their return migration to the south. A few common and sandwich terns can be expected. Little tern may also occur at times, and black terns frequently haunt the water-lily patches during autumn passage as they do on other areas of freshwater in the South West. In winter some sea ducks take advantage of the sheltered water of Slapton, including scaup, red-breasted merganser, common scoter and very occasionally goosander and smew.

The ley is a favourite bathing place for resting flocks of gulls which include large groups of greater black-backed gulls, sometimes several thousand strong. Equally spectacular are the annual congregations of roosting birds which descend in cloud-like wheeling flocks on the reed beds at various times of the year. The most likely to be seen are starlings, swallows, martins and wagtails.

While being a habitat of main interest for water and marsh birds, linnets, whitethroats and stonechats nest in the gorse and bramble patches on the shore, and in the areas of coarse grass skylarks and meadow pipits are particularly common.

Reservoirs

As has already been mentioned in the chapter on heathland, reservoir construction is a constant source of concern to local naturalists in the South West who, with landowners and amenity societies, have fought many battles to prevent important habitats being flooded.

What is of real concern is the lack of long-term planning for water supply, for we cannot afford the present policy of flooding valuable land to provide city dwellers with their two baths or showers per day. The tremendous waste of natural resources in this way is one of the contributing factors in forcing water boards to continue looking for the cheapest way of increasing supplies.

Many of the reservoirs, some already constructed and some proposed, are or will be on well-watered uplands and it is in these areas, in particular, that farm reclamation and afforestation, have also made their inroads on the remaining wilderness areas.

In some small measure the naturalist is compensated for the loss of moorland habitat by the local increase in birds around and on the new reservoirs. However, so far the reservoirs have (with a few exceptions) little of more than general interest to offer the bird watcher, and even less for the botanist. This is due to the lack of shallow water around the banks, so vital for plant growth which in turn supplies food for wildfowl. Tufted duck and mallard have increased on the water but the main gain are the species attracted to reservoirs by the provision of conifer plantations as screens.

The Somerset part of Exmoor has two reservoirs at present, Minehead reservoir at Nutscale, north of Exford, and the Clatworthy reservoir in the Brendon Hills which serves Taunton. A third is proposed, in the National Park this time, the site yet to be decided but probably either at Landacre or a site in the Haddeo Valley.

In Devon, Burrator lies in the Meavy valley about three miles north of Shaugh Prior (see plate p 51). The reservoir at Burrator is surrounded by boulder-strewn slopes and conifer plantations which make quite good habitats for some birds; disappointingly, the water has few wildfowl due to the lack of aquatic vegetation. The conifer belt does, however, have a number of breeding redstart and was formerly a stronghold for woodlark, now much decreased. Fenworthy reservoir, also on Dartmoor, has, like Burrator, little to attract waterbirds but the conifers which have been planted have encouraged two new breeding species for Devon, the siskin and the lesser redpoll.

On the Devon and Cornwall border lies the 50 acre Tamar Lake which unlike the Dartmoor reservoirs has a variety of breeding and migrant waterfowl. Some species are of great interest and during cold weather many rarities have been seen. The diversity of species is due to the presence of shallow water supporting a prolific plant growth together with abundant undergrowth cover on the banks of the reservoir. Other Devon reservoirs are listed in the Appendix, but mention must be made here of the new reservoir under construction at Meldon on the south-west flank of Dartmoor. Here, an area which is both geologically and botanically important, due to the presence of metamorphosed calcareous rocks, is shortly to be flooded.

In Cornwall the reservoirs are more interesting, due to their lower elevation, and new ones such as Siblyback and Stithians increase each year in importance as bird watching locations. As a general rule, reservoirs above 800ft, bordered by moorland or coniferous plantations are poor in wildfowl, as they are isolated areas well away from potential commuting sites such as estuaries. On the other hand, reservoirs below 500ft, surrounded by open

Page 205 (*above*) Old mine walls such as this at Chapel Porth, Cornwall, carry a clifftop flora very rich in maritime species with curtains of thrift, sea campion, plantains and scurvy grass; (*below*) scurvy grass at base of mine wall. This plant was formerly used by sailors as a source of vitamin C

Page 206 (*above*) A damp wall above a small trout stream; typical festoons of ferns and mosses with a good aquatic flora, and rich insect life. Such areas are the haunts of pied and grey wagtails and in higher streams, the dipper; (*below*) roadside verges are important refuges for wildlife. Three-cornered leek, *Allium triquetrum*, and red campion make attractive spring verges to many lanes in the South West

pastureland, are much more attractive to birdlife, although their construction makes necessary the destruction of agricultural land.

The Cornwall Naturalist's Trust has formed a policy for reservoirs in the Duchy which takes into account just such factors as those mentioned; they are trying to make sure that, in the event of any future constructions, some attention will be given to natural history considerations. Inevitably there will be some wild life loss, but with good choice of site and suitable care of the surroundings, waterfowl, at least, can be encouraged.

However, naturalists are not the only interested party in the controversy: there are shooting interests, sailing, fishing, waterskiing and picnickers to consider. Some of these activities are obviously incompatible, but a number of parties will have to be satisfied and each new site is therefore going to need much consideration—and careful management.

CHAPTER ELEVEN

Cultivated land

Farmland–Horticultural land–Animal life

UNLIKE MUCH OF lowland England, the horticultural and farmland of the South West retains great interest for the naturalist as it still contains a wide variety of species as yet relatively little affected by mechanical and chemical developments which have taken place elsewhere.

Farmland

It is difficult to find a greater contrast in agricultural land than that shown by the sheltered, lush, red-soiled fields of the Devon South Hams and the windswept, wet cold-soiled rough grazing land of the Dartmoor granite which forms the Hams northern boundary. High, flower covered, bird-rich stone hedges topped by shrubs and trees to the south of the granite uplands give way to the open uplands with their drystone walls of granite clitter which are well covered by lichens but support little larger than stunted, wind-sculptured hawthorn or blackthorn scrub. Even this is welcome as shelter for the hardy upland stock which graze the coarse grasses.

Much of the pasture land in the South West is of low quality, especially that on the higher granite moors and the badly-drained, cold soils of the Culm measures; such arable farming as takes place, concentrating mainly on barley, oats and mixed corn growing, is much subordinate to stock rearing. It is often difficult to distinguish between temporary and permanent grassland due to the practice of having long leys, for both habitats are rich in plant species and are most welcome to naturalists used to the monoculture grassland 'up country'. The numbers of sheep and cattle grazing the higher moorland have increased in recent years, and the sheep around the lay-bys are becoming almost as familiar a scene as in the Pennines and Forest of Dean. Unfortunately the practice of feeding the animals often leads to road accidents as the animals congregate around busy roads in the hope of free meals, which are therefore not to be encouraged.

The main dairying areas are on the rich pasture land of East Devon and East Cornwall but there are numerous, often very small herds on the Lizard and Land's End peninsulas. A visitor returning to the area after some years absence would notice the alteration in the breeds of cattle, for the shorthorn and traditional Devon Red have made way for increasing numbers of Fresian, Ayrshire and Channel Island breeds.

Most of the fields are small and often enclosed by high hedges. There is a rather primitive, satisfying air of solidarity about a west country hedge, and if one is unfortunate enough to have to try to remove these minor masterpieces of rough stone and fine earth, one feels rather like a vandal. The art of dry hedging is still well known, particularly in Cornwall where many visitors will notice the magnificent warm red and brown stone walls even along recently widened or newly cut roadways, for it is still County Council policy to use traditional hedging techniques rather than the sterile post and fence so common in other parts of the country.

Some hedges consist of a single wall of well chosen stones, often of massive proportions, set into a soft earth bank, so forming the boundaries of many of the deeply-incised lanes in the South West. In areas where the wall is to be freestanding, the hedge consists of a double wall with fine earth and small stone infilling between the two faces with the stones themselves being set again in layers of fine earth. Such walls with their innumerable niches and copious earth supplies form magnificent habitats for animal and plant life to flourish in profusion. There can be few finer sights than a narrow lane in early summer crowded almost

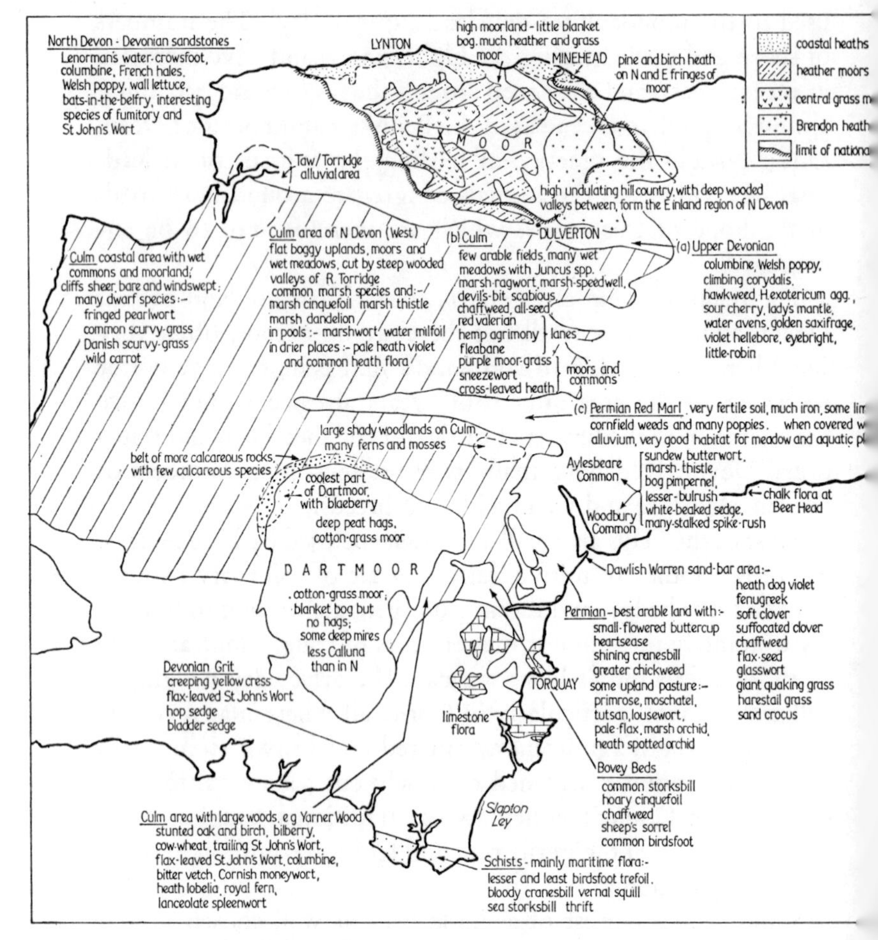

Figure 25 Sketch map of Devon indicating main plant communities associated with various rock types and altitudes. The distribution of the principal habitats on Exmoor is shown in more detail and is based on *The Vegetation of Exmoor* (1970)

into its centre by the brightly coloured flowering spikes of plants such as foxglove, valerian, agrimony, toadflax and betony, while later in the year, golden rod, St John's wort and a variety of heaths and heather add to the colourful community.

The situation of the hedge partly determines the floral composition, particularly that of the usual capping vegetation of shrubs and trees. In sheltered areas, mature stands of trees dominate with typically elm, oak, beech, ash and holly. Areas more exposed to wind have blackthorn and hawthorn as dominant shrubs, while in really exposed conditions near the coast, hedge tops are dominated by gorse and bramble, joined sometimes by the colourful broom, together with a few stunted blackthorn and hawthorn bent away from the prevailing winds. Where pasture land meets cliff edge, the stone hedges are no place for tall shrubs to grow, and even the hardy common gorse *Ulex europaeus* is displaced by the prostrate, mat-forming, natural pin-cushion of western gorse, *U. gallii*. In summer and spring such maritime hedges form colourful natural rock gardens with dense tufts of pink thrift, white sea campion *Silene maritima*, yellow kidney vetch *Anthyllis vulneraria*, and birds foot trefoil *Lotus corniculatus*. Almost concealed among the taller flowers can be found milkwort *Polygala serpyllifolia*, wild thyme *Thymus serpyllum*, and violets.

Most lanes provide considerable shelter from the south-westerly winds, and it is locally held that the diminutive stature of many Cornish people is an adaptation to creeping along out of the wind's path, although geneticists may have considerable misgivings about this deduction. Butterflies find the shelter to their advantage also, and lanes provide some of the richest butterfly habitats. Particularly abundant are small blues, wall butterflies, small coppers, spotted heaths, ringlets and small tortoiseshells, while there is usually a population of red admirals, painted ladies and an occasional fritillary to be seen.

In the general shortage of tree cover in the south-west counties, the hedges and their shrub capping provide very suitable nesting areas. In cracks between stones the loose earth is often washed out by wind and rain and such natural cavities are used by wrens, great tits, coal tits and blue tits, while any man-introduced article such as an old tin or kettle is liable to house a robin family.

During still, hot days in summer the characteristic call of a very typical hedge-breeding bird, the yellow-hammer, is often punctuated by the popping of the ripe gorse seed pods, a source of food for this seed-eating bunting. Yellow-hammers roost in loose colonies in hedges during winter nights. Their less social and much rarer relative the cirl bunting is sometimes seen nevertheless during the winter amongst parties of linnets or chaffinches. First discovered by Montagu in South Devon in 1800 at Kingsbridge, this species has unfortunately still not recovered from the hard winter of 1962–3. The bird is confined to a narrow coastal strip mainly along the South Devon coast, for this is a Mediterranean species at the edge of its range in Great Britain.

Even in winter months the stone hedges have plentiful ferns such as the common polypody to add a touch of green, as does the wall pennywort *Umbilicus rupestris* with its large, round, centre-stalked leaves; these take advantage of the dying-back of other vegetation to store up food supplies for the lean months of summer when most pennywort leaves are covered and smothered by grasses and other herbs, with only the rather drab spike of green flowers showing above the other vegetation. Other typical wall species are wood sage *Teucrium scorodonia*, and the attractive-flowered, succulent-leaved stonecrops.

A typical species list of hedge plants would include:

foxglove	*Digitalis purpurea*
yellow toadflax	*Linaria vulgaris*
betony	*Betonica officinalis*
red campion	*Melandrium dioicum*
greater stitchwort	*Stellaria holostea*
arum lily	*Arum maculatum*
wood sage	*Teucrium scorodonia*
golden rod	*Solidag virgaurea*
herb robert	*Geranium robertianum*
valerian	*Valeriana officinalis*

As with some other habitats in the south-west counties, there are certain species of plants which are rare although of common occurrence further north and east. Good examples are the white deadnettle *Lamium album*, and the harebell *Campanula rotundifolia*.

Compensation is amply given by the profusion of primroses, and in places large stands of orchids at the base of hedges. These man-made habitats are probably among the richest in the peninsula—nevertheless, they seem to have been little studied. We do probably know more about the bryophyte and fern communities of walls and hedges. On lane sides *Epipterygium tozeri* and *Schistostega pennata* may line cracks and overhangs while the ferns are well represented by hard fern *Blechnum spicant*, common polypody *Polypodium vulgare*, and hartstongue fern *Phyllitis scolopendrium*, together with a variety of lichens which characteristically cover the natural stone and slate used in wall construction.

On the drystone walls of stone and earth, mosses are common including *Weissia* spp, *Pottia* spp, and *Bryum donianum* which all root themselves in the soil between stones.

Modern farming is of course bringing changes as ponds are drained and deep ditches dug to run off water from boggy land that formerly held bog or marsh flora. Bulldozers are doing great damage to strips of former wild country as farmers insist on having a tidy edge to their farms. Many coastal farmland areas are overwhelmed by seasonal use as camping and caravan sites, while many acres have been permanently lost to chalet sites, bungalows and, in higher areas, reservoir construction. As land prices rise, profit margins for farmers fall, and the industry becomes more mechanised; one cannot but feel pessimistic about the future of much of the farmland in the South West. Farming practices have in the past helped preserve species indirectly by preserving and creating diverse habitats, but today the farmers are converting diverse habitats into uniform monocultures, sterile as far as wildlife is concerned.

In Devon the woodlark decline may be associated with the destruction of marginal land while the corncrake is no longer a breeding species. Also almost vanished, due to agricultural practices, are the lapwing (as a breeding bird), the partridge, and the moorhen. Although the toxic chemical use is not as yet great compared with some parts of the country, the peregrine falcon has almost been exterminated, and the sparrow-hawk has declined, as has the beneficial barn owl.

Agricultural land affects the flora and fauna indirectly by increasing the nitrate, herbicide and pesticide residues in fresh water. There are still many trout in nearly all the small rivers, but this situation seems unlikely to continue for long. It is in the hands of the farmers, whose ancestors shaped the landscape, either to continue the decline in the wildlife of the South West, or to help with its conservation before it is too late, a great responsibility for a minority body who nevertheless control 86 per cent of the land surface.

Horticultural land

There are still extensive cider-apple orchards in Devon but, unfortunately for the naturalist, many of the older, more interesting ones, as far as wildlife is concerned, have been grubbed out in recent years. Old orchards which are not subject to excessive spraying with fungicide and insecticide are particularly suitable for a large number of arboreal birds, and in many cases they provide very suitable nesting sites. Typical of such habitats are goldfinches, bullfinches, and the great and blue tits. The bullfinch is unfortunately often a bud eater and is therefore hardly welcome; in some soft fruit areas it is trapped and shot.

The rough bark on old pear trees provides many niches for insects to live in dampness and relative seclusion. They are searched out by green woodpeckers, nuthatches and tree creepers, and the leaves and smaller branches are well picked over by the tits. The rapid decline in mistletoe is to be attributed to the grubbing out of the old unprofitable orchards, and with their destruction we also lost many acres of permanent grassland between the trees, a habitat which is often very rich in wild flowers.

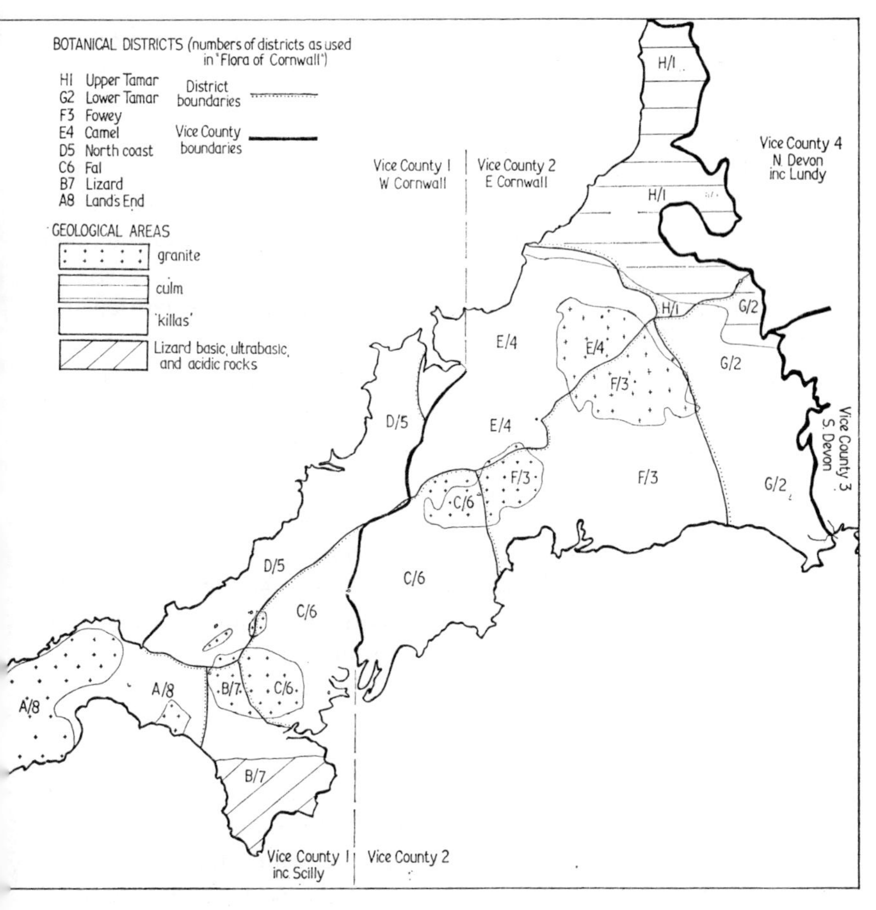

Figure 26 Sketch map showing distribution of vice counties in the South West and district boundaries in Cornwall. District boundaries for Devon will be found in the *Flora of Devon* (1939)

Blackbirds and thrushes feed on overripe fruit and windfalls and even during the depths of winter in old orchards half mummified fruit is still available amongst the tangled grasses for the redwings and fieldfares together with, on occasions, a hare or fox.

Modern well-managed orchards are of little value to birds

due to the vigorously efficient methods used to keep down insect and plant pests, and they do in many cases present a positive hazard to local bird life rather than provide potential nesting and feeding areas.

In Cornwall, Devon and the Isles of Scilly, flower and early vegetable growing is important including special crops such as anemones, narcissus, strawberry, broccoli, spring cabbage, and early potatoes. Among these cultivated crops, a wide variety of weeds, often of great interest, can be found. This is particularly so on Scilly where in early summer the fields produce an interesting second crop of commercially worthless but botanically valuable weeds. These appear after the bulb crop has flowered and the foliage been left to die down before further cultivation takes place (see Appendix, p 265). One of the features of the natural flora in Devon and particularly in Cornwall, is the occurrence of many species not found in other parts of the British Isles and more akin to those in coastal areas of Portugal and Spain; this flora also has many similarities with that of southern Ireland and indicates a mild climate.

The environment is still relatively kind if the problems of wind and salt are tackled. As mentioned in Chapter Two, many trees of both native and imported species have been planted as belts behind which man, his animals and cultivated plants can shelter. The naturalist will notice in the South West a great variety of imported shrubs which are wind and salt tolerant, and many of these plants are from New Zealand. An excellent example of the way in which imported shrubs can change an area is found on the island of Tresco where until the mid eighteen hundreds the site of the now famous Tresco Abbey Gardens was wind-blasted heather land.

A plant familiar to holiday makers is the feathery-leaved tamarisk with its attractive, long, catkin-like spike of pink flowers. This hardy shrub can grow right down to the edge of saltwater and can even withstand sand-blasting as its position at the edge of sand dunes bears testimony. Two species are commonly grown, *Tamarix anglica* with white flowers tinged with pink, and the slightly larger, pale pink-flowered *T. gallica*. An attractive tamarisk hedge grows on each side of the road leading along the exposed peninsula to Trevose lighthouse, south of Padstow.

Of the many plants from the antipodes which grow well, particularly on Scilly, a most attractive shrub is the New Zealand olearia of which there are a number of species. These do well even on exposed heathland areas of Land's End where the silvery undersurfaces of the otherwise green leaves enhance the beauty of many walls and gardens. On Scilly a natural olearia hybrid *Olearia scilloniensis* has arisen on Tresco. Another southern hemisphere shrub is the mutton-bird tree *Senecio rotundifolius* with its attractive red flower. *Cordyline australis*, probably better known as the dracaena or New Zealand cabbage palm, gives a sub-tropical look to many south coast towns, particularly Falmouth were Dracaena Avenue was named in its honour.

Two other characteristic imports are the attractive, aromatic shiny leaves of the escallonias which form dark green, windproof, living filters for gale force winds. The pink flowers attract many insects during the long flowering period, and small birds, for example greenfinches, chaffinches and blackbirds, find shelter for roosting, and a few nests are snugly built in the dense thickets.

Giant pandas at London Zoo have in the past had reason to be grateful to the South West for supplying their staple diet of young bamboo shoots. This giant grass *Arundaria japonica* does extremely well under mild but exposed coastal climates and forms almost impenetrable screens against the wind. Bamboo provides winter roosting quarters for many birds of a variety of species including greenfinch, brambling, blackbird, songthrush and redwing. The two species found in greatest numbers, however, are the chaffinch and starling; in one roost near Bodmin in Cornwall the chaffinches varied between 300 and 3,000, but even this number was small compared with up to 250,000 starlings in the same cover. Ringing studies showed that the roosting chaffinches were of both local and foreign origin (see CBWPS annual report 1968).

Native species of shrub do provide shelter and none more so than the almost ever-blooming gorse which tops most of the stone and earth fences in Cornwall. A double-flowered, orange-yellow variety of the common gorse *Ulex europaeus* occurs naturally on an exposed hillside in the Isles of Scilly and is attractively called Scilly gold. Many other shrubs occur which are best seen in south-west gardens such as Caerhays on the Cornish coast, the Abbey Gardens on Tresco, and a number of resorts with municipal gardens along the South Devon coast.

On the mainland, use of selective weedkillers is having its effects on the weed flora of standing corn crops. Formerly abundant species, such as corn marigold, are now rarely found and have to be sought on waste ground which often supports unexpected rarities or has a good show of commoner plants. Many non-native species of plants will be seen in the south-west counties, as they have escaped from gardens and colonised walls and banks around human dwellings. A good example is the daisy-like Mexican fleabane *Erigeron mucronatus* which is often abundant on Cornish walls, even growing in one of the busiest parts of Truro, Lemon Street.

Other escapees now growing well in the wild are:

greater periwinkle	*Vinca major*
lesser periwinkle	*V. minor*
mind your own business	*Helxine soleirolii*
wallflower	*Cheiranthus cheiri*
alexanders	*Smyrnium olusatrum*
yellow strawberry	*Duchesnea indica*
three-cornered leek	*Allium triquetrum*
pink oxalis	*Oxalis floribunda*
escallonia	*Escallonia macrantha*
shrubby veronica	*Hebe lewissii*
karo	*Pittosporum crassifolium*, wild on Scilly
buddleia	*Buddleia davidii*

bear's breech	*Acanthus mollis*
Russian vine	*Polygonum baldschuanichum*
Japanese knotweed	*P. cuspidatum*

For more details of the interesting flora of wasteplaces and hedgerows see Paton, J. A., *Wild Flowers in Cornwall* (Barton 1968).

Animal life

Unlike the adjacent moorland and heath, cultivated land is richer in birds during winter, with the cirl bunting a characteristic species, as it is in the south along the coastal strip. Low-lying fields close to the shore attract in the colder months many species, among them oystercatchers, golden plover, lapwing, curlew, and sometimes turnstone with generous flocks of black-headed, herring and, less frequently, common gulls. In many regions large flocks of various species, including the thrush family and finches, will be seen foraging on ploughed land and among the dead seedheads of the previous season's weeds. Especially characteristic winter visitors to the South West are redwings and fieldfares, with large influxes of continental song thrushes and blackbirds to supplement the resident population. Among the finches large flocks of goldfinches, linnets, chaffinches and greenfinches are common with lesser numbers of brambling, lesser redpolls and siskins.

In winter the meadow pipits leave the higher moorland and with their numbers supplemented by winter visitors and tree pipits, collect in the lowlands and coastal districts. Members of the crow family can usually be seen scavenging among agricultural crops, and turning over cow and horse droppings on pasture land in search of beetles and fly larvae. Magpies are about the most conspicuous of the family, sometimes occurring in numbers of over twenty in early autumn. By midwinter, however, the pairs are established and remain close together during their foraging expeditions. They are frequently accompanied by mobs of jackdaws which divide their time between their cliff-face breeding-ledges and the fields which act as their feeding-grounds. While carrion crows are far too abundant for the health of small nesting birds, the jay is not frequently seen except where woodland is adjacent to the farmland.

In the winter months few pasture lands are free from the attentions of the continental starling flocks which probe their quarrelsome way systematically among grazing animals, leaving behind a much-pitted grass sward where their probing beaks have been searching for concealed food.

The most obvious wild mammal of cultivated land is the mole who, despite seldom appearing above ground during the winter months, gives ample surface evidence of its presence. The multitude of mole heaps particularly in the areas of fertile and therefore worm-rich soils, are frequently visited by birds who are rewarded with displaced small invertebrates. Despite their liking for rich soil, moles often show their presence in even the poorest soils on cliff tops and even on open heather moors where the worm must be rare indeed. Buzzards, which are frequently seen gliding over open land, probably eat a few moles, and young ones fall prey to the ubiquitous day-flying kestrels and the abundant tawny owls at night.

Disturbed land is highly suitable for foxes to flourish and they make a good living from man's leftovers, supplemented by a plentiful supply of small mammals, particularly the wood-mouse *Apodemus sylvaticus* and short-tailed vole *Microtus agrestis*, which are sometimes a pest on agricultural land and in gardens. The bank vole *Clethrionomys glareolus* is probably less common but in places abundant in earth and stone hedges.

Shrews are often heard though seldom seen alive, among the grass and crevices of the hedges. The badger is familiar and its footprints in damp earth, and well defined trails over walls show his regular movements to forage, mainly for earthworms, in the fields. Badger digging is, unfortunately, still fairly common in the area. There is no excuse for this as insufficient damage is done to warrant such vile 'sport'.

Red deer, particularly on Exmoor, pay usually unwelcome

visits to surrounding farmland, and the little muntjac deer seems to be increasing, moving unseen like the roe deer through thick vegetation, and spreading steadily south-west.

Grey squirrels and the occasional red, live in the tall hedges and scattered woodlands around farmland, and the presence of the grey can often be detected round the edges of corn crops where they cause much damage. Other agricultural pests, the rabbits, seem to build up their populations locally, only to be rapidly reduced by fresh surges of myxomatosis. Even though moles are seldom present on the upland pastures, lower down they are common, but their useful relative, the hedgehog, seems to be less abundant than in former years and the population that does exist is, as elsewhere, subject to dreadful predation at night by the fast car.

CHAPTER TWELVE

The Isles of Scilly

Plantlife—Birds and other animals

THE ISLES OF SCILLY represent the final stages of decay of a once large mountain chain, the Armorican mountains (see p 17). All that remains now are the granite stumps which once formed the roots of the old mountains and today make up a collection of small islands separated by reef-infested shallow sea.

These low-lying, flat topped islands rise to a maximum of only 166ft and represent the first landfall for the westerly winds and primary breakwater of the British Isles against the full Atlantic. Scilly is therefore dominated by wind and sea. Only five of the 145 islands are inhabited, the rest are either bare rock or covered with a low heath vegetation. There are no natural woodlands which means that woodland life is restricted to the few plantations that occur.

The erosion of the granite has produced large quantities of white quartz sand which is spread over the floor of the sea between the islands and is sometimes ridged by wind and tide to form spits which connect islands originally separated by erosion and the sea level rise after the last Ice Age. Wind-blown sand on Tresco reaches about 35ft, and has impounded a large lake of freshwater—the Great Pool—which is popular with waterfowl. St Mary's consists of three islands connected by sand bars whilst Samson and St Agnes are two granite knobs joined by sand in a similar way (see plate p 224).

It is unlikely that the islands have been joined to the mainland of England in recent geological times as between them there is now a deep-water channel. The legendary stories of the lost land of Lyonesse may not be as fanciful as some people suspect.

Page 223 (*above*) A typical Cornish drystone 'hedge' often as here overgrown with bramble and wood sage but supporting a wide variety of attractive species such as foxglove, valerian, goldenrod, toadflax and betony, in summer; (*below*) hen yellowhammer at nest, a characteristic bird of hedges and farmland

Page 224 (*above*) The South east tip of Lundy, showing Rat Island. All now owned by the National Trust which will continue to manage the island in the traditional ways with farming and access for summer visitors. The island is in effect a Nature Reserve, with a large number of sea birds breeding on its precipitous cliffs; (*below*) Isles of Scilly. Looking west with Gugh in the foreground and in the centre, St Agnes, with the former bird observatory, the disused lighthouse. In the background is Annet, a nature reserve, and sanctuary for many breeding seabirds. Note the small bulb fields surrounded by high hedges

A lowering of the sea level to the point that made it possible for forests and peat deposits to grow around the coast of the mainland only a few thousand years ago would mean that Seven Stones reef, of *Torrey Canyon* fame, could well have been habitable islands.

The rough sea crossing from Penzance gives opportunities for some excellent views of common and unusual sea birds, and also possibly marine mammals such as dolphins, seals and porpoise. Particularly on autumn crossings, birds that may be seen include shearwaters, petrels, gannets, phalerope and skuas with some real rarities such as Sabine's gull.

Plantlife

The low islands represent for the naturalist a fascinating assemblage of wildlife. For the botanist the bulb fields, as mentioned in the last chapter, provide most interesting areas for study in the late spring and summer. These fields should only be visited with permission due to the danger of spreading disease. The weeds are abundant and very colourful with one of the brightest combinations that of the large yellow-flowered corn marigold *Chrysanthemum segetum* and whistling jacks *Gladiolus byzantinum* which in May produce contrasting dark reddish-purple flower spikes.

Rosy garlic *Allium roseum* with pale pink flower clusters and the less visually attractive but more pleasantly aromatic musk storksbill *Erodium moschatum* and the yellow-flowered toothed medick *Medicago polymorpha* are all common in the bulb fields. Other plants, some of which are extremely attractive, also bloom after the bulbs have died down and before new cultivation begins; the Spanish iris *Iris xiphium* and the bluebell from the same country *Endymion hispanicus* are two such species.

Together with flowering plants, bryophytes are a feature of bulb fields. The following species appear also on arable and grassland and are characteristic for the South West.

Anthoceros husnotii	*Ditrichum cylindricum*
A. laevis	*Dicranella schreberana*
Riccia glauca	*Bryum rubens*
R. sorocarpa	*Eurhynchium swartzii*

There are large numbers of plants from the southern hemisphere which grow well in the mild climate. Many species from New Zealand and Australia have been introduced within living memory and flourish on Scilly better than anywhere else in Europe.

If exotic plants are exciting, the native flora is varied on the heathlands which have similar plant communities to those found on mainland heaths; but while some new species will be found, such as orange birdsfoot *Ornithopus pinnatus*, others common on the mainland are absent, for example bristle bent grass *Agrostis setacea*, cross-leaved heath *Erica tetralix*, and saw-wort *Serratula tinctoria*.

The islands have very few streams and no natural tree cover; the only mixed woodlands of any real significance are the Abbey Woods on Tresco. Scilly is of interest not only for some of the native plant species that it possesses, many having a Mediterranean or southern Europe affinity, but also for the absence of plants which are found on the mainland only twenty-eight miles to the north-west. Mention has already been made of heathland species that are not found on Scilly but another notable absentee is dog's mercury *Mercurialis perennis*, although the annual form *M. annua* is common. Likewise, the rare form of arum lily *Arum italicum* is common on Scilly while the common mainland form *A. maculatum* is absent, as are cow parsley *Anthriscus sylvestris*, greater stitchwort *Stellaria holostea*, rough chervil *Chaerophyllum temelentum*, and wild teasel *Dipsacus fullonum*.

The exposure of the low granite islands to the westerly winds and absence of native trees necessitates the growing of windbreaks around the bulb fields, a feature seen in the plates on p 224. Many of the hedges are of pittosporum or karo, escallonia, veronica, fuchsia, spindle and tamarisk.

Monteray pine *Pinus radiata* grows well on St Mary's and Tresco and probably regenerates here. The best collection of southern hemisphere plants is in the Abbey Gardens, Tresco, with *Eucalyptus*, *Banksia*, New Zealand flame tree *Metrosideros robusta*, and South American puja flowers.

Many of the subtropical plants produce great quantities of nectar and some of the common birds have discovered this useful source of food. Probably pollination is aided by the attentions of birds such as blackbirds, sparrows, finches, tits and starlings, who often receive a liberal coating of pollen while nectar feeding; yellow-headed blackbirds are occasionally reported on Scilly!

Many of the rocks composing the Isles are bare of vegetation and even the bryophyte flora is sparse. On such rocky outcrops even birds are uncommon but where a little soil accumulates on islands a ground cover is present and often includes tree mallow *Lavatera arborea* and occasionally the rare Cornish mallow *L. cretica*.

Birds and other animals

The small uninhabited isles form the main breeding areas for the many sea birds. Scilly is an excellent place to visit in May and June at nesting time: auks are relatively common although the numbers of puffin now breeding has declined dramatically from around 100,000 in 1909 on Annet alone, to a total breeding population for all Scilly of about 200. Unlike the mainland, razorbills are much more common than guillemots which only breed on three islands. The uninhabited islands and rocks are under the guardianship of the Nature Conservancy and act in effect as nature reserves with restricted access during bird breeding seasons. Although on the mainland razorbills and guillemots are cliff nesting, on Scilly they breed, puffin-like, in tunnels among loose rocks, and sometimes in old rabbit burrows. This is probably due to the lack of suitable rocky ledges along the coast of islands.

Puffins in particular suffer at the beaks of the great black-backed gulls which are now much more common as nesting birds than at the beginning of the century, and more common on Scilly than the mainland. The black-backs not only prey directly upon puffins and shearwaters, but also destroy the habitat by tearing up the grass during courtship display. The ensuing erosion of the soil means that underground breeding for auks and shearwaters becomes impossible, and so the auks decline in numbers. Erosion of topsoil from islands and sea stacks off the mainland together with the predation of the gulls, is rapidly reducing the population of puffins, and it is thought that on the mainland this bird could be extinct within fifty years. Gull numbers would therefore seem to be in urgent need of control.

Annet is a nature reserve which is closed to the public for three months, from 15 April to 15 July, except by permit, during the bird's breeding season. Here are colonies of storm petrels, Manx shearwaters, puffins and gulls.

If the inhabited islands are poor in breeding auks they are well supplied with waders. On Tresco, the Great Pool attracts wild fowl and is the best place in Scilly to study them. Many of the beaches, with their white sand, are relatively poorly occupied by birds, presumably due to the shortage of invertebrate food. More popular with waders are the rocky beaches which face open sea, and which accumulate piles of seaweed and other debris during storms. In such areas waders may be seen at most times of the year except during midsummer when the majority of birds are away at their breeding sites further north. During the spring and autumn there are large numbers of passage migrants with probably the autumn passage being the most exciting. Among the small waders sometimes such rarities as American pectoral sandpipers may be seen and the visiting naturalist in the autumn can expect to see at least one rare bird from North America or South East Europe, eg Phallas's warbler, Baltimore oriole, alpine swift, ortolan bunting, tawny pipit, red-breasted flycatcher or the yellow-browed warbler.

North American birds often turn up after a north-westerly gale and are also aided in their passage by shipping. The reader is referred to an excellent small book by Miss H. M. Quick where a full check list of Scilly bird species will be found with a brief account of many of them.

Reports of the St Agnes Bird Observatory which were formerly published annually have now ceased as the observatory is no longer in operation. Details of the records of birds seen in the islands will be found in the annual reports of the Cornwall Birdwatching and Preservation Society. In 1968 a separate report for the Isles of Scilly was produced and this practice will continue.

Almost anything seems to be capable of turning up on Scilly but a number of mainland birds are here rare, eg rook, jackdaw, magpie, jay, carrion crow and raven. Wood pigeons and woodpeckers are seldom seen, yellow-hammers are uncommon but hoopoes are frequent visitors, particularly in the spring (see Appendix, p 250 for list of breeding birds and migration peaks. A point to bear in mind is that many of the common passerine birds are to be found on beaches in Scilly, right away from their normal habitat, and this may lead to difficulty with identification.

There are few mammals present on Scilly but one of particular interest is the white-toothed shrew *Crocidura sauveolens*. This small insectivore can be found in the Abbey Gardens on Tresco and also in what is said to be its main habitat, amongst bracken and bramble on heathland. The Scilly Island race is a sub-species of the continental race and is called *C. s. cassiteridum* and is not therefore a true species as had been formerly thought. Mammals absent from Scilly are pigmy shrew, short-tailed vole, water shrew, bank vole and stoat. Grey seals are present, however, and do have a small breeding colony whose numbers seem to be almost static.

As with mammals so again with butterflies we find an impoverished species list but a number of interesting island races do occur. The common blue *Polyommatus icarus* has a race confined to the tiny island of Tean while the normal form of this butterfly exists on the adjacent island of St Martins which at one point is only separated by 900ft of sea. On Scilly the common blue is triple-brooded; other breeding species include small copper and green-veined white. Not recorded from the islands are grayling, skippers, brown argus, orange tip or comma. The meadow brown occurs on Scilly as a separate sub-species *Maniola jurtina cassiteridum.* The subspecific name here refers to the islands' former importance in tin trading, for tin deposits were formerly found amongst the granite forming the islands.

The Isles of Scilly reinforce the conclusion reached earlier, that the farther west one goes the less the number of native species of flowering plants, fish and birds. But if typical species farther east in England are less common here, plants and animals of a more southerly maritime nature add considerably to the natural history interest and more than compensate for the losses.

Appendix

Appendix

Butterflies of the South West

(Species listed in order given in *Field Guide to Butterflies of Britain and Europe*, 1970)

Pieris brassicae	Large white, very common
Pieris rapae	Small white, common
Pieris napi	Green-veined white, very common
Pontia daplidice	Bath white, migrant, very rare
Anthocharis cardamines	Orange tip, sometimes common
Colias crocea	Clouded yellow, sometimes in fair number, migrant
Colias hyale	Pale clouded yellow, migrant, numbers variable
Genepteryx rhamni	Brimstone, migrant, not very common
Leptidea sinapis	Wood white, very rare
Danaus plexippus	Milkweed or Monarch, North American, summer vagrant here
Apatura iris	Purple emperor, very rare Devon, not recorded in Cornwall
Limenitis camilla	White admiral, very rare
Inachis io	Peacock, common
Vanessa atalanta	Red admiral, common migrant (breeds)
Vanessa cardui	Painted lady, migrant, often very common spring and summer (breeds)
Aglais urticae	Small tortoiseshell, very common
Polygonia c-album	Comma, spread post-war to West Cornwall, not very common but probably increasing
Argynnis paphia	Silver-washed fritillary, frequent
Mesoacidalia aglaja	Dark-green fritillary, locally fairly common
Fabriciana adippe	High-brown fritillary, not common
Clossiana selene	Small pearl-bordered fritillary, probably decreasing
Clossiana euphrosyne	Pearl-bordered fritillary, frequent
Mellicta athalia	Heath fritillary, rare
Euphydryas athalia aurinia	Marsh fritillary, rare but locally frequent

Melanargia galathea	Marbled white, very rare
Hipparchia semele	Grayling, locally common on heaths
Maniola jurtina	Meadow brown, common
Aphantopus hyperanthus	Ringlet, common
Pyronia tithonus	Gatekeeper, very common
Coenonympha pamphilus	Small heath, common but very few in West Cornwall
Pararge aegeria	Speckled wood, very common
Lasiommata megera	Wall brown, common
Thecla betulae	Brown hairstreak, rare Devon, absent Cornwall
Quercusia quercus	Purple hairstreak, uncommon
Strymonidia w-album	White-letter hairstreak, very rare
Callophrys rubi	Green hairstreak, locally common
Lycaena phlaeas	Small copper, common
Cupido minimus	Little blue, uncommon, SE Devon only
Celastrina argiolus	Holly blue, not common
Maculinea arion	Large blue, very rare North Cornwall and North Devon
Plebejus argus	Silver-studded blue, common some areas eg dunes
Aricia agestis	Brown argus, widespread but probably decreasing
Lysandra coridon	Chalk-hill blue, very rare
Lysandra bellargus	Adonis blue, mainly South East Devon but rare
Polyommatus icarus	Common blue, very common locally
Pyrgus malvae	Grizzled skipper, rather uncommon
Erynnis tages	Dingy skipper, sometimes common on sand-hills
Thymelicus acteon	Lulworth skipper, rare, probably only found in South East Devon
Thymelicus sylvestris	Small skipper, locally common
Ochlodes venatus	Large skipper, quite common

Many downland species may occur near sea shores, where most will be found in sandhills amongst marram grass and other rough vegetation.

Grasshoppers, crickets and their allies (Orthoptera)

The South West has 36 species (Lundy having 3 native and no introduced species, Scilly 4 native and 3 introduced species). Heathland and moorland are the best areas for the group, with Bodmin Moor, Dartmoor and Exmoor excellent hunting-grounds, as are the other smaller heathland areas and sand dunes. As the heathland declines due to spread of people, houses and bracken, so the *Orthoptera* will decrease.

Numbers given after the species name are those of the vice-counties (see p 217) in which the insect occurs. If no number is given this means that the species is found in all the vice-counties of Devon and Cornwall but not Scilly or Lundy unless specifically mentioned. Status is only given where information exists.

A Introduced species

Prickly stick insect	*Acanthoxyla prasina*, Tresco and South Devon
Smooth stick insect	*Clitharchus hookeri*, Tresco
Laboratory stick insect	*Carausinus morosus*, South Devon
Common cockroach	*Blatta orientalis*, also Scilly
American cockroach	*Periplaneta americana*, not 4
Australian cockroach	*Periplaneta australasiae*, 1 only
German cockroach	*Blattella germanica*, not 2
Brown-banded cockroach	*Supella supellectilium*, 3 only
House cricket	*Acheta domesticus*, all but not Scilly

Lundy has no introduced *Orthoptera*

B Native species

(i) Cockroaches	
Dusky cockroach	*Ectobius lapponicus*, not 1
Tawny cockroach	*Ectobius pallidus*
Lesser cockroach	*Ectobius panzeri*, also Scilly and Lundy
(ii) Bush crickets	
Oak bush cricket	*Meconema thalassinum*
Great green	*Tettigonia viridissima*, also Scilly, rough herbage and weeds
Dark bush	*Pholidoptera griseoaptera*, very common
Grey	*Platycleis denticulata*, also Scilly
Bog	*Metrioptera brachyptera*, not 4
Short-winged cone head	*Conocephalus dorsalis*, not 1 and 2
Speckled	*Leptophyes punctatissima*, also Lundy not uncommon
(iii) Crickets	
Wood	*Nemobius sylvestris*, 3 only
Field	*Gryllus lampestris*, rare
Mole cricket	*Gryclotalpa gryllotalpa*, rare
(iv) Grasshoppers	
Large marsh	*Stethophyma grossum*, 2 only
Strip-winged	*Stenobothrus lineatus*
Common green	*Omocestus viridulus*, abundant August to September
Woodland	*Omocestus rufipes*, rare

Common field	*Chorthippus brunneus*, also Lundy and Scilly, very common
Meadow	*Chorthippus parallelus*, common higher meadow land
Lesser marsh	*Chorthippus albomarginatus*, except 4
Rufous	*Gomphocerippus rufus*, locally common north coast alkaline soil on basic intrusive rocks
Mottled	*Myrmeleotettix maculatus*, widespread grassy downs and sand
(v) Ground hoppers	
Common	*Tetrix undulata*
Slender	*Tetrix subulata*
Cepero's	*Tetrix ceperoi*, not 3

Amphibians

Warty newt	*Triturus cristatus cristarus*
Smooth newt	*Triturus vulgaris*, common except possibly in South West Cornwall
Palmate newt	*Triturus helveticus*
Common toad	*Bufo bufo bufo*, common
Common frog	*Rana temporaria temporaria*, still locally common

Reptiles

Snakes and lizards

Slow worm	*Anguis fragilis*, common
Viviparous lizard	*Lacerta vivipera*, locally very common particularly on coastal heathlands
Ringed or grass snake	*Natrix natrix helvetica*, common
Adder or viper	*Vipera berus berus*, locally very common particularly on coastal heathlands and drystone walls

Turtles

Most strandings are of two species of loggerhead; they are by no means common but may always turn up

Common loggerhead	*Caretta caretta*
Kemp's loggerhead	*Lepidochelys kempi*

Check list of Birds of the South West

(Systematic list of bird species in the South West excluding very rare vagrants.) Scientific names as used in the revised edition (1966) of Peterson, et al *Field*

Guide to the Birds of Britain and Europe. Sequence of species as in 1952 BOU check list.

Black-throated diver	*Gavia arctica*, winter visitor and passage migrant, annual but rare
Great northern diver	*Gavia immer*, winter visitor, commonest diver
Red-throated diver	*Gavia stellata*, winter visitor, annual mainland, rare Scilly
Great-crested grebe	*Podiceps cristatus*, winter visitor, rarely breeds Devon not Cornwall
Red-necked grebe	*Podiceps grisegena*, winter visitor possibly annual in Cornwall but rare
Slavonian grebe	*Podiceps auritus*, winter visitor, fairly common
Black-necked grebe	*Podiceps nigricollis*, winter visitor, not common but regular few
Little grebe	*Podiceps ruficollis*, few resident, mainly winter visitors, few breed
Leaches' petrel	*Oceanodroma leucorrhoa*, irregular winter visitor, sometimes 'wrecked'
Storm petrel	*Hydrobates pelagicus*, common and breeds Scilly, summer visitor
Manx shearwater	*Puffinus puffinus*, resident partial migrant, breeds, particularly Scilly
Balearic shearwater	*Puffinus puffinus mauretanicus*, regular passage migrant
Great shearwater	*Puffinus gravis*, irregular visitor in autumn, sometimes large numbers off Land's End
Cory's shearwater	*Procellaria diomedea*, regular autumn visitor between Land's End and Scilly
Sooty shearwater	*Puffinus griseus*, not uncommon 'vagrant' on passage in autumn with Manx
Fulmar	*Fulmarus glacialis*, pelagic, summer visitor to land, breeds, common
Gannet	*Sula bassana*, regular non-breeding visitor, formerly bred Lundy
Cormorant	*Phalacrocorax carbo*, resident, breeds, common
Shag	*Phalacrocorax aristotelis*, resident, breeds, common
Grey heron	*Ardea cinerea*, resident and winter visitor, breeds, common
Purple heron	*Ardea purpurea*, almost annual vagrant, Cornwall
Little egret	*Egretta garzetta*, vagrant on spring migration, usually one per annum, Cornwall
Bittern	*Botaurus stellaris*, rare winter visitor
Little bittern	*Ixobrychus minutus*, very rare vagrant

Spoonbill	*Platalea leucorodia*, winter visitor, regular small numbers
Mallard	*Anas platyrhynchos*, resident and winter visitor, breeds
Teal	*Anas crecca*, resident and winter visitor, breeds occasionally
Green-winged teal	*Anas crecca carolinensis*, vagrant
Garganey	*Anas querquedula*, passage migrant, has bred
Gadwall	*Anas strepera*, winter visitor, regular but not common
Wigeon	*Anas penelope*, winter visitor, very common
Pintail	*Anas acuta*, winter visitor, fairly common
Shoveler	*Anas clypeata*, winter visitor, has bred, local and erratic occurrence
Red-crested pochard	*Netta rufina*, vagrant
Scaup	*Aythya marila*, winter visitor, regular, small numbers
Tufted duck	*Aythya fuligula*, winter visitor, has bred, regular, fair numbers
Pochard	*Aythya ferina*, winter visitor, regular, fairly common
Ferruginous duck	*Aythya nyroca*, vagrant
Goldeneye	*Bucephala clangula*, regular winter visitor, small numbers
Long-tailed duck	*Clangula hyemalis*, regular winter visitor, very small numbers
Velvet scoter	*Melanitta fusca*, winter visitor, regular but uncommon
Surf scoter	*Melanitta perspicillata*, vagrant
Common scoter	*Melanitta nigra*, winter visitor also summer but does not breed, fair numbers
Common eider	*Somateria mollissima*, resident but non-breeding, small numbers
Red-breasted merganser	*Mergus serrator*, winter visitor, regular, locally common
Goosander	*Mergus merganser*, winter visitor, regular but uncommon, increasing Cornwall
Smew	*Mergus albellus*, winter visitor, regular, small numbers
Shelduck	*Tadorna tadorna*, resident and winter visitor, breeds, common
Grey lag goose	*Anser anser*, irregular winter visitor
White-fronted goose	*Anser albifrons*, winter visitor, regular but not in large numbers
Pink-footed goose	*Anser brachyrhynchus*, irregular winter visitor

Brent goose	*Branta bernicla*, winter visitor, regular, increasing
Barnacle goose	*Branta leucopsis*, irregular visitor, decreasing
Canada goose	*Branta canadensis*, resident, breeds occasionally Cornwall, about 200 in Devon, spreading after introduction 1949
Mute swan	*Cygnus olor*, resident, breeds, common
Whooper swan	*Cygnus cygnus*, winter visitor, fairly regular, small numbers, most in hard winters
Bewick's swan	*Cygnus bewickii*, winter visitor, regular, small numbers, increasing
Buzzard	*Buteo buteo*, resident, breeds, common
Sparrow-hawk	*Accipiter nisus*, resident and passage migrant, breeds
Goshawk	*Accipiter gentilis*, vagrant
Red Kite	*Milvus milvus*, irregular visitor, has bred
Marsh harrier	*Circus aeruginosus*, irregular visitor
Hen harrier	*Circus cyaneus*, winter visitor, formerly bred
Montagu's harrier	*Circus pygargus*, uncommon summer visitor, breeds
Osprey	*Pandion haliaetus*, rare passage migrant, formerly bred
Hobby	*Falco subbuteo*, summer visitor, breeds, increasing, regular
Peregrine	*Falco peregrinus*, resident, breeds, very small numbers but increasing
Merlin	*Falco columbarius*, resident and winter visitor, breeds, not common
Kestrel	*Falco tinnunculus*, resident, breeds, common, some passage spring/autumn
Red grouse	*Lagopus lagopus*, resident, breeds, introduced and uncommon
Black grouse	*Lyrurus tetrix*, resident, decreasing, may still breed
Red-legged partridge	*Alectoris rufa*, resident, breeds locally, uncommon
Partridge	*Perdix perdix*, resident, breeds, not very common possibly decreasing
Quail	*Coturnix coturnix*, irregular summer visitor, breeds sporadically, possibly slightly increasing
Pheasant	*Phasianus colchicus*, resident, breeds, introduced, fairly common
Water rail	*Rallus aquaticus*, winter visitor and passage migrant, breeds Cornwall and Scillies
Spotted crake	*Porzana porzana*, breeds Somerset, uncommon passage migrant Cornwall, irregular visitor Devon
Corncrake	*Crex crex*, passage migrant, formerly bred Devon, rarely breeds Cornwall and Scilly

Moorhen	*Gallinula chloropus*, resident, breeds, big increase in winter numbers in Cornwall and Scilly
Coot	*Fulica atra*, resident and winter visitor, breeds, increasing in large numbers in winter particularly in Devon
Oystercatcher	*Haematopus ostralegus*, resident and winter visitor, breeds, common
Lapwing	*Vanellus vanellus*, resident, winter visitor and passage migrant, breeds, common
Ringed plover	*Charadrius hiaticula*, resident, passage migrant and winter visitor, breeds Devon
Little ringed plover	*Charadrius dubius*, vagrant but spreading from east, may soon breed
Kentish plover	*Charadrius alexandrinus*, scarce passage migrant
Grey plover	*Pluvialis squatarola*, winter visitor and passage migrant, fairly common
Golden plover	*Pluvialis apricaria*, resident and very common winter visitor, breeds, also passage migrant
Dotterel	*Eudromias morinellus*, passage migrant, rare Cornwall, more common Devon
Turnstone	*Arenaria interpres*, passage migrant, winter visitor and non-breeding summer visitor, common
Short-billed dowitcher	*Limnodromus griseus*, annual vagrant
Snipe	*Gallinago gallinago*, resident and winter visitor, breeds, most common in winter
Jack snipe	*Lymnocryptes minima*, winter visitor and passage migrant, regular small numbers
Woodcock	*Scolopax rusticola*, winter visitor, has bred, very common West Cornwall in winter
Curlew	*Numenius arquata*, resident and winter visitor, very common, increasing as nesting species
Whimbrel	*Numenius phaeopus*, passage migrant, common in small numbers
Black-tailed godwit	*Limosa limosa*, winter visitor and passage migrant, quite common recently
Bar-tailed godwit	*Limosa lapponica*, passage migrant and winter visitor, non-breeding summer visitor, common, increasing
Green sandpiper	*Tringa ochropus*, passage migrant and winter visitor, regular in small parties
Wood sandpiper	*Tringa glareola*, passage migrant, regular small numbers

Common sandpiper	*Tringa hypoleucos*, summer visitor, passage migrant and winter visitor, breeds, few in Devon and declining, common on passage migration
Redshank	*Tringa totanus*, resident and winter visitor, very common, few breed in Devon and possibly Cornwall
Spotted redshank	*Tringa erythropus*, passage migrant and winter visitor, fairly common small numbers, increasing
Lesser yellowlegs	*Tringa flavipes*, annual autumn vagrant
Greenshank	*Tringa nebularia*, passage migrant and winter visitor, small numbers, fairly common, increasing
Knot	*Calidris canutus*, winter visitor and passage migrant, common, increasing
Purple sandpiper	*Calidris maritima*, winter visitor, locally common, small numbers
Little stint	*Calidris minuta*, passage migrant, regular but not common
Pectoral sandpiper	*Calidris melanotos*, vagrant but commonest American wader in Britain
Dunlin	*Calidris alpina*, resident, passage migrant and winter visitor, few breed (Cornwall is most southerly breeding site for species in British Isles), mainly winter visitor and passage migrant, very common
Curlew sandpiper	*Calidris ferruginea*, irregular but fairly common passage migrant
Sanderling	*Calidris alba*, passage migrant, winter visitor and non-breeding summer visitor, small numbers, usually fairly common
Buff-breasted sandpiper	*Tryngites subruficollis*, almost annual vagrant
Ruff	*Philomachus pugnax*, winter visitor and passage migrant, regular small numbers
Avocet	*Recurvirostra avosetta*, winter visitor, not common but increasing
Black-winged stilt	*Himantopus himantopus*, vagrant
Grey phalarope	*Phalaropus fulicarius*, passage migrant, uncommon, sometimes 'wrecked'
Red-necked phalarope	*Phalaropus lobatus*, vagrant
Stone curlew	*Burhinus oedicnemus*, vagrant
Pratincole	*Glareola pratincola*, vagrant
Arctic skua	*Stercorarius parasiticus*, passage migrant, pelagic, small numbers
Great skua	*Stercorarius skua*, irregular visitors
Pomarine skua	*Stercorarius pomarinus*, irregular visitor

Long-tailed skua	*Stercorarius longicaudus*, vagrant
Great black-backed gull	*Larus marinus*, resident and winter visitor, breeds, common, increasing
Lesser black-backed gull	*Larus fuscus*, summer visitor and passage migrant, breeds (not commonly), mainly passage migrant
Herring gull	*Larus argentatus*, resident, breeds, very common
Common gull	*Larus canus*, abundant winter visitor and passage migrant
Glaucous gull	*Larus hyperboreus*, scarce and irregular winter visitor
Iceland gull	*Larus glaucoides*, scarce and irregular winter visitor
Mediterranean Gull	*Larus melanocephalus*, vagrant
Little gull	*Larus minutus*, passage migrant and winter visitor, not common but regular
Black-headed gull	*Larus ridibundus*, resident and winter visitor, irregular breeder, common winter visitor and passage migrant
Sabine's gull	*Larus sabini*, annual vagrant
Kittiwake	*Rissa tridactyla*, resident, breeds, common, increasing
Black tern	*Chlidonias niger*, passage migrant, uncommon Cornwall, regular Devon
Common tern	*Sterna hirundo*, passage migrant, has bred Devon, still breeds on Scilly, few remain for summer in Cornwall and Devon, most common April to October
Arctic tern	*Sterna paradisea*, passage migrant, not common
Roseate tern	*Sterna dougallii*, passage migrant, few breed on Scilly, rare on mainland, most off West Cornwall
Little tern	*Sterna albifrons*, passage migrant, regular but few
Sandwich tern	*Sterna sandvicensis*, passage migrant, formerly bred Scilly, common passage migrant, increasing in Devon
Razorbill	*Alca torda*, resident, breeds, common but decreasing
Little auk	*Plautus alle*, rare but recorded most years, sometimes 'wrecked', irregular winter visitor
Guillemot	*Uria aalga*, resident, breeds, common but decreasing
Black guillemot	*Cepphus grylle*, vagrant
Puffin	*Fratercula arctica*, resident, breeds, fairly common but rapidly declining
Stock dove	*Columba oenas*, resident and winter visitor, breeds, fairly common spreading west
Rock dove	*Columba livia*, formerly resident and bred in Devon, few pure-bred birds in Cornwall

Wood pigeon	*Columba palumbus*, resident and winter visitor, very common
Turtle dove	*Streptopelia turtur*, summer visitor, breeds, never common
Collared dove	*Streptopelia decaocto*, resident, common, increasing, breeds
Cuckoo	*Cuculus canorus*, summer visitor, breeds, common, probably increasing last two years after decline
Barn owl	*Tyto alba*, resident, breeds, never common and decreasing in Cornwall, widespread outside breeding season
Little owl	*Athene noctua*, resident, breeds, very local, not common, probably decreasing
Tawny owl	*Strix aluco*, resident, breeds, common
Long-eared owl	*Asio otus*, irregular visitor, may have bred in Devon
Short-eared owl	*Asio flammeus*, winter visitor and passage migrant, has bred in small numbers
Nightjar	*Caprimulgus europaeus*, summer visitor, breeds locally, quite common but decreasing
Swift	*Apus apus*, summer visitor, breeds, common
Kingfisher	*Alcedo atthis*, resident, breeds, widely distributed, probably stable population, never common
Hoopoe	*Upupa epops*, passage migrant, frequent records, single birds mostly, spring passage
Green woodpecker	*Picus viridis*, resident, breeds, common
Great spotted woodpecker	*Dendrocopos major*, resident, breeds fairly common in Devon, rarer in Cornwall
Lesser spotted woodpecker	*Dendrocopos minor*, resident, breeds, not very common, very few breed in Cornwall
Wryneck	*Jynx torquilla*, scarce passage migrant, has bred, rarely overwinters
Woodlark	*Lullula arborea*, resident, breeds, decreasing, thinly distributed Devon, rarely breeds Cornwall, some passage migrants
Skylark	*Alauda arvensis*, resident and winter visitor, breeds, common
Swallow	*Hirundo rustica*, summer visitor and passage migrant, breeds
House martin	*Delichon urbica*, summer visitor, breeds, common
Sand martin	*Riparia riparia*, summer visitor, breeds, common but local

Golden oriole	*Oriolus oriolus*, irregular spring passage migrant, has bred in Devon
Raven	*Corvus corax*, resident, breeds, fairly common
Carrion crow	*Corvus corone*, resident, breeds, common
Hooded crow	*Corvus cornix*, irregular visitor
Rook	*Corvus frugilegus*, resident, common, breeds
Jackdaw	*Corvus monedula*, resident, breeds, common
Magpie	*Pica pica*, resident, abundant, breeds
Jay	*Garrulus glandarius*, resident, breeds, fairly common
Chough	*Pyrrhocorax pyrrhocorax*, vagrant in Devon, formerly bred, one individual until recently resident in Cornwall
Great tit	*Parus major*, resident, breeds, common
Blue tit	*Parus caeruleus*, resident, breed, common
Coal tit	*Parus ater*, resident, breeds, common probably increasing
Marsh tit	*Parus palustris*, resident, breeds, fairly common
Willow tit	*Parus montanus*, resident, breeds, rather local, not common
Long-tailed tit	*Aegithalos caudatus*, resident, breeds, fairly common
Bearded tit	*Panurus biarmicus*, vagrant, formerly bred in Devon
Nuthatch	*Sitta europaea*, resident, breeds, fairly common
Tree creeper	*Certhia familiaris*, resident, breeds, common
Wren	*Troglodytes troglodytes*, resident, breeds, common
Dipper	*Cinclus cinclus*, resident, breeds, common
Mistle thrush	*Turdus viscivorus*, resident, breeds, common
Fieldfare	*Turdus pilaris*, winter visitor, regular, common
Song thrush	*Turdus philomelos*, resident and winter visitor, breeds, common
Redwing	*Turdus iliacus*, winter visitor, common
Ring ouzel	*Turdus torquatus*, summer visitor, breeds, well distributed
Blackbird	*Turdus merula*, resident and winter visitor, breeds, very common
Wheatear	*Oenanthe oenanthe*, summer visitor, breeds, fairly common locally
Stonechat	*Saxicola torquata*, resident, breeds, locally quite common
Whinchat	*Saxicola rubetra*, summer visitor, breeds, not uncommon
Redstart	*Phoenicurus phoenicurus*, summer visitor, breeds, in-

	creasing and spreading from Devon to Cornwall where they breed in east
Black redstart	*Phoenicurus ochruros*, passage migrant and winter visitor, has bred, regular in small numbers
Nightingale	*Luscinia megarhynchos*, summer visitor, breeds Devon, very rare Cornwall, passage migrant, eg Porthgwarra
Bluethroat	*Cyanosylvia svecica*, rather scarce passage migrant
Robin	*Erithacus rubecula*, resident, breeds, common, autumn immigration
Grasshopper warbler	*Locustella naevia*, summer visitor, breeds, fairly common locally, increasing
Reed warbler	*Acrocephalus scirpaceus*, summer visitor, breeds, passage migrant, extending range, not common in Cornwall, widely distributed in Devon
Marsh warbler	*Acrocephalus palustris*, vagrant, breeds sporadically, scarce summer visitor
Sedge warbler	*Acrocephalus schoenobaenus*, summer visitor, breeds, locally common
Melodious warbler	*Hippolais polyglotta*, scarce passage migrant (mainly autumn)
Icterine warbler	*Hippolais icterina*, scarce passage migrant
Blackcap	*Sylvia atricapilla*, summer visitor, breeds, some over-winter, fairly common and increasing
Garden warbler	*Sylvia borin*, summer visitor, breeds, less common than blackcap and rare in Cornwall
Whitethroat	*Sylvia communis*, summer visitor, breeds, common
Lesser whitethroat	*Sylvia curruca*, summer visitor, breeds increasing but scarce
Dartford warbler	*Sylvia undata*, resident, breeds, Devon, very rare
Willow warbler	*Phylloscopus trochilis*, summer visitor and passage migrant, breeds, common
Chiff-chaff	*Phylloscopus collybita*, summer visitor and passage migrant, breeds, common, few in winter
Wood warbler	*Phylloscopus sibilatrix*, summer visitor, breeds, locally common
Goldcrest	*Regulus regulus*, resident and winter visitor, breeds, common, increasing
Firecrest	*Regulus ignicapillus*, passage migrant and winter visitor, widespread in small numbers in winter, most on autumn passage

Spotted flycatcher	*Muscicapa stricta*, summer visitor, breeds, fairly common
Pied flycatcher	*Ficedula hypoleuca*, summer visitor, breeds, regular on spring and autumn passage; small numbers breed regularly now in Cornwall
Red-breasted flycatcher	*Ficedula parva*, scarce passage migrant mainly on Lundy
Dunnock	*Prunella modularis*, resident, breeds, common
Meadow pipit	*Anthus pratensis*, resident and winter visitor, breeds, common
Tree pipit	*Anthus trivialis*, summer visitor, breeds, regular but not abundant, less in west
Rock and water pipits	*Anthus spinoletta petrosus*, resident, breeds, common *Anthus spinoletta spinoletta*, passage migrant, rare visitor, not common
Pied and white wagtails	*Motacilla alba* (a) *Motacilla alba yarrellii*, resident and passage migrant, breeds common (b) *Motacilla alba alba*, passage migrant, has bred (Lundy), local, small numbers
Grey wagtail	*Motacilla cinerea*, resident, breeds, common
Yellow and blue-headed wagtails	*Montacilla flava* (a) summer visitor and passage migrant, breeds, local breeder but common passage migrant (b) passage migrant, has bred, scarce and irregular
Waxwing	*Bombycilla garrulus*, irregular winter visitor
Great grey shrike	*Lanius excubitor*, irregular winter visitor
Red-backed shrike	*Lanius collurio*, scarce summer visitor, breeds, also irregular passage migrant
Starling	*Sturnus vulgaris*, resident and winter visitor, breeds, common, increasing
Hawfinch	*Coccothraustes coccothraustes*, resident and winter visitor, breeds rarely and irregularly
Greenfinch	*Carduelis chloris*, resident and winter visitor, breeds, common
Goldfinch	*Carduelis carduelis*, resident, breeds, common
Siskin	*Carduelis spinus*, resident and winter visitor, breeds, fairly common, locally increasing in Devon, on autumn passage in Cornwall
Linnet	*Acanthis cannabina*, resident and winter visitor, breeds, common
Twite	*Acanthis flavirostris*, vagrant, has bred, decreasing

Lesser redpoll	*Acanthis flammea*, resident and winter visitor, breeds, recently increasing but still uncommon, now breeds in Cornwall since 1968
Serin	*Serinus serinus*, vagrant
Bullfinch	*Pyrrhula pyrrhula*, resident, breeds, common
Crossbill	*Loxia curvirostra*, irregular visitor, breeds sporadically
Chaffinch	*Fringilla coelebs*, resident, winter visitor and passage migrant, breeds, common
Brambling	*Fringilla montifringilla*, winter visitor, occasionally large flocks, normally small numbers
Yellowhammer	*Emberiza citrinella*, resident, breeds, common
Corn bunting	*Emberiza calandra*, resident, breeds irregularly, increasing locally in West Cornwall but declining in Somerset
Cirl bunting	*Emberiza cirlus*, resident, breeds, coastal, not common but probably increasing
Ortolan bunting	*Emberiza hortulana*, passage migrant, regular now on Lundy, very few on mainland
Reed bunting	*Emberiza schoeniclus*, resident, breeds, fairly common
Lapland bunting	*Calcarius lapponicus*, passage migrant, regular on Lundy, few on mainland
Snow bunting	*Plectrophenax nivalis*, passage migrant and winter visitor, small numbers but regular
House sparrow	*Passer domesticus*, resident, breeds, common
Tree sparrow	*Passer montanus*, winter visitor, breeds sporadically, regular but uncommon winter visitor

Bird migration in the South West

The following list, which is probably typical, is based on observations at Porthgwarra S W 3721 Cornwall, by members of the Cornwall Bird Watching and Preservation Society. The list of species is not comprehensive but indicates what may be seen and roughly when.

Spring passage	
End February	Lesser black-backed gull
Early to mid-March	Wheatear
	Chiff-chaff
Early April	Sand Martin
	Swallow

	Willow warbler/chiff-chaff
	Wheatear
	Blackcap
	Goldcrest
	Redstart
Mid-April	Whitethroat
	Grasshopper warbler
	House martin
	Redstart
	Corn bunting
	Ring ouzel
End April	Whitethroat
	Swallow
	Turtle dove
	Spotted redshank
	Yellow wagtail
	Cuckoo
	Swift
	Sedge warbler
Mid-May	Spotted flycatcher
	Swift
	Yellow wagtail
	Turtle dove
	Sedge warbler
	Whitethroat

End May, still considerable migration
Autumn migration, start in early August

Mid-August	Wheatear
	Swift
	Pied flycatcher
	Redstart
	Yellow wagtail
	Chiff-chaff
	'Waders'
	Whitethroat
	Linnet
	Goldfinch
Late August	Tawny pipit
	Hobby
	Golden plover
	Sandwich tern
	Swift

	Swallow
	Martin
	Tree and meadow pipit
	Yellow wagtail
	Whitethroat
	Garden warbler
	Phylloscopus warblers (mainly willow warbler and chiff-chaff)
	Pied and spotted flycatchers
	Wheatear
	Redstart
	Crossbill
	Montagu's harrier
	Merlin
	Reed warbler
Early September	Similar to above but also:
	Hippolais warblers
	Sooty shearwater
	Woodwarbler
	Spotted crake
	Melodious warbler
	Richard's pipit
Early October	Ring ouzel
	Short-eared owl
	Firecrest
	Mistle thrush
	Snow bunting
	Brambling
Mid-October	Fieldfare
	Redwing
	Redpoll
	Firecrest
	Blue and great tits
	Goldcrest
	Chiff-chaff
	Red-breasted flycatcher
	Pied flycatcher
	Black and common redstarts
	Lesser whitethroat
	Blackcap
	Baltimore oriole
	Yellow-browed warbler

	Great grey shrike
	Barred warbler
End October, late migrants and winter visitors	
	Many chaffinch
	Brambling
	Siskin
	Starling
	Long-tailed tit
	Richard's pipit
	Redpoll
	Ortolan bunting
November	Lapland bunting
	Common tern
	Little auk
	Short-eared owl

Birds of the Isles of Scilly (based on H. M. Quick *Birds of the Scilly Isles*)

Bird watching: Main seasons or months for watching

March: small passerine migrants arrive

April: very good month for migrant waders but few by the end of the month

May: swifts, spotted flycatchers, golden oriole, whinchat, ortolan bunting

June: sea birds very good—nesting

July to August: quiet months for birds on Scilly, some return passage migrants

September to October: very good months, many passerines and waders going through: American pectoral sandpiper, red-breasted flycatcher, Lapland and ortolan buntings, tawny pipit, curlew, sandpipers, little stint, purple sandpiper. Some at least will be seen—if not all.

Where to watch:

(a) St Mary's:
Lower and Upper Moors, marshy ground; Bar-Point, good for waders at times; Peninnis Point, wheatears and other migrants and for sea watching.

(b) Bryher:
Rushy Pool, waders at times.

(c) Tresco:
Sandy shores for waders; Great Pool and Abbey Pool, duck and waders; Moorland at north end.

(d) St Agnes: on which is the former bird observatory in the old lighthouse:
Priglis and Per'killier beaches, excellent for waders in autumn, often unusual birds on St Agnes.

(e) Sampson Hill: at south end colony of lesser black-backed gulls:
Best out of tourist season; pleasure boats from St Mary's will leave most days in good weather to take people to the four 'off Islands' and collect them at the end of the day.

Breeding birds (*Scilly*): residents and summer visitors are included:

Resident

Cormorants } proportion shag:
Shag } cormorant 50:1
Mallard
Teal
Gadwall
Shoveler
Shelduck
Mute swan
Kestrel—few
Water rail
Moorhen
Coot
Oystercatcher
Ringed plover
Great black-backed gull
Herring gull
Wood pigeon
Skylark
Wren
Songthrush
Blackbird
Stonechat
Robin
Goldcrest
Hedge sparrow
Rock pipit
Starling
Greenfinch
Goldfinch
Linnet
Chaffinch
House sparrow
Carrion crow—few on St Mary's

Summer visitors

Storm petrel*
Manx shearwater*
Fulmar
Lesser black-backed gulls early February
Kittiwake—end of March
Common tern ..about 23 April
Roseate tern..from West Africa
Razorbill*
Guillemot*
Puffin*
Turtle Dove
Cuckoo
Swift
Swallow
Wheatear
Sedge warbler
Willow warbler } some possibly
Chiff-chaff } overwinter

* All arrive off Bishop Rock about March 25

Resident	*Summer visitors*
Great tit } few	
Blue tit }	

Species absent including:

Raven	Owls
Rook	Yellowhammer
Jackdaw	Corn bunting
Magpie (occasionally)	Reed bunting
Jay	Bullfinch
Woodpecker	Mistle thrush
Nuthatch	Coal tit
Treecreeper	Long-tailed tit

Birds seen from cliff tops

An example of what may be seen from good cliff observation points in the South West based on sea watches and migrant studies at Prawle Point. This is the most southerly point in Devon. Based on reports in *Devon Birds.*

Resident	Buzzard, kestrel, raven, cirl bunting, yellowhammer
Autumn passage migrants mainly after east winds followed by calm clear weather; best in the early morning	Willow warbler, chiff-chaff, whitethroat, garden warbler, blackcap, grasshopper warbler, pied flycatcher, tree pipit, whinchat, wheatear
Coastal passage migrants	Wagtails, pipits and swallows usually moving west
Waders peak migration: early to mid-september	Oystercatchers, turnstone, curlew, whimbrel, dunlin, redshank, spotted redshank, common sandpiper, grey plover, knot, bar-tailed godwit
Sea birds	Gannet, kittiwake, terns, herring gull, common gull and black-headed gull, latter often seen moving west in evenings to roost near Salcombe. Shags also common after gales in September, good for westerly passage of sea birds; gannet, sandwich tern, great and Arctic skua, kittiwake, lesser black-backed gull, manx shearwater, common and Arctic tern, razorbill, guillemot

Mammals

Common and scientific names as used in *The Handbook of British Mammals*, Southern (ed).

Insectivores

Hedgehog *Erinaceus europaeus*, quite common but not abundant
Mole *Talpa europaea*, common but not on heathland
Common shrew *Sorex araneus*, common
Pygmy shrew *Sorex minutus*, locally very common
Water shrew *Neomys fodiens*, probably common, sometimes found on heathland amongst heather
Lesser white-toothed shrew *Crocidura suaveolens cassiteridum*, widely distributed on Scilly Isles in variety of habitats but prefers heathland

Chiropterans

Greater horseshoe bat *Rhinolophus ferrumequinum*, locally common, particularly in limestone caves in Devon
Lesser horseshoe bat *Rhinolophus hipposideros*, locally common
Whiskered bat *Myotis mystacinus*, probably fairly common
Natterer's bat *Myotis nattereri*, probably fairly common
Bechstein's bat *Myotis bechsteini*, rare but recorded from Somerset
Daubenton's bat *Myotis daubentoni*, locally common
Parti-coloured bat *Vespertilio murinus*, recorded from Plymouth early in the last century only
Serotine *Eptesicus serotinus*, locally fairly common
Leisler's bat *Nyctalus leisleri*, rare but recorded from both Somerset and Devon
Noctule *Nyctalus noctula*, common
Pipistrelle *Pipistrellus pipistrellus*, commonest bat
Barbastelle *Barbastella barbastellus*, probably not common
Long-eared bat *Plecotus auritus*, probably fairly common

Lagomorphs

Rabbit *Oryctolagus cuniculus*, seems to be re-establishing itself after myxomatosis but local populations often quickly reduced by the disease which flares up sporadically
Hare *Lepus europaeus*, very rare in Cornwall in 1955 survey but since have increased on sand dunes and old airfields, widespread elsewhere and increasing in Cornwall

Rodents

Red squirrel *Sciurus vulgaris*, widespread in Cornwall, small numbers locally increasing perhaps

American grey squirrel *Sciurus carolinensis*, common
Bank vole *Clethrionomys glareolus*, quite common but numbers fluctuate, not found on Lundy or Scilly
Short-tailed vole *Microtus agrestis*, very common but not found on Lundy or Scilly
Water vole *Arvicola amphibius*, common in suitable habitats
Wood mouse *Apodemus sylvaticus*, very common on mainland but only found on St Mary's and Tresco in the Scilly Isles and absent from Lundy
Yellow-necked mouse *Apodemus flavicollis*, not recorded from Devon or Cornwall but may be present if looked for
Harvest mouse *Micromys minutus*, still fairly common
House mouse *Mus musculus*, seems to be not very common in Cornwall
Black rat *Rattus rattus*, still present on Lundy and possibly around ports on the mainland
Brown rat *Rattus norvegicus*, very common on agricultural land and water courses, seems to increase as effluent increases
Dormouse *Muscardinus avellanarius*, a rare and seemingly declining species now

Carnivores

Red fox *Vulpes vulpes*, very common, sometimes seen on shores
Stoat *Mustela erminea*, not very common since decline of rabbits but seen occasionally and possibly increasing: absent from Lundy and Scilly
Weasel *Mustela nivalis*, widespread but seldom common although more so than stoat. Not found on Lundy or Scilly
American mink *Mustela vison*, well established in Devon and Cornwall as far as Land's End and still increasing
Polecat *Mustela putorius*, may still be a few wild in Devon and Cornwall
Badger *Meles meles*, very common in most places
Otter *Lutra lutra*, seems to be declining although still said to be fairly common in north-east Cornwall. Frequently this is a coastal species in the South West
Grey seal *Halichoerus grypus*, fairly common off rocky shores, breeds in North Cornwall, Scilly and Lundy

Artiodactyls

Muntjac *Muntiacus* spp, probably more common than records suggest, may be increasing
Fallow deer *Dama dama*, some in parks others now feral and increasing in wooded areas
Red deer *Cervus elaphus*, widespread and probably still spreading from main centre of population on Exmoor, should become increasingly common in the area

Sika deer *Cervus nippon*, feral herds in Devon and Somerset also probably soon in Cornwall

Roe deer *Capreolus capreolus*, widespread in Devon and have spread into East Cornwall, probably will continue to increase range in Forestry Commission and similar plantations

Wild goat *Capra hircus*, feral herds on Lundy and one on Land's End peninsula

Cetaceans

Killer whale *Orcinus orca*, sometimes seen off shore

Common porpoise *Phocoena phocoena*, the most commonly seen cetacean

Lesser rorqual *Balaenoptera acutorostrata*, seems to migrate down north coast of our region

Common rorqual *Balaenoptera physalus*, some strandings but probably less common than at beginning of century

Pilot whale *Globicephala melaena*, rarely stranded although perhaps not uncommon

Bottle-nosed whale *Hyperoodon ampullatus*, stranded occasionally

Risso's dolphin *Grampus griseus*, sometimes stranded on south and west coasts

Euphrosyne dolphin *Stenella styx*, very rare indeed but stranded sometimes in extreme South West

Bottle-nosed dolphin *Tursiops truncatus*, fairly frequent in English Channel

Common dolphin *Delphinus delphis*, the most common dolphin seen off shore

White-sided dolphin *Lagenorhynchus acutus*, rarely stranded, but one injured washed in at Gwithian near Hayle in September 1970

White-beaked dolphin *Lagenorhynchus albirostris*, possibly quite common

Common mainland species of plants

The following list is composed of species that, although not generally common in the British Isles, are so common that no distribution records are needed locally for them as all are of widespread distribution in suitable habitats in the south-west peninsula. The species list is a modified version of that published by Camborne and Redruth Natural History Society in their journal of 1969.

Common names are those used in Collins' *Pocket Guide to Wildflowers* by McClintock & Fisher (1955) and the star system has also been adopted from that publication. This indicates the degree of rarity of the species mentioned as a wild plant in the British Isles as a whole. One star indicates that the plant is only locally common, two stars indicates a scarce plant growing in a limited area while three stars indicates a real rarity as far as the other parts of the British Isles is concerned.

The flowering period is given for each species mentioned (or spore production time for ferns) but plants may be found in flower outside the limits set which is only an average. A star indicates after a month that flowering continues probably until frosts, or right through the winter sometimes in the sheltered areas.

Habitats in which the plants are usually found are also given but it must be remembered that this is only a rough guide and plants may be found in habitats other than the ones indicated for each species by a tick.

Records for other species should be sent to the county recorder concerned via the appropriate naturalists trust or natural history society for the area. Details of the addresses will be found on p 282–3.

Q

	Common name	Flowering period	Habitats
**Achillea ptarmica*	sneezewort	Jun, Jul, Aug	Heath, bog, marsh
**Agropyron pungens*	sea couch	Jun, Jul, Aug, Sept	Cliff, salt marsh
**Agrostis setacea*	bristle bent	May, Jun, Jul	Heath
***Allium triquetrum*	three-cornered leek	Apr, May, Jun	Dunes, hedge
**Anagallis tenella*	bog pimpernel	Jun, Jul, Aug	Bog, wet cliff
Anthyllis vulneraria	kidney vetch	May, Jun, Jul, Aug*	Cliff, grassland
Armeria maritima	thrift	May, Jun, Jul, Aug*	Marsh, cliff, salt marsh
Asplenium adiantum-nigrum	black spleenwort	Jun, Jul, Aug*	Hedge
**A. marinum*	sea spleenwort	Jun, Jul, Aug, Sept (spores)	Cliff, old buildings
Aster tripolium	sea aster	Jul, Aug, Sept*	Salt marsh
Athyrium filix-femina	lady fern	Jul, Aug (spores)	Woodlands, hedge
***Barbarea verna*	American land cress	Apr, May, Jun	Hedge, wasteland
Betonica officinalis	betony	Jun, Jul, Aug, Sept*	Heath, cliff, hedge
Blechnum spicant	hard fern	Jun, Jul, Aug (spores)	Heath, woodlands
**Calamintha ascendens*	common calamint	Jul, Aug, Sept	Wasteland, grassland
Calluna vulgaris	ling	Aug, Sept	Heath, cliff, hedge, woodland
**Carduus tenuiflorus*	seaside thistle	May, Jun, Jul, Aug	Dunes, cliff, wasteland, grassland
Carex paniculata	tussock sedge	May, Jun	Marsh, woodlands
***Catapodium marinum*	darnel fescue	May, Jun, Jul	Cliff
**C. rigidum*	fern grass	May, Jun, Jul, Aug, Sept	Cliff
Centranthus ruber	red valerian	May, Jun, Jul, Aug*	Cliff, hedge, wasteland
**Cerastium atrovirens*	dark green mouse ear	Apr, May, Jun, Jul	Cliff, wasteland

	Common name	Flowering period	Habitats
★Chamaemelum nobile	common chamomile	Jun, Jul, Aug	Heath, grassland
★Chrysanthemum parthenium	feverfew	Jul, Aug, Sept★	Hedge, wasteland, farmland
★C. segetum	corn marigold	Jun, Jul, Aug★	Wasteland, farmland
★Chrysosplenium oppositifolium	golden saxifrage	Mar, Apr, May	Marsh, woodlands, hedge
★Cichorium intybus	chicory	Jun, Jul, Aug★	Wasteland, grassland
Cochlearia danica	early scurvy grass	Feb, Mar, Apr, May, Jun, Jul, Aug, Sept	Dunes, cliff, shore, hedge
★Coronopus didymus	slender wart cress	May, Jun, Jul, Aug, Sept	Hedge, wasteland, farmland
★Crithmum maritimum	rock samphire	Jun, Aug, Sept	Cliff
★★Crocosmia x *crocosmiflora*	montbretia	Jun, Aug	Cliff, hedge, wasteland
★Cuscuta epithymum	common dodder	Jun, Aug, Sept	Heath, sand dunes
Cymbalaria muralis	ivy-leaved toadflax	Apr, May, Jun, Jul, Aug★	Hedge
Dactylorchis maculata	heath spotted orchid	May, Jun, Jul	Heath, bog
★D. praetermissa	marsh orchid	Jun, Jul	Marsh, dunes,
Daucus carota spp *gummifer*	wild carrot	Jun, Jul★	Cliff
and spp *carota*		Jun, Jul★	Dunes, cliff, grassland
Deschampsia cespitosa	tufted hair grass	May, Jun, Jul	Heath, woodland, wasteland, farmland
Digitalis purpurea	foxglove	Jun, Jul, Aug, Sept	Woodlands, hedge, wasteland
★Drosera rotundifolia	common sundew	Jun, Jul, Aug	Heath, bog
★Dryopteris borreri	golden-scaled male fern	Jul, Aug (spores)	Woodlands, hedge

★*Eleocharis multicaulis*	many-stalked spike rush	Jul, Aug	Bog
★*Epilobium adnatum*	square-stemmed willow herb	Jul, Aug	Marsh, woodlands
★*E. lanceolatum*	spear-leaved willow herb	Jul, Aug★	Hedge, wasteland
Erica cinerea	bell heather	May, Jun, Jul, Aug★	Heath, hedge
E. tetralix	crossleaved heath	Jun, Jul, Aug★	Heath, bog
Eriophorum angustifolium	common cotton grass	Apr, May	Heath, bog
★★*Erodium maritimum*	sea storksbill	May, Jun, Jul, Aug	Dunes, wasteland, grassland
Foeniculum vulgare	fennel	Jul, Aug★	Hedge, wasteland, farmland
Fumaria bastardii	fumitory	May, Jun, Jul★	Wasteland, farmland
F. muralis spp *boraei*		May, Jun, Jul★	Hedge, wasteland, farmland
★*Geranium columbinum*	long-stalked cranesbill	May, Jun, Jul, Aug★	Hedge, grassland
★★*G. versicolor*	pencilled cranesbill	May, Jun, Jul	Hedge, grassland
★★*Helxine sloeirolii*	mind your own business	May, Jun, Jul, Aug	Hedge, wasteland
Hydrocotyle vulgaris	marsh pennywort	Jun, Jul, Aug	Heath, bog, marsh, dune, slack
★*Hypericum androsaemum*	tutsan	Jun, Jul, Aug	Cliffs, woodlands, hedge
★*H. elodes*	marsh St John's wort	Jun, Jul, Aug, Sept	Bog, marsh, freshwater
★*Impatiens glandulifera*	Himalayan balsam	Jun, Jul, Aug★	Marsh, freshwater, wasteland
★*Iris foetidissima*	roast beef plant	Jun	Dunes, cliffs, wasteland
★*Jasione montana*	sheep's bit	Mar, Apr, May★	Heath, cliffs, grassland, hedge
★*Kickxia elatine*	sharp-leaved fluellen	Jul, Aug★	Hedge, wasteland, farmland

	Common name	Flowering period	Habitats
***Lavatera arborea*	tree mallow	Jul, Aug, Sept	Cliffs, hedge, wasteland
**Lepidium heterophyllum*	Smith's peppercress	May, Jun, Jul, Aug	Hedge, wasteland, farmland, grassland
**Linum bienne*	pale flax	May, Jun, Jul, Aug, Sept	Heath, wasteland, grassland
**Lithospermum officinale*	common gromwell	Jun, Jul	Dunes, hedge
Lotus corniculatus	birdsfoot trefoil	May, Jun, Jul, Aug*	Dunes, cliffs, grassland
Luzula multiflora	heath woodrush	May, Jun	Heath, woodlands
L. sylvatica	great woodrush	Jun, Jul	Woodlands
Lythrum salicaria	purple loosestrife	Jul, Aug	Marsh, freshwater
**Medicago arabica*	spotted medick	Apr, May, Jun, Jul, Aug, Sept	Dunes, cliffs, wasteland, farmland
Melampyrum pratense	common cow wheat	May, Jun, Jul, Aug, Sept	Woodlands
***Melissa officinalis*	balm	Jul, Aug, Sept	Hedge, wasteland
Molinia caerulea	purple moor grass	Jul, Aug, Sept	Heath, marsh
Nardus stricta	mat grass	Jun, Jul, Aug	Heath, bog
**Narthecium ossifragrum*	bog asphodel	Jul, Aug	Heath, bog
**Oenanthe crocata*	hemlock water dropwort	Jul, Aug, Sept	Marsh, freshwater
**Oenothera erythrosepala*	large evening primrose	Jun, Jul, Aug*	Dunes, hedge, wasteland
Orchis mascula	early purple orchid	Apr, May, Jun	Woodland, hedge, grassland
**Oxalis corniculata*	sleeping beauty	May, Jun, Jul, Aug, Sept	Wasteland, farmland
***Parentucellia viscosa*	yellow bartsia	Jun, Jul, Aug*	Wet grassland, dune, slacks

Parietaria diffusa	pellitory of the wall	Jun, Jul*	Hedge
Pedicularis sylvatica	lousewort	May, Jun, Jul, Aug, Sept	Heath, bog, marsh
**Pentaglottis sempervirens*	green alkanet	Apr, May*	Hedge, wasteland
Petasites fragrans	winter-flowering heliotrope	Jan, Feb, Mar, Nov, Dec	Hedge, wasteland
Phyllitis scolopendrium	hart's tongue fern	Jul, Aug (spores)	Woodland, hedge, cliff
Plantago coronopus	buck's horn plantain	May, Jun, Jul	Dunes, cliffs, salt marsh
P. maritima	sea plantain	Jun, Jul, Aug	Cliffs, shore, salt marsh
Polygala serpyllifolia	heath milkwort	May, Jun, Jul, Aug*	Heath, grassland
P. vulgaris	common milkwort	May, Jun*	Grassland
**Polygonum cuspidatum*	Japanese knotweed	Sept, Oct	Hedge, wasteland
**Polystichum setiferum*	soft shield fern	Jul, Aug (spores)	Woodland, hedge
**Potentilla anglica*	trailing tormentil	May, Jun, Jul*	Heath, grassland
P. erecta	tormentil	May, Jun, Jul*	Heath, cliffs, grassland
Primula veris	cowslip	Apr, May	Heath, dunes, hedge, grass-land
P. vulgaris	primrose	Mar, Apr, May	Woodland, hedge, grassland
Prunus spinosa	blackthorn	Apr, May	Cliffs, woodland, hedge, wasteland
***Quercus cerris*	Turkey oak		Woodland
Q. ilex	holm oak		Hedge
**Ranunculus lenormandii*	Lenormande's buttercup	Mar, Apr,May, Jun, Jul, Aug	Freshwater
**Rosa pimpinellifolia*	burnet rose	May, Jun, Jul	Heath, dunes, cliffs, grassland
**Rubia perigrina*	wild madder	Jun, Jul, Aug	Heath, cliffs
**Sagina maritima*	sea pearlwort	Jun, Jul, Aug, Sept	Heath, cliffs, grassland

	Common name	*Flowering period*	*Habitat*
Salicornia agg	glasswort	Aug, Sept	Shore, salt marsh
Saponaria officinalis	soapwort	Jul, Aug, Sept	Hedge, wasteland
★★*Sarothamnus scoparius* spp *maritimus*	broom (prostrate variety)	May, Jun	Cliffs
★*Scilla verna*	vernal squill	Apr, May, Jun	Heath, cliff, grassland
★*Scirpus cernuus*	small bristle club rush	May, Jun, Jul	Heath, bog, cliffs, grassland
S. fluitans	floating spike rush	May, Jun, Jul, Aug, Sept	Freshwater
★*S. setaceus*	bristle club rush	May, Jun, Jul	Marsh, freshwater
★*Scutellaria minor*	lesser skullcap	Jul, Aug★	Damp heath
Sedum acre	wall pepper	Jun, Jul	Dunes, cliffs, wasteland
★*Sedum anglicum*	English stonecrop	Jun, Jul, Aug	Freshwater, dunes, cliffs
★*Serratula tinctoria*	sawwort	Jul, Aug, Sept	Heath, cliffs, grassland
★*Silene gallica*	small-flowered catchfly	Jun, Jul★	Wasteland, farmland
S. maritima	sea campion	Jun, Jul, Aug	Dunes, cliffs, shore, hedge
S. vulgaris	bladder campion	Jun, Jul, Aug	Wasteland, grassland, cliff
★*Smyrnium olustratum*	Alexanders	Apr, May, Jun	Cliffs, hedge, wasteland
★*Solanum nigrum*	black nightshade	Jun, Jul, Aug, Sept	Wasteland, farmland
Solidago virgaurea	golden rod	Jul, Aug, Sept	Heath, hedge
★*Spergularia rupicola*	cliff spurrey	Jun, Jul, Aug, Sept	Cliffs, hedge
★*Stachys arvensis*	field woundwort	Apr, May	Wasteland, farmland, grassland, hedge
★*Symphoricarpos rivularis*	snowberry	Jun, Jul, Aug, Sept	Hedge
★*Tamus communis*	black bryony	May, Jun, Jul★	Woodland, hedge
Teucrium scorodonia	wood sage	Jun, Jul, Aug, Sept	Heath, dunes, hedge

Thymus drucei	wild thyme	Jun, Jul, Aug	Heath, dunes, cliffs, hedge, grassland
⋆*Trifolium media*	zigzag clover	Jun, Jul, Aug	Heath, hedge, grassland
⋆*T. micranthum*	slender yellow trefoil	May, Jun, Jul, Aug	Hedge, grassland
Ulex europaeus	gorse (furze)	Mar, Apr, May, Jun, Jul, Aug, Sept, Oct, Nov⋆	Heath, cliffs, hedge, wasteland, farmland, grassland
⋆*U. gallii*	western gorse (dwarf)	Jul, Aug, Sept	Heath, cliffs, wasteland
Ulmus carponifolia var *cornubiensis*	Cornish smooth elm	Feb, Mar, Apr	Woodlands, hedge, farmland
⋆*Umbilicus rupestris*	wall pennywort	Jun, Jul, Aug	Hedge
Vaccinium myrtillus	bilberry	Apr, May, Jun	Heath, woodlands
Valeriana officinalis	valerian	Jun, Jul, Aug	Hedge, wasteland, grassland
⋆*Verbena officinalis*	vervain	Jun, Jul, Aug, Sept	Wasteland, grassland
⋆⋆*Veronica filiformis*	slender speedwell	Apr, May, Jun	Marsh, grassland
⋆*Vinca major*	greater periwinkle	Mar, Apr, May, Jun, Jul	Wasteland
⋆⋆*V. minor*	lesser periwinkle	Apr, May, Jun, Jul, Aug⋆	Hedge, wasteland

Southern plant species in the South West

Many of the species found are Atlantic species but a few belong to extreme South West Europe, Portugal, North Spain and Atlantic coast further south. These Lusitanian species probably survived the glaciation by maintaining a foothold in south-west England away from the ice fronts.

Lusitanian species

Ranunculus tripartitus	Very rare, April to July; pools
Fumaria martinii	Very rare, cultivated ground
Hypericum undulatum	Wavy-leaved St John's wort, very common, marshy and wet places, July to September
Hypericum linariifolium	Flax-leaved St John's wort, very rare, dry rock banks, June to July
Lotus hispidus	Short-podded bird's foot trefoil, mainland rare, dry banks and pasture near coasts, June to September, frequent Scilly and Lizard
Lobelia urens	Heath lobelia, damp pastures and boggy ground, local and rather rare, August to October
Erica ciliaris	Dorset heath, moorland, July to September
Erica vagans	Cornish heath, introduced Dartmoor, heathland, July to September, locally abundant in Cornwall
Verbascum virgatum (native only in Devon and Cornwall)	Large-flowered mullein, rather rare, dry banks and cliffs, June to September
Scrophularia scorodonia	Balm-leaved figwort, hedges and banks, locally frequent, common Tresco, June to August
Sibthorpia europaea	Cornish moneywort, shady damp places, locally common, June to September
Euphorbia hyberna	Irish spurge, shady woods, very local, June to July
Rumex rupestris	Shore dock, cliffs, local, rather rare, June to September
Agrostis setacea	Bristle-bent grass, very common, heaths and moors, June to July
Wahlenbergia hederacea	Ivy-leaved bellflower

Species with a European distribution

Mecanopsis cambrica	Welsh poppy, rare, dry banks and orchards, May to June
Limonium binervosum	Rock sea lavender, rocky places by sea, local, June to September
Pinguicula lusitanica	Pale butterwort, bogs and marshy places, locally common, June to September

Euphorbia portlandica	Portland spurge, rough cliff and sandy seaside areas, April to September

Plants with a Mediterranean distribution

Mathiola sinuata	Great sea stock, native Devon, naturalised now in Cornwall, sandy beaches and cliffs, May to August
Polycarpon tetraphyllum	Four-leaved all-seed, very rare, dry banks and stony places, frequent Scilly bulb fields and walls, June to July
Geranium purpureum	Little Robin, rare rocky banks and cliffs, May to September
Bupleurum opacum	Hare's ear, Devon only, cornfield weed, rare
Daucus carota sp *gummifer*	Wild carrot, cliffs, common, June to September
Galium debile	Slender marsh bedstraw, Devon (only East), pond margins, very rare
Romulea columnae	Sand crocus, Dawlish Warren on grassy sea slopes, local and very rare in Cornwall, April to May
Lagurus ovatus	Harestail grass, casual Cornwall, also Dawlish Warren in Devon, June to August

All the above species are found in Devon and Cornwall unless otherwise stated.
Cornwall has 51 species that do not occur in Devon;
Devon has 103 species not recorded from Cornwall;
Cornwall has 20 species not recorded from other counties in Britain.

Flora of the Isles of Scilly

Interesting species are found on Scilly during late spring and early summer with probably the best month May. Many of the species listed are found in the bulb fields which are only cultivated after the bulbs have died down. Permission to look for these flowers must be obtained from the owners of the land to avoid the possibility of disease spread.

Bulb fields

Bermuda buttercup	*Oxalis pes-caprae*
Fingered saxifrage	*Saxifraga tridactylites*
Changing forget-me-not	*Myosotis discolor*
Wall speedwell	*Veronica arvensis*
Spring beauty	*Montia perfoliata*
Shepherd's needle	*Scandix pecten-veneris*
Annual mercury	*Mercurialis annua*
Four-leaved all-seed	*Polycarpon tetraphyllum*
Western fumitory	*Fumaria occidentalis*

Scilly buttercup	*Ranunculus muricatus*
Lesser quaking grass	*Briza minor*
Corn marigold	*Chrysanthemum segetum*
Whistling Jacks	*Gladiolus byzantinum*
Rosy garlic	*Allium roseum*
Musk storksbill	*Erodium moschatum*
Toothed medick	*Medicago polymorpha*
Rare lords and ladies	*Arum italicum*
Several species of:	*Mesembryanthemum*
Green nightshade	*Solanum sarrachoides*
Wormwood	*Artemisia absinthium*
Common penny cress	*Thlaspi arvense*
Spanish bluebell	*Endymion hispanicus*
Spanish iris	*Iris xiphium*
Pot purslane	*Portulaca oleracea*

On dunes

African lily	*Agapanthus orientalis*
New Zealand flax	*Phormium tenax*
Babington's leek	*Allium babingtonii*

Flora of the Lizard

Some typical species, many of which are rare and always appear to have been so; others formerly more widely distributed are now rare in the British Isles generally but still locally common on the often magnesium-rich soils of the Lizard.

* rarity rating, see p 255 (see Collins' *Pocket Guide to Wild Flowers*).

**	*Anagallis minima*	Chaffweed
*	*Anagallis tenella*	Bog pimpernel
***	*Asparagus officinalis prostratus*	Sea asparagus
***	*Briza minor*	Lesser quaking grass
**	*Cicendia filiformis*	Slender cicendia
***	*Corrigiola littoralis*	Strapwort
**	*Erica ciliaris*	Dorset heath
**	*Erica vagans*	Cornish heath
not listed	*Fumaria occidentalis*	Fumitory
***	*Genista pilosa*	Hairy greenweed
***	*Herniaria cilliata*	Rupture wort
**	*Hypericum undulatum*	Wavy St John's wort
**	*Hypochoeris maculata*	Spotted cat's ear
***	*Isoetes histrix*	Sand quill wort

★★★	*Juncus capitatus*	Dwarf rush
★★★	*Juncus mutabilis*	Pigmy rush
	Lycopodium selago	Fir clubmoss
★★	*Melittis melissophyllum*	Bastard balm
★★	*Mentha pulegium*	pennyroyal
★★	*Pinguicula lusitanica*	Pale butterwort
★★	*Pilularia globulifera*	Pillwort
not listed	*Poa infirma*	Variety of meadow grass
★★	*Ranunculus parviflorus*	Small-flowered buttercup
★	*Ranunculus sardous*	Hairy buttercup
not listed	*Ranunculus tripartitus*	(One of world's rarest buttercups)
not listed	*Sarothamnus scoparius* sub sp *maritimus*	Prostrate broom
★★	*Scilla autumnalis*	Autumn squill
★★	*Sibthorpia europaea*	Cornish moneywort
★★★	*Trifolium bocconei*	Twin-flowered clover
★	*Trifolium medium*	Zigzag clover
not listed	*Trifolium molinerii*	No common name
not listed	*Trifolium occidentale*	No common name
★★★	*Trifolium strictum*	Upright clover
★★	*Trifolium suffocatum*	Suffocated clover
★★	*Vicia bithynica*	Bithynian vetch
★★	*Vicia lutea*	Yellow vetch

Probably the best months for seeing the Lizard flora are May, June and July. Many of the dwarf species found are genetic dwarfs and not simple ecotypes. Some of the species mentioned are not listed in the *Pocket Guide* because of their rarity.

The Predannack Downs Nature Reserve has been established on the Lizard to conserve some of this remarkable collection of plants. Other important cliff sites are held by the National Trust and almost all are of Nature Reserve status. Only one of the species mentioned above seems to be in great danger locally and this is the Strapwort which was formerly abundant at Loe Pool but has declined since the water level of the pool was stabilised. The general problem of over use of an area by feet and car tyres will become of increasing concern as the Lizard area is visited by more and more tourists.

Nature trails

Before visiting it is advisable to check with the organisation responsible for the trail that it is in fact open.

DBPS Devon Birdwatching and Preservation Society

DTNC Devon Trust for Nature Conservation
CNT Cornwall Naturalists' Trust
CBWPS Cornwall Birdwatching and Preservation Society
NT National Trust property
STNC Somerset Trust for Nature Conservation
SSSI Sites of Special Scientific Interest
SPNR Society for the Promotion of Nature Reserves
NC Nature Conservancy

Devon

Arlington Court, about 5 miles north-east of Barnstaple. Open March to October from 11 am to 6 pm. Parkland, shrubs and trees, river, pond, lakes, woodland and wilderness area. Heronry and wildfowl refuge. The trail, which is 2 miles long, starts at the Court where booklets are available. Car park provided. NT.
Bellever Forest Walk, Postbridge, map 175/656761. Open all year. A managed coniferous woodland in Dartmoor Forest. Wildlife and archaeology interest. Trail 1–3 miles with guide obtainable on site or from Forestry Commission, Flowers Hill, Brislington, Bristol 4, Telephone 78311.
Bolberry Down, South Devon. A trail jointly organised by the NT and Shell, SX 6939. Open June and July, coastal trail with a cliff walk leading to beach at Sewer Mill Cove. Trail about 1 mile long.
Braunton Burrows National Nature Reserve (South West Region Nature Conservancy, Taunton). Starts at carpark at American Road, 163/463349, this is the Flagpole trail through sand dunes and is about 1½ miles long. A second trail, also 1½ miles, called the Lighthouse trail, covers sea shore and sand dunes, starting from Broad Sands, 163/465325. Open all year by arrangement. Booklets from Warden, Pounds Mead, Hills View, Braunton, North Devon. Telephone Braunton 552.
Dunsford Wood Nature Reserve (DTNC). Open all year. Entrance Steps Bridge, SX 8088, about 7 miles west of Exeter. Woodland and riverside walk, wild daffodils in spring. Walks of 1–2½ miles. Leaflets can be bought on site or at Steps Bridge Hotel. By post from K. Watkins, Butterbrook, Hareford, Ivybridge, Devon.
Heddon Valley, Parracombe, North Devon. Open all year. Woodland, watermeadows, rapid river, open moorland, scree areas and sea shore. The 2 mile walk starts at Hunters Inn Hotel, SS 6548. Booklets can be bought at hotel. Carpark at hotel.
Hemsbury Woods, South Devon, SX 7268. Open September. NT/Shell trail through coppice oak wood in valley of river Dart.
Stoke Woods, Exeter Forest. Start at 176/928964. Forest walk with notes available on natural history of the area at various points along trail. Guide from Exeter City Information Office, 18 Queen Street, Exeter.

Trowlesworthy Warren, South Devon, SX 5664. NT/Shell trail. Open July to August. Woodland walk overlooking upper part of river Plym on south-west flank of Dartmoor.
Welsford Moor, Hartland Forest, SS 2720. Open all year, coniferous woodland with marshy areas and open 'rides'. Booklet on forestry problems from Forestry Commission or Warden's House near trail. About 2½ miles long.
Yarner Wood National Nature Reserve near Bovey Tracey. Start from entrance to reserve near Yarrow Lodge, SX 787789. This is an educational trail run in association with Devon Schools' Museum Service. Heathland and mixed woodland on east edge of Dartmoor. Open all year but must make prior booking with the warden. Booklets from Warden, Yarrow Lodge, Yarner, Bovey Tracey, Devon. Telephone Bovey Tracey 2330.

Somerset

North Hill, Minehead, SS 9447. Organised by STNC. Open all year. Bird migration watch-point and effect of man on landscape. Woods and moorland. About 3 miles long, starts west of harbour, 9647. Guide from Exmoor National Park Information Centre, The Parade, Minehead.

Cornwall

Chapel Porth, St Agnes, SW 6949. Cornwall CC Cliff and valley walk. Birds, butterflies, wild flowers, geology. Guide 10p from County Hall, Truro.
Coombe Valley, nr Bude, SX 2111. Oakwood and plantation, guide 15p from M. S. Henchley, Stamford Hill, Bude.

Areas of natural history interest

(see List of Abbreviations, p. 267–8)

Cornwall

Argal Reservoir, SW 7633 and 7632. Water birds.
Ardevora and *Trelonk* saltings on the Fal. See under Ruan Marshes.
Bodmin Moor, Crowdy and Redhill Marshes, SX 1880, 3 miles north-west of Alternun. Very good bog and moorland plants, particularly in June.
The Cheesewring, SX 2572. Quarry exposing typical Bodmin granite. Some topaz found locally in the granite.
Dozmary Pool, Bodmin Moor, SX 1974. Large, desolate sheet of open water surrounded by high moorland. Little aquatic vegetation but some water birds.
Camel Estuary, North Cornwall. Most birds above Trewornan Bridge (SW 9874) or Burniere Point (SX 9874) where there is a CBWPS hide (for members). Best at high tide for waders and in winter up to 100 white-front geese in the Walmesley Sanctuary, SX 9974. Waders common most times of year.
Cargreen. CNT foreshore reserve, river Tamar, SX 4362. Wintering duck and

waders including avocet, some from breeding colony in East Anglia, others from Holland.
Chapel Porth (SW 6949 to 6847) to Porthtowan Cliffs. NT with excellent coastal heathland, rich flora with some sand patches providing local calcareous heath. Headlands good for sea watches. Old copper and tin mines of scenic and geological interest, well colonised by bryophytes and lichens.
Clicker Tor Quarry, Menheniot, SX 2861. An unusual outcrop of picrite.
Cligga Head near St Agnes, SW 7353. Greizened granite at contact with 'killas', many minerals in cliff face veins and loose beach boulders, including wolfram. Cliffs have good flora and formerly a stronghold of peregrine falcons, now rare.
Crousa Downs, Lizard, SW 7618. Pliocene gravels and interesting moorland and bog plants.
Crowan Reservoir, SW 6434. Good in autumn for waders, including greenshank, spotted redshank and ruff, also duck and terns.
The Dizzard, near Crackington, SX 60987. A most unusual dwarf oakwood on steep exposed cliffs on Culm, which is much slipped. Excellent for lichens and bryophytes but little known of its natural history. NT, SSSI.
Dodman Point, SX 0039. Headland with Bronze Age fort. Excellent sea-watching point and good beaches and cove. NT.
Drift Reservoir, SW 4329, near Penzance. CNT hold shooting rights over the water and have a small woodland reserve and shore area near head of reservoir. Before visiting a permit must be obtained from Mr Scobie, Chyandour Estate Office, Chyandour, Penzance.
Dunmere and Pencarrow Woods, near Bodmin, Forestry Commission SX 0468 and 0469. Varied woodland, good for fungi in autumn. Permission from FC.
Ethyl and Lerryn, SX 1256 and 1356. NT woodland beside the river Lerryn.
Fal River Estuary has many muddy side creeks wooded down to water. These creeks are good for waders but main channel is poor in birds; cormorants, herons and shelduck all year; in autumn terns and black-headed gulls with wide variety of waders.
Gannel, SW 8060 and 7961. Small estuary, mainly sandy, part-owned by NT. Small salt marsh at head. Many gulls and some waders.
Gunwalloe Cove, SW 6620, The Lizard. NT area, sand dunes and good flora.
Hawke's Wood, Wadebridge, SW 9870. CNT reserve, 9 acres, leased. Coppiced oak wood with sycamore and ash.
Hayle Estuary, SW 5437. A very important bird area suffering increasingly from human activities particularly with road-widening affecting the causeway. Very good in autumn for waders and gulls and ducks. Some good saltings also. Private nature sanctuary with accommodation at Woodcote, Lelant.
Helford River. Wooded river valley and estuary with rocky entrance but good muddy creeks higher up. Waders and excellent for marine biology on extensive *Zostera* beds at Helford Passage, SW 7626.

Hell's Mouth and Godrevy Point, SW 6043 and 5943. Cliff and coastal heathland good for flora and breeding sea birds, mainly auks, fulmars and shags with raven and buzzard; grey seals offshore. NT.
Holywell, Gull Rock or Crater's Rock, SW 7559. Many breeding seabirds, guillemot, razorbill and puffin. Also sand dunes at Holywell. Good flora but much disturbed in holiday season.
Kelsey Head, near Crantock, SW 7861. SSSI area of dunes, many birds and mammals, including hare and rabbits with seals offshore. Also good flora.
Kingsmill Creek. See Tamar Estuary, SX 4261.
Lanhydrock House, SX 0863. NT gardens and woodland. Important in Cornwall for redstarts and pied flycatchers which nested in 1966 for first time in county. Some butterflies including silver-washed fritillary and wood white have been seen in recent years
Lizard Cliffs, SW 6813. NT heathland on serpentine with unique plant community. Also good for geology including various metamorphic and basic igneous rocks. Cliffs good for bird migration watches. See also Predannack entry.
Loe, The. Fine 150 acre freshwater lagoon, SW 6424 and 6425. Formed by shingle barrier pool; good for wintering duck, well wooded banks also good habitat for birds. Path on west side of Loe Pool open to public through Penrose estate except on Sundays.
Lowland Point, SW 8019. Ice Age raised beach with good views of the Manacles rocks off which sharks may be seen. NT.
Luckett Woods on banks of Tamar, SX 3972. Nature reserve of CNT: 19 acres leased from Duchy of Cornwall. Partly cleared woodland and old gardens with interesting plants and butterflies. To visit contact first Mrs A. I. Graham Campbell, Coombshead, Lewannick, near Launceston. Telephone Coad's Green 250.
Lye Rock, SX 0689. Largest puffin colony in Cornwall; also other auks breeding in summer.
Marazion Marsh, near Penzance, SW 5031 and 5131. One of the best bird habitats in Cornwall with the marsh resting on an old submerged forest. Most famous locality for trans-Atlantic immigrants but in spring and autumn excellent for waders and passerine migrants on passage. In winter many divers and grebe.
Melancoose Reservoir, near Newquay, SW 8662.
Minions, north of Liskeard, SX 263713. Old granite quarry below the Cheesewring and also partly colonised mine waste north of Phoenix buildings, SX 265722. Interesting plants but more information needed especially on flora of mine heaps.
Millook Haven, SS 1800. Excellent example of zigzag folding in Culm measures, well exposed in cliff.

Mounts Bay, off Penzance. Good locality for sea birds in winter, mainly divers and grebe with sea ducks. Harbour wall at Penzance good watching place or from *Scillonian* en route to Scilly.
Mousehole, near Penzance, SX 4726. RSPB bird hospital and sanctuary.
Mullion Island, SW 6617. CNT reserve leased from NT. Many breeding sea birds, in particular kittiwakes. Island is inaccessible.
National Trust Land. See Trust handbook for full details but all their property in the South West is of interest to naturalists including a number of SSSI's. The Trust has field days at various sites during the summer.
Pencalenick, near Truro, SW 8543. Woodland and riverside path to Malpas, excellent for flora. Salt marshes with many birds, one small freshwater pond with duck and other waterbirds.
Pentire Point, SW 9280. Good cliff exposures of Devonian spilitic pillow lavas. Good footpath, excellent in spring and autumn for flowers, butterflies of coastal heathland with seals offshore. NT.
Penjerrick, SW 7730. Subtropical gardens with great variety of plants. Seasonal access (free).
Peter's Wood, SX 1190, east of Boscastle in Valency Valley. Comprises 25 acres of sessile oak woodland on Culm measures. Leased by CNT from NT.
Porthcothan, SW 8671. A privately owned valley held under agreement with owner by CNT as nature reserve. Open April, May and June only. Permission to visit from Hon Warden and owner, Mr T. O. Drake, Glencoe, Porthcothan Bay, Padstow. Telephone St Merryn 393.
Porthgwarra Cliffs, SW 3721. CBWPS ringing and bird observation site. Excellent for spring and summer migration studies. Land owned by St Levan Estates. For permission to work in the valley, cliffs or heathland, contact Mr J. Williams of Roskestal Farm. Cars must only be left in carpark near cove.
Predannack Cliff area between Porth Mellin and Predannack Wollas on west side of Lizard peninsula, SW 6615 and 6616, etc. CNT have lease of this area as nature reserve from NT. Partly grazed cliffs on serpentine and hornblende schist rocks with rich flora.
Predannack Downs (lower), SW 6814, and Kynance Cliff, SW 6813 and 6912. SSSI. An area of NT land of about 640 acres of which 215 acres is leased to CNT as nature reserve. Open heathland on serpentine with *Erica vagans* common and a unique flora, much ling *Calluna vulgaris*, with bog rush *Schoenus nigricans* in wetter areas. Good area for land bird migrations.
Roche Rock, SW 9959. Classic outcrop of schorl rock, a tourmalinised granite on top of which is an ancient hermitage overlooking Goss Moor which has much wet heathland with cotton grass.
Rosemullion Head, SW 7927. NT land with cliff footpath around headland. Good flora, also birds and butterflies.
Ruan Marshes and Ardevora, SW 8740. Comprises 3 miles of foreshore on east

bank of Fal river leased by CNT from NT. Saltings with excellent population of waders and waterfowl. No land access to Ardevora part of reserve but Fal and Ruan river areas can be reached through Trelonk Farm. No permission necessary to visit but contact Mr T. F. Byass at farm, telephone Veryan 234 beforehand.

Scilly, Isles of. Almost the whole collection of islands of great ecological interest with many plants and animals at edge of range. Some island races of butterflies. See also p 265 on the flora.

Tresco Abbey, SV 8914. Subtropical gardens, many exotic shrubs. Open weekdays (free).

Annet Island, SV 8608. A bird sanctuary under the control of the Nature Conservancy. Access controlled and closed, except by special permit, from 15 April to 15 July. St Mary's has a natural history museum.

St Agnes, SV 8808. Formerly a bird observatory.

Siblyback Reservoir. A new construction near Liskeard. Casual access on foot after getting permission from keeper but for regular use contact East Cornwall Water Board at Treswithian, near Liskeard.

St Agnes Head, SW 6951. Breeding auks and large colony of kittiwakes, also ravens. Heathland with excellent flora. Many butterflies, lizards and adders.

Sand Pits, SW 7050. Pleistocene, possibly glacial, deposits at base of *St Agnes Beacon* which is NT land, having interesting heathland and extensive views across Cornwall.

Field centre at *Goonvrea*, SW 711498, run by the author.

St Erth, SW 5535. Old sand pits of Pleistocene Age, with rich fossil fauna, now much overgrown.

Stithians Reservoir, SW 7336. A new reservoir of importance for water birds.

St Ives 'Island', SW 5241. Best mainland location in Cornwall for seabird watches, particularly after north-west gales in autumn when many offshore birds are blown close to the headland.

St John's Lake, SX 4254. Tidal mudflats south of Torpoint. Excellent for passage migrant, wintering waterfowl and waders.

Tamar Estuary from Cargreen to Skinham Point and including Kingsmill Lake, SX 4260 to 4362 and 4162. CNT nature reserve leased from Duchy of Cornwall. Comprises 6 miles of foreshore with mud and salt marsh. Excellent feeding grounds for waders and other water birds.

Trebetherick Point, SW 9277. Pleistocene shore deposits of geological interest.

Tregargus Quarry, St Stephen, SW 9454. Classic china stone deposits.

Trethias Island, SW 8573. CBWPS nature reserve. Breeding seabirds, no access.

Trevone Bay, SW 8975. Very good coast for wildflowers. Also sandflats and good rock pools at St Cadoc's Point.

Ventongimps Moor, SW 7851, near Callestick. CNT nature reserve. Wet and dry heathland with some bog and willow and alder carr in stream valley. Interesting

flora and insect populations but great problem of management as the area invaded by gorse *U. europaeus.*
Zennor and *Zennor Quoit,* SW 4439. Headland with good cliff flora and cromlech. NT.

Devon

(*Note:* DTNC reserves which are 'closed' act as sanctuaries which can only be visited by permission of executive committee of Devon Trust.)
Arlington Court, SS 6140. NT nature reserve. Heronry and duck refuge, red deer, buzzard and raven. Woodland walk by lake and river with nature trail. Booklets from Court.
Ashclyst Forest, SX 9999 to 0099. Hardwood of oak with typical Devon woodland plants and birds.
Anstey and *Molland Commons,* SS 8728, west-north-west to 8130 near South Molton. Large area of unreclaimed moorland on southern flank of Dartmoor.
Axmouth—Lyme Regis (Devon/Dorset) national nature reserve, SY 2589 to 3391. Natural ashwood in land-slip cracks. Access off footpath by permit only from Nature Conservancy.
Axe Estuary, SY 2591 and 2590. One of the smaller estuaries in South Devon, about 1 mile long with only a small area of mud but good marshes on west of the estuary and north of Axmouth. In marshes, lapwing, curlew and snipe with gulls and waders on mud; good account with map, list of and status of local birds in *Devon Birds,* vol XIX, no 3, October 1966.In autumn sandpipers (green, wood and common), also godwits, ruff, spotted redshank, etc.
Becky Falls, SX 760801. Excellent area for mosses and lichens on junction between Dartmoor granite and metamorphosed country rock.
Beer Head, SY 2287. Lyme Bay. Interesting chalk cliffs with good clifftop calcareous vegetation on one of most westerly outcrops of chalk. Short turf downland and scrub with privet, hawthorn and dogwood, wayfaring tree and old man's beard. Also herbs: nodding thistle, yellow mullein. Good watchpoint for seabirds' movements in autumn, also for landbird migrations, particularly from September.
Bellever Forest, SX 6577. Dartmoor coniferous plantation which holds first Devon breeding population of lesser redpolls and siskin, also a forest walk in this Forestry Commission plantation, together with a nature trail.
Berry Head, SX 9456, east of Brixham. Breeding auks, kittiwakes and fulmars.
Bicton Common, SY 0386. See entry under Lowland Heaths.
Bicton Gardens, East Budleigh, SY 0786. Formal garden including pinetum and waterfowl collection.
Blackadon Down, SX 7073. Leusdon open nature reserve, 90 acres. DTNC.
Black Tor Copse, SX 5770. Forest nature reserve, 73 acres. Access by permit only. NC and Duchy of Cornwall.

Bovey Valley Woodlands, SX 7582 to 8078. Nature reserve since 1963, 179 acres including Rudge, Woodash and Houndstor Woods with excellent native hardwood areas. Access off footpath by permit only.
Braunton Burrows, SS 4437 to 4631. National nature reserve of 560 acres with facilities for scientific study over a further 932. Large sand dune system of great botanical interest. Also important for migrant birds in autumn.
Brendon Commons, SS 7644. Unreclaimed typical heather moorland of Exmoor.
Bridford Wood, SX 8088. Oak wood of 84 acres on hillside and banks of river Teign near Steps Bridge. NT with woodland walks.
Bradley Pond, Bovey Tracey, SX 828778. Open DTNC.
Buckfastleigh, SX 7466. Caves, including Joint Mintor with Pleistocene fossils. SPNR 11 acre reserve. Also Pengelly Caves (Higher Kiln Quarry) reserve of DTNC.
Bull Point, North Devon, SS 4646. Migration point for autumn bird migration.
Burrator Reservoir, SX 5568, Meavy valley (approximately 700ft), Dartmoor. Surrounded by conifers and clitter-strewn hillsides, scrub, mixed woodland, variety of birds but much disturbed by visitors and shallow water not present at edge so poor in waterfowl; woodlark and redstart in surrounding area, mallard, tufted duck, common and green sandpipers, teal, goldeneye, greenshank and pochard.
Buzzards Withleigh, SS 910116. In valley of Little Dart, 82 acres. Coppiced woodland and water meadows for 1 mile on both sides of river. NT.
Chapel Wood, SS 4841, Spreacombe, near Barnstaple. RSPB and DBPS reserve in wooded 13 acre valley with the usual woodland birds and breeding ravens and buzzard. Access by permit only (no charge); apply to Hon Warden, C. G. Manning, 18 Pottington Road, Barnstaple, Devon.
Chudleigh, SX 8678 to 8979. Geology, Dunscombe Farm Quarry, Upper Devonian goniatite limestone. Chudleigh Cave, classic fissure site, many Pleistocene fossils.
Chudleigh Knighton Heath, SX 840770. DTNC (open), 180 acres. Important heathland much with typical wet heath vegetation. Much ruined by development. Formerly a good area for nightingales which are relatively rare in Devon.
Colaton Raleigh Heath, SY 0787. See under Lowland Heaths.
Combe Park, Lynton, 163, SS 735475. In 45 acres of woodland. NT.
Combe Wood, Combe Raleigh, ST 1601, near Honiton. Comprises 18 acres of woodland. NT.
Cranmere Pool, SX 6085, Dartmoor. Not much more than a bog except after heavy rain when temporary lake. Interesting for bryophytes and typical boggy ground flora.
Cowsic, Blackbrook, 596752, Dartmoor. Gravel pit, good soil profile. SSSI.

Dartington Hall, SX 7962. School estate managed as local nature reserve.
Dartmoor National Park. Confirmed 1951. In 365sq miles of moors, tors and granite uplands. Very good botanically, many prehistoric remains. Much owned by Duchy of Cornwall.
Dart estuary, South Devon. Scenically very beautiful. Steep wooded banks but not rich in waterfowl, few spoonbills in winter of interest.
Dart Valley, SX 6772. DTNC (open) reserve between Dartmeet and New Bridge, 450 acres.
Dawlish Warren, SX 9879. Degenerate dune system still of interest for coastal erosion studies and for salt marsh plants and waders. Early September peak of migration for waders.
Dendles Wood, SX 6161. National Nature Reserve since 1965. Comprises 73 acres. Access by permit only.
Dunsford and *Meadhaydown Woods*, SX 8189, Dunsford. DTNC (open) reserve with nature trail in 132 acres.
East Budleigh Common, SY 0384. See under Lowland Heaths.
Eggesford Forest, SS 6710. River Taw Valley conifer plantation.
Exmoor area. See under Heddons Mouth and Woody Bay.
Exmouth, around SX 9980.
Exmouth Aquarium, founded 1951 (about 70 species).
Exmouth Zoo (about 60 species).
Exe Estuary, National Wildfowl Refuge.
Fernworthy Forest, SX 8365, etc. Dartmoor conifer forest.
Fernworthy Reservoir, SX 8466, at 1,100ft, south-west of Chagford. Surrounded by rough Dartmoor moorland and conifer plantations. Lack of shallow water at edge so few aquatic plants or water birds. Habitats varied and some breeding duck including mallard and teal with a small number of ducks in winter.
Froward Point, Kingswear, SX 9049. A closed nature reserve. DTNC, 52 acre site.
Gittisham Common, SY 1496 and 1497. Elevated common with interesting flora.
Golden Cove, SS 565477, west of Combe Martin, 10 acres of wooded cliff.
Great Haldon Hill area around SX 8983. Forestry Commission afforested moorland.
Halwill Forest, SX 5297 and 4398. Large Forestry Commission conifer plantation on reclaimed moorland on Culm.
Hartland Point, SS 2227 to Speke Valley, SS 2223. Area protected by DTNC almost as nature reserve. Good for autumn bird migration watches.
Heddons Mouth, SS 6549. SSSI woodland within Exmoor National Park. Unspoilt steep-sided straight valley with vegetation on acid and base rich soil. Much damp woodland rich in ferns but also areas of dry scree. Moorland area leads up to Trentishoe Common. All NT (with nature trail) totalling over 900 acres.

Hembury, near Buckfastleigh, SX 726684. Comprising 25 acres of woodland: some young oak and coppice, also beechwood.

Hennock Reservoir, SX 8085 to 8082. Three lakes totalling 140 acres about 4 miles north of Bovey Tracey at about 800ft amongst conifers. Steep sides to lakes so little vegetation; few ducks in winter including tufted, pochard and teal, also coot.

Holne Woods, SX 7271, west bank of Dart. Comprising 165 acres of natural oak woods.

Hope's Nose, SX 9463. Largest kittiwake colony in Devon, about 150 pairs.

Ilfracombe Zoo Park, SS 5246. Gardens, admission free.

Killerton Park, SX 9897. Woodland with heronry; also roe deer.

Kingsbridge Estuary, SX 7441, etc. Unique estuary in having no large river draining into it. Shallow creeks known locally as lakes are of great interest to marine biologists and bird watchers. In winter has wigeon, shelduck, mallard, teal and many waders. Like Dart estuary it has a deep, narrow, rocky entrance.

Lady's Wood, Wrangaton, SX 6757. DTNC open reserve of 8 acres.

Lannacombe (SX 8037), *Start Point* (SX 8337), *Hallsands* (SX 8138). Area protected by DTNC. Good flora and birds.

Lundy. Many breeding sea birds and rare migrants. One unique plant, Lundy cabbage. Observatory since 1947. Lundy Field Society. NT, almost nature reserve, excellent botanically and for bird migration, 1,100 acres. Boats from Bideford and Ilfracombe.

Lundy Field Station and Bird Observatory. Visitors to field station must be members of Lundy Field Society; hostel-type accommodation at 25p per night. Accommodation office: A. J. Vickery, 4 Taw View, Bishops Tawton, Barnstaple. Booking for hotel or one of cottages: Resident Agent, Manor Farm Hotel, Lundy, Bristol Channel via Bideford, Devon. Access by MV *Lundy Gannet*: Mr A. Beasley, Tadworthy, Northam, Bideford, or during summer season by Campbells Steamers from Ilfracombe.

Lowland Heaths: East of Exe Estuary, heather and grass moors with scattered pines and scrub in contrast to Dartmoor. Interesting birds species: crossbill and redpolls, formerly nightingales and red-backed shrikes. Much affected by population pressure for amenity, so slowly losing wildlife importance.

Lydford Gorge, SX 5083. Valley of Lyd. Deep ravine, pothole succession; steep valley with oak woodland, White Lady Waterfall (90ft), 'river capture' example. NT.

Lympstone Common, SY 8402. See under Lowland Heaths.

Lynmouth, Watersmeet, 163: SS 7448. Both sides of Lyn Valley, 508 acres. Woodland and river interest. NT.

Merton (see also Winkleigh entry), north of Hatherleigh, SS 5012. North Devon Clay Co works; for permission to visit consult the manager. Willow tit and lesser redpoll amongst birds of interest.

Mill Bottom, Lustleigh, SX 7582, 2 miles north-west of Lustleigh. Open nature reserve. DTNC.
Molland Common. See under Anstey Common.
Molton Forest. Coniferous forest in similar situation to Eggesford Forest.
Mort Bay, SS 4445, Baggy Point to Mort Point. Mainly NT land. Fine cliffs, many sea birds and migration observation point, also sand dunes at Woolacombe Warren.
New Cross Pond, SX 8674, Kingsteignton. DTNC, 20 acres, closed reserve.
Northam Burrows, SS 4430 and 4431. Good sand dunes on south side of Taw/Torridge estuary.
Paignton, SX 8859. Zoological and botanical gardens, also seashore life aquarium.
Pengelly Caves, SX 7466, Buckfastleigh. DTNC, 5 acres, closed nature reserve.
Prawle Point, SX 7735. Headland in probably Pre-cambrian metamorphic rocks similar to those at Lizard Point. Good observation point for autumn bird migration and sea watches; also seals offshore.
Preston, SX 8574. Kingsteignton Nature Reserve. DTNC, closed.
Plym Bridge Woods, SX 5255. Wooded valley on both banks of river Plym, 111 acres. NT.
Plym Estuary, SX 5055, etc. Ruined by industry but still has some waders with godwits, dunlin, redshank, golden plover and curlew in autumn. This is an unusual estuary in that it is good for birds at low tide. At high tide waders fly to Saltram meadows.
Plymouth. The headquarters of the Marine Biological Society of the United Kingdom is at Plymouth and much research is carried on in the waters of the channel and the local estuaries.

In 1968 the Society produced a second revision of its species check list. There is a named collection of the commoner seaweeds which is available for visiting workers and for the general public. An aquarium is open containing about 90 species. New guide (1970).
Rockbeare Hill, SY 0694. Comprises 22 acres of woodland and heath on hill top. NT.
Salcombe Estuary, SX 7338. See also under Kingsbridge. Excellent area for marine biology, rich mudflats, little spoilt.
Scabbacombe Head, SX 9251. Breeding seabird cliff.
Sidmouth Cliffs, SY 1387. DTNC, 17 acres, open nature reserve.
Slapton, SX 8244. Slapton Ley Field Study Centre of Field Studies Council. Varied habitats include freshwater ley, shingle beach with many birds, particularly freshwater duck, also many insects and varied flora. Nature reserve can be visited by permit from field centre warden. Also bird observation station of the DBPS who have a cabin to sleep 6. Information from P. F. Goodfellow, 6 Dunraven Drive, Highfields, Roborough, Plymouth.
Sourton Quarry, Bridestowe, SX 5289. DTNC, 8 acres, closed nature reserve.

Stanton Moor, Loddiswell, SX 7248. DTNC, 54 acres, closed nature reserve.

Start Point, SX 8337. See also Prawle Point entry. Good place to view seabird migration in autumn, also night migrations viewed from Start Point lighthouse.

Stoke Woods, Exeter Forest, SX 9296 to 9396. Mixed woodland with nature trail.

Tamar Lake, SS 2911. Regional wildfowl refuge, 75 acres on Devon/Cornwall border, shallow water at edge so good aquatic plant growth and good for birds, marsh on three sides, fields and rough grazing on other. Breeding coot, mallard, moorhen, teal and little grebe, good for winter visitors and passage migrants.

Tamar Estuary. See entries for Cornwall side of estuary, also Warleigh Point (SX 4461) and Weir Quay (SX 4365). Winter visitors: duck, waders, including avocet, godwits, golden plover, wigeon.

Teign Estuary, SX 9372 to 8872. Common species of waders but despite wide foreshore and good mudflats, rather few species.

Tod Moor, SX 6254, near Ivybridge. DTNC, 17 acres, open nature reserve.

Taw/Torridge Estuary. Main estuary on North Devon coast for waders and duck, probably declined in importance due to disturbance from RAF Chivenor, a power station and a road. See also Braunton Burrows entry and Northam Burrows.

Torquay: aquarium, aqualand and gardens, at Lummaton Quarry rich fossiliferous Devonian limestone, also Kent's Cavern (9263), Pleistocene to Stone Age bone cave.

Warleigh Wood, around SX 4561. DTNC, 31 acres, closed nature reserve.

Watersmeet, SS 7448. NT property in east Lyn river gorge, 344 acre site. SSSI. Woodlands of oak with rich ground flora including many liverworts and mosses. In damp flushes alder and ash predominate with heathland capping higher ground.

Welsford Moor, Hartland Forest, SS 2720. Conifer woodland, Forestry Commission nature trail.

Wembury Bay and *Yealm Estuary*, SX 530480. Mostly NT. Formerly CBWPS reserve, now naval, but access by permission. Very good for waders and migrants. Mr L. I. Hamilton, 8 Grosvenor Road, Crownhill, Plymouth, has species list. See also *Devon Birds*, May 1965.

Winkleigh, north-east Hatherleigh, SS 6307, old airfield. North Devon Clay Co old working. Willow tit, lesser redpoll nesting.

Wistland Pound Reservoir, SS 6441, 12 miles north-east of Barnstaple in rough grassland on edge of Dartmoor. Some conifer plantations on banks, interesting for bird life: willow tits and whinchats breed.

Wistman's Wood, SX 6177. Forest Nature Reserve, 63 acres. Duchy of Cornwall and NT.

Woodbury Common, SY 0387. Most important for birds but see under Lowland Heaths.
Woody Bay, SS 6749. NT and Exmoor Society nature reserve, 115 acres. Some wooded steep slopes, also moorland and cliff.
Wolborough Decoy, Newton Abbot, SX 8570. DTNC, 15 acres, closed nature reserve.
Yarner Wood, SX 7779. National Nature Reserve, 361 acres. Visit by permit only. Also nature trail (with booklets). *Q. petraea* (sessile oak) and hazel.
Yealm, SX 5550. Small acre of mudflat in upper part of estuary. Wildfowl in moderate numbers. See also under Wembury Bay.

Somerset

Avill Valley. Woodland between Timberscombe and Dunster. In this valley most of the commercially valuable timber has been removed but some good woods of amenity value.
Barle Valley. The wooded part of this quiet, not easily accessible, valley runs from Dulverton north-west to Withypool. A good marked footpath however exists along the entire valley length on the river bank and in the area are three woodland SSSI's. Much of the oak woodland is coppiced and birch is widespread together with some standard oak and beech. Conifers, mainly spruce, pine, hemlock, Douglas fir and larch.
Birch Cleave, SS 7739. Beechwood planted prior to 1840 along Barle river at Simonsbath. One of the highest beechwoods in the country, up to 1,200ft, but the trees are now past their prime.
Brendon Hills. Outlier on east of Exmoor with large Forestry Commission woodlands on the north slopes. This area of woodland, including Luxborough Valley, is mostly conifers which also form a blanket over the top of Croydon Hill (SS 9740). Brendon Forest is the main Forestry Commission holding in Somerset, covering 3,000 acres. Walkers are welcome along the forest rides but cars are not.
Burridge Wood. A 54 acre site to the north-west of Dulverton (SS 9128) with well preserved partly coppiced oakwood which is so characteristic of this area.
Coastal Woods. These form a unique feature of the Exmoor National Park. Most of the cliff face trees are coppiced oak some replanted, however, with beech, sweet chestnut, plus Douglas fir and other conifers. The south-west peninsular coastal footpath passes through some of this region. There are many footpaths through these woods connecting with the moorland inland.
Dulverton Churchyard, SS 9127. Belfrey tree, a sycamore of great age and girth.
Dunkery, Holnicote Estate, astride A39 for 6 miles from north coast. Comprises 6,720 acres of moorland and woodland with Dunkery (SS 8941) and Selworthy (9147) Beacons. See also under Holnicote Estate.
Dunster Castle Estate, SS 9943. Douglas fir planted in Broadwood south-east

of Dunster (9941) in 1874, now over 155ft high with girths up to 12ft, some of the finest specimens of this species in the British Isles. Also eighteenth-century plantations of oak.

Glenthorne, SS 7949. In the mid-nineteenth century the cliffs here were only colonised by scrub, the rest being bare. Plantations of Monteray Cypress *Cupressus macrocarpa* were established to form a shelter belt behind which were planted beech, larch, Scots and Corsican pines; now well wooded cliffs and combes. Later Yenworthy (8049) and Stag's Head Woods were established on bare sites on coasts.

Haddeo Valley, SS 9529, 9429 and 9428. Good walk available along a private drive running by the river for almost the whole length of the valley. Woods at west end large and sheltered with fertile soil clothed by mainly oak coppice. Smaller woods at east end are largely replanted with pine, larch and spruce.

Hoar Oak, SS 748431. This marks the edge of the 'Forest of Exmoor' and the county boundary between Devon and Somerset. The present tree is a poor specimen: the original tree fell in 1658, a second was planted in 1662 which fell in 1916, after which several replanted but only one remains.

Holnicote Estate, SS 8844, etc, including Horner Valley and Hawkcombe. All the estate is an SSSI giving a profile of Exmoor fauna and flora from seashore through valley woodland to high open moorland up to 1,700ft at Dunkery Beacon. Good walks, camping sites and views. Horner valley owned by NT; Somerset County Council own west half of Hawkcombe Wood (8745). Latter mainly oak and oak coppice with few beech.

Knaplock and *North Barton Woods*, SS 7448. An 80 acre area of steep valley side with deciduous oakwood with interesting local variations in vegetation.

National Trust Woodlands. Leaflets for their wooded properties are available from Killerton Estate Office. Areas covered: Heddon's Mouth, Woody Bay and Watersmeet near Lynmouth.

Nettlecombe Court, ST 0537. A field centre run by the Field Studies Council. Weekly courses for students and amateurs in a variety of subjects. Some excellent oaks in the estate grounds.

North Hill, Minehead, SS 9447. A nature trail in coastal woodlands organised by TNC.

Oare Valley, SS 8346. Containing Weir Wood at east end. This is an ancient oak coppice woodland of almost natural origin. Other valley woodlands of oak and beech plus a few areas of pine, spruce and larch.

Porlock Coastal Area. See map, p 149, for coastal birds. The marshes are good for migrants.

Quantocks. Longstone Hill, ST 141407. Open moorland, 61 acres.
Shervage Wood, ST 1640. Oak wood, oak coppice and moorland, 136 acres.
Willoughby Cleeve, ST 151410. Woodland, agricultural land and moorland, 77½ acres.

Quarme and *Exe Valley* from SS 9136 along rivers to SS 9326. An important tourist route and acts as divider between the main mass of Exmoor and the South Brendon Hills. Although this valley is heavily used in the tourist season the woods are rarely entered by visitors. They consist of mainly oak standard and coppice with some scrub oak. Also present are some good beech, sycamore and ash. Conifers are represented by larch, spruce and Douglas fir, some in pure stands.
Seven Wells Bridge, ST 1737. Quantock forest trail of Forestry Commission (Nature Trail).
Winsford Hill, Exmoor, SS 8734. Comprises 1,288 acres of moorland between Exford and Dulverton.

Map list

Ordnance Survey one inch to the mile maps which cover the area dealt with in this book are sheet numbers 163, 164, 174, 175, 176, 185, 186, 187, 188, 189 and 190. These sheets make up the 100km squares SS, SX and SV and the western parts of ST and SY.

A description of the one-inch Tourist Map of Dartmoor area will be found in *Dartmoor* by D. Brunsden, published by the Geographical Association in 1968.

One-inch geology maps available

New series, all drift editions

311	Exeter	349	Ivybridge
326/340	Sidmouth and Lyme Regis	350	Torquay
335	Trevose Head	351/358	Penzance
336	Camelford	352	Falmouth, Truro, Camborne and Redruth
337	Tavistock		
338	Dartmoor Forest	353/354	Mevagissey
339	Teignmouth	355	Kingsbridge
346	Newquay	356	Start Point
347	Bodmin and St Austell	357/360	Isles of Scilly
348	Plymouth and Liskeard	359	Lizard

Societies, naturalists' trusts and field centres

Blundell's School Science Society, Tiverton
Breanoc Field Centre, Goonvrea, St Agnes, Cornwall (Warden Roger Burrows)
British Naturalists' Association, local branches (Devon):
East: Mr R. C. Hodgson, Oakdene, Higher Brook Meadow, Sidford, Sidmouth

North: Miss D Feist, Marina, Golf Links Road, Westward Ho!
South: Mr C. A. Fletcher, Beachcroft, Marine Parade, Dawlish
All the branches hold field meetings

Camborne and Redruth Natural History Society, Hon Sec Mrs. M. I. Williams, Mount Pleasant, Tehidy, Camborne

Cornwall Bird Watching and Preservation Society, including Scilly
Records for mainland to Rev J. E. Beckerlegge, St Crowan Vicarage, Praze, Camborne
For Scilly to Miss H. Quick, St Agnes, Isles of Scilly

Cornwall Naturalists' Trust, Hon Sec Mr J. K. Williams, Mount Pleasant, Tehidy, Camborne

Dartmoor Preservation Association, Hon. Sec, 23 Well Park Close, Exeter

Devonshire Association for the Advancement of Science, Hon Sec, 7 The Close, Exeter

Devon Bird Watching and Preservation Society, Hon Sec Mr P. Ellicott, Exminster Hill, Exminster, near Exeter

Devon Trust for Nature Conservation, Slapton Ley Field Centre, Devon

Exeter Field Club, Hon Sec, 16 High Street, Ide, near Exeter

Exmoor Society, Membership Secretary, Parish Rooms, Dulverton, Somerset

Lizard Field Club, Hon Sec Mrs M. C. Holden, Kernyk, Housel Bay, The Lizard

Lundy Field Society, Lundy Field Station and Conservatory, via Bideford, Devon

National Trust Regional Office, information from Saltram House, Plympton, Plymouth

Nettlecombe Court Field Centre, Somerset, Field Studies Council

Ramblers' Association Devon and Cornwall, area office: 6 Norwood Avenue, Topsham Road, Exeter

Royal Geological Society of Cornwall

Slapton Ley Field Centre, Devon, Field Studies Council

Somerset Archaeological and Natural History Society, Hon Sec, c/o Taunton Castle, Taunton, Somerset

Somerset Trust for Nature Conservation, enquiries to A. C. Hingley, Stangman's Heale, Curry Rivel, Langport

South Western Naturalists' Union, Hon Sec Mrs Phoebe Beer, Shorton Manor, Shorton, Paignton, Devon. Telephone 50519

Visitors should send species record to the appropriate naturalists' trust or local society.

Information on natural history in the South West and names of experts willing to give advice or help can be obtained from the Hon Sec, South Western Naturalists' Union.

Bibliography

Abrahams, H. M. 'Britain's National Parks', *Country Life* (1959)

Annual reports of Somerset Archaeological and Natural History Society, reports on Somerset birds, Newsletter 'Goldeneye'

Bannister, R. T. 'Additional List of Cornish Coleoptera', *CNT Bulletin*, no 7 (1968)

Barnes, E. F. *Flora of Devon—The Mosses and Liverworts* (Torquay 1958)

Barton, R. M. *An Introduction to the Geology of Cornwall* (Truro, 1969)

Bere, R. A. *Wildlife in Cornwall* (Truro, 1970)

Burton, S. H. *Exmoor* (1970)

Christy, M. and Worth, R. H. 'The ancient dwarfed oak woods of Dartmoor', *Trans Devons Ass*, no 54 (1922), pp 291–342

Claydon, B and Manley, D. J. R. 'The soils of the Dartmoor granite', *Dartmoor Essays*, ed Simmons (1964)

Cornwall Bird Watching and Preservation Society, *Annual Reports*, 1930–

Dark, T. O. *The Cornish Chough* (Truro, 1971)

Davey, F. Hamilton. *Flora of Cornwall* (Penryn, 1909)

Davis, P. 'A list of the birds of Lundy', *Exeter Lundy Field Society* (1954)

Dent, A. *The Pure-bred Exmoor Pony* (1970)

Devon Birds, *Journal of the Devon Bird Watching and Preservation Society* (1948) (see also annual reports)

'Exmoor Review', *Journal of the Exmoor Society* (Dulverton, 1959)

Forestry Commission
Booklet no 6, *National Forest Parks* (1961)
Booklet no 10, *The New Forests of Dartmoor* (1964)
Frost, L. C. and Coombe, D. E., 'The Heaths of the Cornish Serpentine', *J Ecol*, no 44 (1956), pp 226–56
Harris, G. T. 'Ecological notes on Wistman's Wood and Black Tor Copse', *Trans Devons Ass*, no 53 (1921), pp 232–45
Harvey, L. A. 'The natural history of the shores of Scilly', *The Scillonian*, nos 172–3 (1968)
Harvey, L. A. 'The marine flora and fauna of the Isles of Scilly,' *J Nat Hist*, vol 3 (1969)
Harvey, L. A. and Gordon, D. St L. *Dartmoor* (1953)
HMSO. *National Park Guide—Exmoor* (1970)
Hepburn, I. *Flowers of the Coast*, New Nat Series (1950), with references to papers on vegetation of the Camel estuary and Cornish cliff flora
Higgins, L. G. and Riley, N. D. *Butterflies of Britain and Europe* (1970)
Holt, E. G. 'Autumn migration along the Bristol Channel', *Brit Birds*, xliii (1950), 271–3
Howell, B. R. and Shelton, R. G. J. 'The effect of china clay on the bottom fauna of St Austell and Mevagissey Bay', *J Mar Biol Ass*, UK, vol 50, no 3 (1970)
Johns, C. A. *A Week at the Lizard* (1848)
Flowers of the Field (1853)
Keble Martin, W. and Fraser, G. T. *Flora of Devon* (Arbroath, 1959)
Kidson, C. 'Dawlish Warren', *Trans Inst Brit Geog*, no 16 (1952)
Lack, D. 'The chaffinch migration in North Devon', *Brit Birds*, vol 1 (1957)
Lewis, J. R. *The Ecology of Rocky Shores* (1964)
Lloyd, E. R. *Red Deer of Exmoor* (1970)
Loyd, L. R. W. *Lundy, its History and Natural History* (1952)
Lundy Field Society Annual Report (1947–)
Maund, H. B. *Fish of Exmoor* (1970)

McClintock, D. and Fitter, R. S. R. *Pocket Guide to Wild Flowers* (1956)
Mercer, I. D. 'The Natural History of Slapton Ley', *Nature Reserve Field Studies 2* (1966)
Moore, R. *The Birds of Devon* (Newton Abbot, 1969)
Nicholson, E. M. 'Britain's Nature Reserves', *Country Life* (1957)
Orwin, C. S. *The Reclamation of Exmoor Forest* (1929)
Palmer, M. G. (ed). *Ilfracombe Flora and Fauna* (Exeter, 1946)
Palmer, E. M. and Ballance, D. K. *The Birds of Somerset* (1968)
Pennallurick, R. D. *Birds of the Cornish Coast* (Truro, 1969)
Paton, J. *Wildflowers in Cornwall and Isles of Scilly* (Truro, 1968)
'A bryophyte flora of Cornwall' *Trans Brit Bryological Soc*, vol 5 (1968), 4
Peterson, Mountford and Hollom. *A Field Guide to the Birds of Britain and Europe* (1966)
Plymouth Report on 'Torrey Canyon' Pollution (Cambridge, 1967)
'Faunal list revision of chek list', *Mar Biol Ass* (1968)
Proctor, M. C. F. 'The phytogeography of Dartmoor bryophytes', in *Dartmoor Essays*, Simmons, I. G. (ed), *Devons Ass* (1964)
Quick, H. M. *Marsh and Shore Bird Watching on the Cornish Coast* (1948) *Birds of the Scilly Isles* (Truro, 1964)
Ryves, B. H. *Bird Life in Cornwall* (1948)
Sargent, H. B. *A Natural History of Porthleven* (1961)
Simmons, I. G. 'The blanket bog of Dartmoor', *Trans Devons Ass*, no 95 (1963)
Sinclair, G. *The Vegetation of Exmoor* (1970)
Slapton Bird Observatory Annual Report (1960–)
Stamp, Sir L. D. *Nature Conservation in Britain* (1969)
Steers, J. A. *The Coastline of England and Wales* (1962)
Stidston, S. T. A. 'List of the Lepidoptera of Devon', *Torquay Times and Devonshire Press* (1952)
Tansley, A. G. *The British Isles and their Vegetation* (Cambridge, 1949)
The Lizard (1957) (The Lizard Field Club publication)

Thurston, E. and Vigurs, C. C. *A Supplement to Davy's Flora of Cornwall* (1922)

Townsend, C. 'List of Scilly Plants', *Journal of Botany* (1964)

Trebilcock, G. D. 'A guide to and local list of insects in north-west Cornwall', *Bull Amat Ent Soc*, no 268 (1965)

Turk, F. M. 'Notes on Cornish Mammals', annual reports in *Newsletter* of Cornish Naturalists' Trust

Turk, S. M. 'Molluscs of the Lizard peninsula', *The Lizard*, vol 14, no 4 (1964)

Turk, S. M. *Seashore life in Cornwall* (Truro, 1971)
Newsletter of Cornish Naturalists' Trust

Victoria County Histories of the Counties of England
Cornwall (1906)
Devon (1906)

Wallace, J. J. 'Ecology of Dawlish Warren', *Trans Devons Assoc*, no 85 (1953)

Watson, W. 'Cryptogamic vegetation of the sand dunes of the west coast of England', *J Ecol*, no 6 (1918), 126

Willis, A. J., Hope-Simpson, J. F. and Yemm, E. W. 'Braunton Burrows', *J Ecol*, no 47 (1959)

Worth, R. H. 'The physical geography of Dartmoor', *Trans Devons Assoc*, no 94 (1930)

Acknowledgements

THE MATERIAL USED in the preparation of this book has come from a variety of sources both via articles and books and also discussion and written correspondence with other naturalists.

The interpretation of other people's work is, of course, my own; I take full responsibility for any errors that may occur and I would welcome constructive comment from both resident and visiting naturalists. If this book should be produced in a new edition full acknowledgement of all help given will be made.

Most of the individual naturalists whose publications I have consulted have been acknowledged in the bibliography, but I would also like to thank a number of naturalists whose names do not appear on those pages. In particular my thanks to Russell Gomme who, during the gestation stages of the book, provided much useful information and comment, and two members of the Cornwall Naturalists' Trust, Ken Williams and Rene Bere, whose conversation helped to fill in a number of details.

My thanks are also due to a large number of students and members of staff from a variety of educational establishments throughout the British Isles who have stayed at my field centre in Cornwall and by their knowledge and enthusiasm have helped with much of the field work which has been incorporated into the book.

For the difficult task of deciphering my writing and correcting numerous errors I would like to thank my wife Isobel and two long-suffering typists, Merle Cox and Betty Tompkins.

Roger Burrows

Index

Italic figures indicate illustrations